The Central Nervous System
and Fish Behavior

The Central Nervous System and Fish Behavior

EDITED BY

David Ingle

The University of Chicago Press

Chicago and London

Library of Congress Catalog Card Number: 68-24558

THE UNIVERSITY OF CHICAGO PRESS, CHICAGO 60637
The University of Chicago Press, Ltd., London W.C. 1

Foreword

The papers in this volume were presented at a meeting in April, 1967, at the University of Chicago. The symposium was jointly sponsored by the United States Air Force Office of Scientific Research (Contract F44620–67–C0083), the Comparative Physiology Division of the American Zoological Society (National Institutes of Health Grant 5–R13–GM–10062–04), and the academic journal *Perspectives in Biology and Medicine*.

The purpose of the meeting was to promote an interdisciplinary attack on brain function, and specifically to give impetus to the study of teleost fishes. The symposium was dedicated to the memory of the pioneering neuroanatomist C. Judson Herrick, who spent much of his long and productive research life a few blocks from our meeting place. Although only one paper deals explicitly with Herrick's ideas, the symposiasts shared his implicit conviction that anatomists, physiologists, and psychologists should educate and challenge one another in a common effort to translate the underlying language of the brain.

DAVID INGLE
Editor

v

Contents

vii

Part I Anatomy and Function of the Fish Visual System

Anatomy of Visual Centers in Teleosts

Horst O. Schwassmann / Lawrence Kruger

Physiological Research Laboratory, Scripps Institution of Oceanography
University of California, San Diego

Department of Anatomy, School of Medicine, and Brain Research Institute
University of California, Los Angeles

Introduction

The analysis of visual physiology in fishes is still in its infancy. Development in this field has been limited to a large extent by the relatively restricted morphological information available. It therefore seems expedient to consider some of the important unsolved problems amenable to experimental analysis in order to place present knowledge into an appropriate context. If this attempt to summarize some of the recent results concerning structure and possible function of teleost visual centers should provide more questions than solutions, the intent of this presentation will have been achieved.

Original material was selected for a comparison of visual centers from several species which are known to rely on vision as the dominant sense: rainbow trout, *Salmo gairdneri* (Salmonidae); bluegill, *Lepomis macrochirus* (Centrarchidae); velvet Oscar, *Astronotus ocellatus* (Cichlidae); four-eyed fish, *Anableps microlepis* (Cyprinodontidae); northern anchovy, *Engraulis mordax* (Engraulidae); opaleye, *Girella nigricans* (Girellidae); Jack mackerel, *Trachurus symmetricus* (Carangidae); sand bass, *Paralabrax nebulifer* (Serranidae). For comparative purposes, the brown bullhead, *Ictalurus nebulosus*, of the catfish family Ictaluridae, was chosen to represent a fish with a poorly developed visual system. In addition, the carp, *Cyprinus carpio*, and the goldfish, *Carassius auratus*, both of the Cyprinidae, were selected as probably intermediate between the two extremes. Serial sections of the brains of the above species were available, cut in one or more of the three principal planes, and stained according to Klüver and Barrera (1953) or silver-impregnated by a modified Bodian method (Ziesmer 1952).

The Principal Visual Pathways

The primary optic pathways have been examined in histological preparations of normal and some experimental material in a variety of teleosts. It is generally agreed that optic nerve axons, originating in retinal ganglion cells, cross completely at the optic chiasm. In the majority of species, this decussation is a simple crossing-over. With the exception of some flatfish families, either the right or the left nerve can be dorsal to the other within a given species (Parker 1903; Larrabee 1906; Hubbs and Hubbs 1944). An interdigitating chiasm occurs in some teleosts in which bundles of the optic nerve of one side separate and penetrate through corresponding bundles of the opposite nerve. In a herring (*Clupea harengus*) one nerve simply perforates the other (Weber 1827). In the European bream (*Abramis brama*) a large ventral and a small dorsal bundle interlace with those of the other nerve (Gross 1903). Ströer (1939) reported that in *Salmo salar* each optic nerve consists of two bundles which interdigitate and, without reuniting, form the medial and lateral fascicles of the optic tracts. Two separate bundles interdigitating with three were found in the bitterling (*Rhodeus amarus*) by Lissner (1923), and three with four in *Engraulis encrasicholus* (Solger 1877). Greater variety was found in the northern anchovy (*Engraulis mordax*) where three with four, or two with three interlacing bundles were observed (Schwassmann 1965). The largest number of mutually perforating optic nerve fiber bundles is found in the squirrel fish family (Holocentridae) where each optic nerve forms six to nine separate bundles at the chiasm (Meader 1934).

Before reaching the anterior level of the optic tectum the optic tract divides into a medial and a lateral branch. Fibers of the medial branch spread over the anterior and dorsal portions of the tectum, while those of the lateral branch terminate in the lateroventral and posterior tectal parts.

The Optic Thalamus

Before we consider the fine structure of the optic tectum and the orderly topography of tectal termination of optic nerve fibers, a few nuclear structures of the diencephalon should be mentioned. Two distinct nuclear groups of the teleostean diencephalon, nucleus geniculatus lateralis and nucleus praetectalis, appear to be related to the optic tract. Although both are said to have optic fiber connections (Schnitzlein 1962), possibly only through termination of collaterals of optic axons (Bellonci 1888), reliable evidence from experimental degeneration studies seems to be lacking. The nucleus corticalis (Ariëns Kappers 1906) may also be related to the visual pathway. It appears from the material available for comparison that the degree of development in size and differentiation of these three nuclei is correlated with the development of the visual system.

Nucleus Geniculatus Lateralis

The lateral geniculate body is located laterally between the dividing medial and lateral branches of the optic tract. A fiber bundle lateral to this nucleus was termed fasciculus geniculatus tracti optici (Meader 1934), and the variable appearance of this nucleus in several species of fish was described by Franz (1912). The nucleus usually consists of two parallel layers of small neurons separated by a dense network of fine fibers. It is not a distinct nucleus in the catfish and appears poorly differentiated in carp and goldfish. It is better developed in more visually oriented species in which, with the exception of the anchovy, it exhibits considerable folding.

Nucleus Praetectalis

This nucleus has been described by a variety of authors but its exact limits vary in different descriptions (Ariëns Kappers, Huber, and Crosby 1936, p. 924). It is located caudal and medial to the lateral geniculate. The pretectal nucleus is easily identified as a distinct cell group in most species studied, but in catfish, carp, and goldfish it is difficult to delineate and may be represented by only a cluster of large cells in this region.

Nucleus Corticalis

The cortical nucleus lies lateral and dorsal to the pretectal nucleus in the anteroventral part of the tectum. It consists of a limited number of large cells (25–100), which are arranged either in a spherical cluster, as in bluegill and mackerel, in a disklike fashion, as in the opaleye, or in a sickle-shaped cluster of cells, as in the anchovy. A few large cells which are scattered through the anteroventral tectum probably represent this nucleus in the trout. It could not be detected in the catfish and in the two cyprinids, although Schnitzlein (1962) mentions a few large cells in the goldfish brain which could represent the cortical nucleus.

Other diencephalic nuclei of the fish brain probably play a role in vision, since there are fiber connections between them and the optic tectum. However, the differing opinions among authors and the confusing inconsistency of terminology (Ariëns Kappers, Huber, and Crosby 1936; Schnitzlein 1962) indicate the need for additional evidence from experimental degeneration studies. A massive tectal projection to the nucleus rotundus of birds has been demonstrated in this manner in the pigeon (Karten and Revzin 1966) and is supported by electrophysiological evidence (Revzin and Karten 1966/67). The avian and reptilian nucleus rotundus projects upon the paleostriatum as judged by its retrograde atrophy following restricted lesions of that region of the telencephalon (Powell and Cowan 1957, 1961; Kruger and Berkowitz 1960; Powell and Kruger 1960). It would be important to know the corresponding structure in the fish diencephalon. Although the teleostean nucleus rotundus (Schnitzlein 1962) bears some resemblance to the avian structure of the same name in gross appearance and location, it is not certain whether these two nuclei in the different classes are homologous (Schnitzlein 1962).

The Optic Tectum

The optic tectum of teleosts, the main structure of termination of retinal ganglion cell axons, appears to reflect the degree of dominance of the visual sense. It is larger than telencephalon or cerebellum in most teleosts studied, except for the catfish and the two cyprinids, which exhibit a relatively large cerebellum. Superficial inspection reveals some species differences in the gross appearance of the optic tectum, aside from the size variation mentioned above. In the carp, the relatively large valvula cerebelli within the optocoele is the apparent cause for a considerable lateral shift of the dorsal part of the tecta, especially at the caudal end. This is also the case in the goldfish, but to a lesser degree. In most teleosts, the dorsomedial edges of the right and left tecta are adjacent throughout their longitudinal extent and connect medially to the torus longitudinalis, a paired median structure which is not found in other vertebrates. Rostrally the two lateral parts of the torus longitudinalis are fused together and join the commissura posterior.

In the marine families Carangidae and Scombridae, as in other tuna-related families, the medial and lateral branches of the optic tract spread over separate anterior bulges of the optic tectum, and this horizontal indentation of the anterior tectum extends for about a third to half of its length, the larger caudal portion of the optic tectum displaying the usual single semicircular cross section.

With these few exceptions, the gross anatomical structure of the optic tectum displays little variation among different species of teleosts. In *Anableps*, in which the visual system is adapted to simultaneous vision in air and water, specialization is determined by optical features in the eye and does not affect the external appearance of the optic tectum (Schwassmann and Kruger 1965*b*).

The cytoarchitecture and fiber architecture of the teleostean optic tectum have been studied in detail by numerous workers. Despite some species differences, the spectacular laminar pattern, indicating morphological specialization, exceeds that of the superior colliculus of primates, its presumptive mammalian homologue. From six to sixteen separate

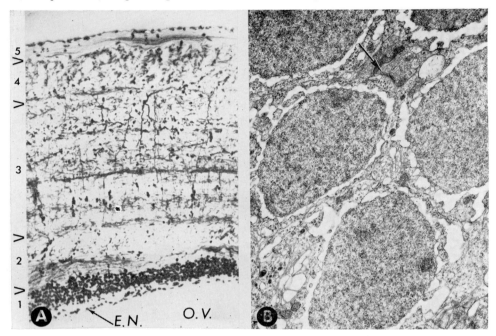

FIG. 1. *a*, Transverse section of part of the optic tectum of the northern anchovy showing the five principal layers: 1, stratum griseum periventriculare; 2, stratum fibrosum profundum; 3, stratum griseum centrale; 4, stratum plexiforme et fibrosum externum; 5, stratum fibrosum marginale: *o.v.*, optocoele; *e.n.*, ependymal cell nuclei. Bodian-silver impregnation. ×300. *b*, electron micrograph of subependymal matrix in the optic tectum of the bluegill. The presence of axosomatic synapses (one shown at arrow) indicates that these small and poorly differentiated cells must include neurons. The dilation of endoplasmic reticulum and nuclear envelope is probably related to the method of preservation. ×15,000.

layers of this laminar structure were distinguished by different workers, depending to a large extent on the species studied, e.g., Fusari (1887), van Gehuchten (1894), P. Ramón y Cajal (1899), and Leghissa (1955).

Inspection of the fine structure of optic tecta from a large variety of teleost fish suggests a division into five principal layers, most of which can be further subdivided, depending on the degree of differentiation present in the different species. The following classification is based principally on the recent description by Leghissa (1955) (Fig. 1*a*).

Stratum Griseum Periventriculare

This innermost layer contains many small cell nuclei. Those lining the optic ventricle are the nuclei of ependymal cells which extend their processes through the entire thickness of the tectum to form endfeet under the external "pial" membrane. The ultrastructure of these ependymal cells in the fish tectum has been described recently (Kruger and Maxwell 1966). Some of the cells in the subependymal matrix layer could be undifferentiated neuroblasts. This view is supported by the observation that in very young fish the space below the developing mesencephalic roof is filled with these cells which gradually concentrate into the final periventricular gray layer during formation of the optocoele. The optocoele appears as two lateral vesicles separated by a medial accumulation of these small cells which differentiate here into torus longitudinalis and valvula cerebelli (Schwassmann 1965). Kirsche and Kirsche (1961) found in regeneration experiments that sparing of this "matrix" layer was essential for tectal regeneration. Based on evidence from Golgi studies, P. Ramón y Cajal (1899) and Leghissa (1955) classify numerous cells in this periventricular gray as small pyriform neurons extending their processes into peripheral tectal layers, and electron-microscopic evidence demonstrates synapses on some of these elements (Fig. 1*b*). The presence of axosomatic contacts on some of these cells renders it likely that this layer is not simply a functional pluripotential "reservoir." Further studies to differentiate the cells in this layer are currently in progress. There seems to be no significant difference in the appearance of this cellular layer among species; its relative thickness and cell density are greatest in immature fish.

Stratum Fibrosum Profundum

Little interspecies variability is noted in this heavy layer of fibers which are probably efferent from the tectum, although Leghissa (1955) lists centrifugal as well as centripetal fibers. Bundles of fibers penetrate the periventricular gray near the midline dorsally and cross to the contralateral tectum as the intertectal commissure, or enter the torus longitudinalis. The separation of the periventricular cell and fiber layers is indistinct in the lateral and ventrolateral portions of the tectum, where heavy fiber tracts penetrate the periventricular gray, forming the tractus tectobulbaris and tractus tectospinalis.

Stratum Griseum Centrale

This is the layer of greatest thickness in the fish tectum. It contains numerous kinds of neurons which have been described from Golgi preparations (P. Ramón y Cajal 1899; S. Ramón y Cajal 1911; Leghissa 1955), but is chiefly a synaptic neuropil. Pyramidal neurons with radially oriented dendritic trunks as well as multipolar neurons with horizontally directed dendrites can be seen in silver-impregnated preparations. Further subdivision of this neuropil layer is easily accomplished in the optic tecta of those fish with presumably better vision. Ramification of dendritic arborizations at rather precise horizontal levels results in the appearance of two or more plexus layers. The differentiation of horizontal plexus layers is quite distinct in opaleye, anchovy, mackerel, bass, bluegill, and trout, and even more precise in the cichlid. A few conspicuously large neurons are seen slightly below the heaviest plexus layer in the anchovy tectum. These cells appear to be enveloped by thickly impregnated fibers extending into this plexus and also into the external plexiform layer. Electron-microscopic examination of the fine structure of the optic tectum, especially of the central gray layer, indicates even further complexity. Despite the relative scarcity of cells apparent in light microscopy, well-developed and easily identifiable neurons are readily encountered (Fig. 2). Tectal neurons display the distinctive arrays of rough endoplasmic reticulum and Golgi membranes characteristic of vertebrate neurons. On the basis of nuclear morphology alone, they are usually easy to differentiate from glial cells. The latter are relatively sparse compared with mammalian brain, but astrocytes, oligodendrocytes, and ependymal cells have been identified (Kruger and Maxwell 1966, 1967). The number of neurons in the central gray is surprisingly small, especially in relation to the enormous richness of the synaptic neuropil (Fig. 3a) in which the density of axon terminal knobs is greater than in mammalian cerebral cortex. Since the vast majority of terminals make axodendritic rather than axo-somatic contacts (Fig. 3a and Fig. 2 inset), it would seem probable that either the dendritic arborizations of tectal neurons have not been fully impregnated in Golgi preparations reported to date, or that some of the dendrites are derived from neuron somata outside the tectum, a less likely alternative.

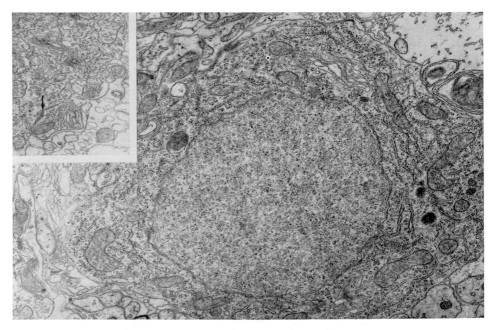

FIG. 2. Electron micrograph of a typical neuron in the stratum griseum centrale of the bluegill optic tectum. Note the relatively homogeneous nucleoplasm, extensive granular endoplasmic reticulum, free ribosomes, and Golgi apparatus. ×22,900. *Inset,* Axosomatic synapse (arrow) from the central gray layer of bluegill optic tectum. ×29,500. (From Fig. 15, Kruger, L., and Maxwell, D. S. 1967. *J. Comp. Neurol.* 129: 139, with permission of the Wistar Institute of Anatomy and Biology.)

Stratum Plexiforme et Fibrosum Externum

This layer, in its external part, contains optic nerve fibers spreading over the tectum, and probably some of their terminations in the inner plexiform portion. This latter plexiform portion is of particular interest in electrophysiological studies of the fish tectum. Maximal unit activity, responding to luminous stimulation of the contralateral eye, can be recorded when the tip of the microelectrode is in this layer, below the optic nerve fiber bundles. The optic fiber layer is most conspicuous in those fish species with well-developed vision; it is thicker near the dorsomedial and the ventrolateral edge of the tectum from where the fibers spread over the tectal surface. Electron micrographs demonstrate that, although the majority of axons in this layer appear to be myelinated, huge clusters of fascicles of unmyelinated axons are interspersed (Fig. 3b). Unfortunately, the lack of success in tracing optic axon degeneration beyond the external fiber layer with present methods has severely limited the experimental approach to identifying the site and mode of termination of different fiber groups.

Stratum Fibrosum Marginale

This external fibrous layer, described by Leghissa (1955), is apparent in certain regions of the tectum. It consists of relatively few bundles of long fibers, which are frequently found to traverse all tectal layers obliquely toward the torus longitudinalis.

Insufficient experimental evidence prevents identification of the different tectal strata with regard to their role in vision. However, some of the results obtained by Leghissa (1950, 1955) might be mentioned in this context. In comparing the thickness of the different layers

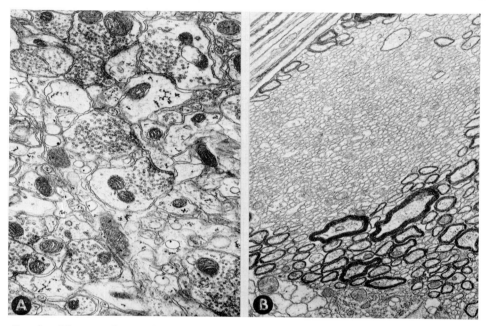

Fig. 3. *a*, Electron micrograph of synaptic neuropil in the central gray of the bluegill optic tectum. Note the presence of axodendritic synapses. ×21,700. *b*, electron micrograph from the stratum fibrosum externum of the bluegill optic tectum showing a large fascicle of unmyelinated axons surrounded by myelinated axons. ×35,200.

of the right and left optic tecta several months after unilateral eye removal, a considerable reduction was noted not only in the optic nerve fiber layer, but also in the external and the plexiform portions of the central neuropil (Leghissa 1955). In another reported experiment, removal of one eye at an early larval stage and inspection of the tectum two years later in silver-impregnated sections revealed the apparent absence of certain types of neurons in the outer as well as the inner portion of the neuropil (Leghissa 1950). Considering the known selectivity and poor reproducibility of silver-impregnation methods, additional evidence from experimental degeneration studies would appear necessary in order to clearly establish a functional classification of tectal elements. The results obtained by Wawrzyniak (1962), employing histochemical methods, corroborate in principle those reported by Leghissa.

Retinotectal Topographic Relations

Experimental degeneration studies have provided evidence for an orderly projection of retinal quadrants onto the optic tectum of fishes (Lubsen 1921; Ströer 1939; Akert 1949; Leghissa 1955) and corresponding results were obtained for other vertebrates. Tracing regenerating optic nerve axons from selected retinal regions to their terminations on the optic tectum, Attardi and Sperry (1963) demonstrated the local specificity of these regenerating fibers and obtained a map of the retinotectal projection. Microelectrode mapping techniques have further demonstrated the precision of the visual field projection onto the tectum (Jacobson and Gaze 1964; Schwassmann and Kruger 1965a, b). The method of electrophysiological mapping of the fish tectum will be described briefly.

The anesthetized fish is mounted in a tank of Lucite. Aerated anesthetic solution (MS-222, Sandoz) flows over the gills of the fish through a fitted mouthpiece. The water level is adjusted so that the eyes are submerged but the exposed midbrain remains above the water. The left eye of the fish is positioned in the center of a water-filled hemisphere of Lucite which is mounted vertically, its plane surface forming the side of the tank. A grid of coordinates, consisting of a vertical and a horizontal meridian which intersect at the center of the lateral visual field, and their 10° parallels is marked on the convex hemispheric surface where luminous stimuli are presented. A steel microelectrode, insulated except for the fine tip (Green 1958), is mounted on the shaft of a micrometer head which is attached to a micromanipulator. This allows calibrated movement of the electrode in all three planes. Using conventional amplifying and recording methods, the electrode is placed on the surface of the right tectum and slowly advanced to a depth at which a maximum of unit activity influenced by luminous stimulation of the left eye is encountered. The photic stimulus for mapping receptive fields consists of a brief pulse of light transmitted from a glow modulator tube through a flexible fiber optics bundle with an effective circular aperture of 0.5° when displayed at the hemispheric surface. This stimulus is moved over the hemisphere in small steps and the area from which unit activity can be influenced is marked on the surface, constituting a multiunit receptive field. The entire dorsal surface of the tectum is explored by moving the electrode in equal 0.5- or 0.25-mm steps. The ventral portions of the tectum are reached by passing the electrode through the dorsal layers and optic ventricle, using the same lateral and longitudinal coordinates. The entire surface of the tectum can be mapped in this manner, resulting in a complete map of the visual field where each of the small receptive field outlines corresponds to a particular point on the optic tectum (Schwassmann and Kruger 1965a). By utilizing the horizontal and vertical coordinates of the many small receptive fields and relating them to their corresponding recording sites, the visual field coordinates can be outlined on the optic tectum (Fig. 4).

The general orientation of the visual field projection onto the optic tectum is the same in all teleosts investigated to date, and agrees with that of other vertebrate classes. The dorsal half of the visual field projects to the dorsal tectal surface, and the ventral field to the ventral tectum. Nasal fields have an anterior tectal projection, while temporal portions are represented posteriorly. For several species of freshwater fish the projection of the visual field is essentially linear on the tectal surface (see Fig. 4). For example, an approximately even spacing of the 10° parallels appears in the tectal maps of the freshwater bass and the carp (Fig. 4a, b). These fields are represented on the tectum with no obvious distortions (Schwassmann and Kruger 1965a). For certain species, however, distortions of retinotectal topography can occur.

Nonlinear Tectal Projections

An example of the nonlinear projection to the tectum was noted when studying the visual system of *Anableps*, the so-called four-eyed fish (Schwassmann and Kruger 1965*b*). In this species, a horizontal band just above the water line occupies a disproportionately large projection area (Schwassmann and Kruger 1965*b*). From Figure 4*c* the wide spacing between the horizontal meridian in the lateral tectum and the dorsal 10° parallel is apparent. Furthermore, the spacing between the 10° and 20° parallels is also wider than that between the parallels within the rest of the dorsal or ventral fields. Within this magnified band, there is a denser concentration of visual receptive fields than is found elsewhere.

A second example of expanded tectal representation within a particular region of the tectum occurs in three marine serranids of the genus *Paralabrax*. The spotted bass is shown as an example in Figure 4*d*, and comparable results were obtained from the kelp bass and from the sand bass. For these fish, a disproportionately large region of the anteroventral

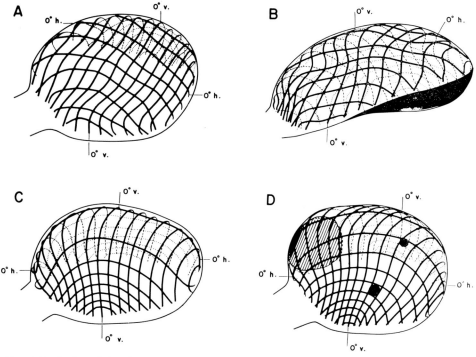

FIG. 4. Projection of the visual field of the left eye onto the right optic tectum in four species of teleosts. *a*, Large-mouth freshwater bass; *b*, carp; *c*, four-eyed fish *Anableps*; *d*, spotted marine bass. The four optic tecta are shown as seen from above; anterior is to the left, medial is down. The horizontal meridian (0° *h*) with its 10° dorsal and ventral parallels and the vertical meridian (0° *v*) with its 10° rostral and temporal parallels are shown as solid lines on the dorsum of the tectum, as broken and dotted lines in the underlying lateroventral aspect of the tectum. The projection of the approximately 10° area of foveal vision is indicated by slanted lines in *d;* it lies in the ventral curvature of the tectum. The projections of equally large areas of the dorsal and of the ventral visual field are shown by the two small dark circles. (*a* and *b* from Figs. 5 and 8, Schwassmann, H. O., and Kruger, L. 1965. *J. Comp. Neurol.* 124: 120, 121, with permission of the Wistar Institute of Anatomy and Biology. *c* from Fig. 6, Schwassmann, H. O., and Kruger, L. 1965, *Vision Res.* 5: 276, with permission of Pergamon Press.)

tectum is activated by a small area within the anterior visual field. The receptive fields of visual units are smaller and more concentrated within this 10° area. Figure 4*d* illustrates the tectal representation of this area, and outlines the projections of other 10° regions from different parts of the field for comparison.

Magnification of the projection from a specific region in the visual field indicates a specialized retinal region, usually called the "area centralis." High cone density is usually found as a basic feature of this area centralis in the fish eye (Tamura 1957; O'Connell 1963), but the density of ganglion cells may also be a good criterion. In *Anableps* the number of ganglion cells per unit area correlates directly with the magnification of the area just above the water surface. A similar correlation has been demonstrated by Jacobson (1962) in a species of frog, where a horizontal band of higher tectal magnification is found. The location of the "area centralis" (perhaps more appropriately called "area temporalis" in this circumstance) in the serranid retina is easily detected in histological sections by the high ganglion cell density. The ganglion cells here are arranged in three to five rows as compared to the single row elsewhere in the retina. The presence of a fovea as a shallow depression inside the area can also be recognized in histological preparations. Several morphological features are characteristic for the foveal region, e.g., thinner and more densely packed cones, and an external nuclear layer containing fewer nuclei than elsewhere in the retina; the foveal depression is accompanied by a reduction in thickness of the optic nerve fiber layer, emphasized by a thickening of this layer at the foveal periphery. The apparent thinness of the fiber layer in the fovea, despite increased number of ganglion cells, is a consequence of the tendency of optic axons from the more temporal retina to pass around instead of through the foveal region.

Other marine teleosts are known to possess a foveate retina (Kahmann 1934, 1936). In the serranids we have investigated, the region of foveal vision lies in the anterior binocular field. Binocular convergent movements are necessary to superimpose the foveal fields of both eyes. The significance of binocular as well as monocular fixation movements noted in behavioral experiments should be correlated with these anatomical findings.

Functional Significance of the Retinotectal Projection

The orderly retinotectal topography is a well-documented feature of the fish visual system. It has its morphological basis in the precise anatomical arrangement of optic nerve fiber endings in the optic tectum, presumably a consequence of neurochemical specificity (Sperry 1955, 1965) which enables these fibers to terminate and to make synaptic contact with tectal elements only at a specific tectal locus. It remains to be demonstrated to what extent the tectal topography of optic fiber terminations is important for higher-order visual processes. Previous experiments by Wichers and Dijkgraaf (reported in Healey 1957) had already indicated such a dependency. After partial ablation of the right optic tectum in *Phoxinus*, Wichers and Dijkgraaf noted the absence of feeding and fixation reactions to appropriate stimulation within the presumptive topographically corresponding region of the visual field of the left eye.

In order to demonstrate in greater detail the dependence of visual function on the retinotectal topography, an attempt was made in our laboratory to show if localized lesions in the optic tectum would result in scotomata corresponding in location to the lesion, in conformity with the retinotectal projection pattern. Classical cardiac conditioning, recording the electrocardiogram by means of implanted wire electrodes (McCleary and Bernstein 1959; McCleary 1960), was employed as a convenient method for examining the visual field before and after tectal lesions. The conditional stimulus was a one-half degree circular luminous stimulus of one second duration which could be displayed anywhere in the visual field of the left eye. During conditioning, the conditional stimulus was followed by a brief electric shock (unconditional stimulus), resulting in a conditioned response, apparent as a delay in successive heart beats. After conditioning, a lesion was placed in the right optic tectum with an iridectomy knife. Resulting scotomata could be identified and delimited by the absence or presence of the conditioned response when displaying the luminous stimulus in different areas of the visual field. The visual projection onto the optic tectum was subsequently mapped by the electrophysiological method described above, and the brain was preserved for histological examination.

Aside from providing some additional information concerning the visual role of specific fiber tracts, these experiments clearly demonstrated the importance of the retinotectal topographic pattern. A localized lesion in the optic tectum impairs or abolishes vision in a specific and limited area of the visual field. The scotomata found in these experiments were relatively large, 20°–50° in diameter, and were possibly the result of damage in deeper tectal layers.

Concluding Comments

Comparative anatomical study of visual centers in teleost fish reveals some variability among different species. The noted differences predominantly concern the degree of development in relative size and differentiation of the optic tracts and tectum and certain diencephalic structures which can be implicated in vision. The optic tectum is the site of termination of the majority of optic tract fibers. It is of relatively large size and exhibits the highest degree of differentiation into separate distinct layers, indicative of specialized function, in those fish which rely on vision as the dominant sense. Insufficient evidence from experimental degeneration studies makes it difficult to assign specific visual functions to certain substructures of the optic tectum and to other mesencephalic and diencephalic nuclei. A few of these nuclei have been referred to in this presentation which are probably concerned with vision and for which fiber connections with optic tract and tectum have been claimed. They were selected here because they are found to be well developed in those species which rely predominantly on vision, and are less conspicuous in fish with apparently poor vision.

An orderly topographic pattern has been demonstrated for the projection of the visual field onto the optic tectum. Specialization of this retinotectal projection is present in some species where certain areas of the visual field have a magnified representation in the tectum. Magnification of the projection areas at the tectal level is due to specialization of the retina, the presence of an "area centralis." This area is a horizontal band in the eye of *Anableps* and a circular "area temporalis" in some marine bass eyes where, in addition, a shallow fovea is found within the area. A correlation exists between the degree of tectal magnification of visual areas and the ganglion cell density in the retina.

Little experimental evidence exists concerning the possible function of the optic tectum in fish vision other than a detailed knowledge of the precise topographic relations between retina and tectum. The demonstrated directionality of eye movements in response to electrical stimulation of different regions of the dorsal tectal surface (Akert 1949; Leghissa 1950) should not lead one to regard the tectum exclusively as a center for optomotor reflexes. Electrophysiological investigations of the response characteristics of single visual units have been successful (Jacobson and Gaze 1964) but difficulties exist in interpreting these data with respect to optic tectum function. Although the fish optic tectum is currently the subject of intensive research in neurophysiology and neuroanatomy, it is evident that even relatively complete knowledge of the role of the retina and optic tectum is not likely to solve all problems in visual physiology of fishes.

Acknowledgment

We are greatly indebted to Mrs. Olga Fiorello, Mrs. Sharon Sampogna, and Dr. David Maxwell for valuable assistance. This study was supported by grants from the United States Public Health Service (B-04578) and the National Science Foundation (GB-2796).

References

Akert, K. 1949. Der visuelle Greifreflex. *Helv. Physiol. Acta* 7:112–34.

Ariëns Kappers, C. U. 1906. The structure of the teleostean and selachian brain. *J. Comp. Neurol.* 16:1–109.

Ariëns Kappers, C. U.; Huber, G. C.; and Crosby, E. C. 1936. *The comparative anatomy of the nervous system of vertebrates, including man.* 3 vols. Reprinted 1960 by Hafner, New York.

Attardi, D. G., and Sperry, R. W. 1963. Preferential selection of central pathways by regenerating optic fibers. *Exp. Neurol.* 7:46–64.

Bellonci, J. 1888. Über die centrale Endigung des Nervus opticus bei den Vertebraten. *Z. Wiss. Zool.* 47:1–46.

Franz, V. 1912. Beiträge zur Kenntnis des Mittelhirns und Zwischenhirns der Knochenfische. *Folia Neurobiol.* 6:402–41.

Fusari, R. 1887. Untersuchungen über die feinere Anatomie des Gehirns der Teleostier. *Int. Monatsschr. Anat. Physiol.* 4:275–300.

Gehuchten, A. van. 1894. Contribution à l'étude du système nerveux des téléostéens. *Cellule* 10:255–95.

Green, J. D. 1958. A simple microelectrode for recording from the central nervous system. *Nature* 182:962.

Gross, J. 1903. Über die Sehnervenkreuzung bei den Reptilien. *Zool. Jahrb. Abt. Anat. Ontog. Tiere.* 17:763–99.

Healey, E. G. 1957. The nervous system. In *The physiology of fishes*, ed. Margaret E. Brown, 2:1–119. New York: Academic Press, Inc.

Hubbs, C. L., and Hubbs, L. C. 1944. Bilateral asymmetry and bilateral variation in fishes. *Papers Mich. Acad. Sci.* 30:229–310.

Jacobson, M. 1962. The representation of the retina on the optic tectum of the frog: Correlation between retino-tectal magnification and retinal ganglion cell count. *Quart. J. Exp. Physiol.* 47:170–78.

Jacobson, M., and Gaze, R. M. 1964. Types of visual response from single units in the optic tectum and optic nerve of the goldfish. *Quart. J. Exp. Physiol.* 49:199–209.

Kahmann, H. 1934. Über das Vorkommen einer Fovea centralis im Knochenfischauge. *Zool. Anz.* 106:50–55.

———. 1936. Über das foveale Sehen der Wirbeltiere. I. Über die Fovea centralis und die Fovea lateralis bei einigen Wirbeltieren. *V. Graefe's Arch. Ophthalm.* 135: 265–76.

Karten, H., and Revzin, A. M. 1966. The afferent connections of the nucleus rotundus in the pigeon. *Brain Res.* 2:368–77.

Kirsche, W., and Kirsche, K. 1961. Experimentelle Untersuchungen zur Frage der Regeneration und Funktion des Tectum opticum von *Carassius carassius*, L. *Z. Mikroskopisch-anat. Forsch.* 67:140–82.

Klüver, H., and Barrera, E. 1953. A method for the combined staining of cells and fibers in the nervous system. *J. Neuropath. Exp. Neurol.* 12:400–403.

Kruger, L., and Berkowitz, E. C. 1960. The main afferent connections of the reptilian telencephalon as determined by degeneration and electrophysiological methods. *J. Comp. Neurol.* 115:125–41.

Kruger, L., and Maxwell, D. S. 1966. The fine structure of ependymal processes in the teleost optic tectum. *Amer. J. Anat.* 119:479–98.

———. 1967. Comparative fine structure of vertebrate neuroglia: Teleosts and reptiles. *J. Comp. Neurol.* 129:115–42.

Larrabee, A. P. 1906. The optic chiasma of teleosts: A study of inheritance. *Proc. Amer. Acad. Arts and Science* 42:215–31.

Leghissa, S. 1950. Il sostrato anatomico dei riflessi ottico-oculomotori nei teleostei. *Monit. Zool. Ital. Suppl.* 59:1–11.

———. 1955. La struttura microscopica e la citoarchitettonica del tetto ottico dei pesci teleostei. *Z. Anat. Entwicklungsgesch.* 118:427–63.

Lissner, H. 1923. Das Gehirn der Knochenfische. *Wiss. Meeresunt. Helgoland* 14: 125–84.

Lubsen, J. 1921. Over de projectie van het netvlies op het tectum opticum bij een beenvisch. *Ned. T. Geneesk.* 2:1258–61.

McCleary, R. A. 1960. Type of response as a factor in interocular transfer in the fish. *J. Comp. Physiol. Psychol.* 53:311–21.

McCleary, R. A., and Bernstein, J. J. 1959. A unique method for the control of brightness cues in study of color vision in fish. *Physiol. Zool.* 32:284–92.

Meader, R. G. 1934. The optic system of the teleost *Holocentrus*. I. The primary optic pathways and the corpus geniculatum complex. *J. Comp. Neurol.* 60:361–407.

O'Connell, C. P. 1963. The structure of the eye of *Sardinops caerulea, Engraulis mordax*, and four other pelagic marine teleosts. *J. Morph.* 113:287–330.

Parker, G. H. 1903. The optic chiasma in teleosts and its bearing on the asymmetry of the *Heterosomata* (flatfishes). *Bull. Mus. Comp. Zool.* 40:221–42.

Powell, T. P. S., and Cowan, W. M. 1957. The thalamo-striate projection in the avian brain. *J. Anat.* 91:571.

———. 1961. The thalamic projection upon the telencephalon in the pigeon. *J. Anat.* 95:78–109.

Powell, T. P. S., and Kruger, L. 1960. The thalamic projection upon the telencephalon in *Lacerta viridis*. *J. Anat.* 94:528–42.

Ramón y Cajal, P. 1899. El lobulo optico de los peces. *Rev. Trimestr. Micrograf.* 4:87–107.

Ramón y Cajal, S. 1911. *Histologie du système nerveux de l'homme et des vertébrés*. Paris: Maloine, 2 vols.

Revzin, A. M., and Karten, H. 1966/67. Rostral projections of the optic tectum and the nucleus rotundus in the pigeon. *Brain Res.* 3:264–76.

Schnitzlein, H. N. 1962. The habenula and the dorsal thalamus of some teleosts. *J. Comp. Neurol.* 118:225–68.

Schwassmann, H. O. 1965. Functional development of visual pathways in larval sardines and anchovies. *Mar. Res. Comm. Cal. Coop. Oceanic Fish. Invest. Rept.* 10:64–70.

Schwassmann, H. O., and Kruger, L. 1965*a*. Organization of the visual projection upon the optic tectum of some freshwater fish. *J. Comp. Neurol.* 124: 113–26.

———. 1965*b*. Experimental analysis of the visual system of the four-eyed fish, *Anableps microlepis. Vision Res.* 5:269–81.

Solger, B. F. 1877. Über das noch nicht beschriebene Chiasma nervi optici von *Engraulis. Sitz. Ber. Naturforsch. Ges. Halle* 1877:10–11.

Sperry, R. W. 1955. Functional regeneration in the optic system. In *Regeneration in the central nervous system*, ed. W. F. Windle, pp. 66–76. Springfield, Ill.: Thomas.

———. 1965. Embryogenesis of behavioral nerve nets. In *Organogenesis*, ed. R. L. De Haan and H. Ursprung, pp. 161–86. New York: Holt, Rinehart and Winston.

Ströer, W. F. H. 1939. Zur vergleichenden Anatomie des primären optischen Systems bei Wirbeltieren. *Z. Anat. Entwicklungsgesch.* 110:301–21.

Tamura, T. 1957. A study of visual perception in fish, especially on resolving power and accommodation. *Bull. Jap. Soc. Sci. Fish.* 22:536–57.

Wawrzyniak, M. 1962. Chemoarchitektonische Studien am Tectum opticum von Teleostiern unter normalen und experimentellen Bedingungen. *Z. Zellforsch.* 58:234–64.

Weber, E. H. 1827. Beim Häring durchbohrt der Sehnerv des rechten Auges den des linken. *Meckel's Arch. Anat. Physiol.* 1827:317.

Ziesmer, C. 1952. Silberfärbung an Paraffinschnitten. Eine weitere Verbesserung der Bodian-Methode. *Mikroskopie* 7:415–17.

2

Physiology of Fish Vision

Marcus Jacobson

Thomas C. Jenkins Department of Biophysics
The Johns Hopkins University, Baltimore

Functional organization in the fish visual system has been investigated along two interconnected main lines. First, the operational characteristics of the components have been analyzed
to find out how information is processed at various levels in the visual system. In this field
it is much easier to obtain experimental results, usually electrical potentials, than to interpret
them. Functional localization is the second main problem. Advances have been slow because methods of marking the tip of the microelectrode, and other localizing techniques,
are not yet good enough. Although electrical responses are as a rule easily recorded, it is
often very difficult to determine their origin in a tissue as complex as the retina or optic
tectum. It appears that a combination of anatomical and physiological methods is needed to
work out the functional connections in the visual system.

In 1963 Marks showed by microspectrophotometry of single cones that there are three
kinds of cones, each with a single pigment, which have difference spectra with maxima in
the blue (467 nm), green (533 nm), and red (620 nm) (Marks 1963, 1965; Liebman and Entine
1964). This knowledge has made it possible to start interpreting the chromatic responses
recorded from units in the retina proximal to the receptors. The outputs from the three sets
of differently pigmented cones combine when they converge on more proximal neurons. As a
result the spectral sensitivities of units in the retina, optic nerve, and visual centers in the
brain may be very complex.

The electrical responses which Tomita (1965) has obtained directly from the cones appear to be derived in a relatively simple way from the cone pigment absorption spectra. The
cone responses are maintained negative potentials with three kinds of monophasic spectral
response curves, each with a peak roughly corresponding with the maximum of one of the
cone pigments in the blue, green, or red. These responses do not show area summation and
their receptive fields are very small, as is to be expected if they originate in single cones. These
results, then, are consistent with the Young-Helmholtz theory of color vision. Unlike the

17

cone responses, many of the electrical responses recorded proximal to the receptors are biphasic, like the opponent processes of the Hering theory. This transformation of the output after it has been delivered from the cones to the proximal neurons has been studied mainly by recording the S-potentials from fish retina.

S-potentials were first recorded from fish retina by Svaetichin (1953, 1956). They are sustained during retinal illumination, graded with the intensity of the stimulus, and may be negative or positive depending on the wavelength of the stimulus. There are two types: L-responses and C-responses (MacNichol and Svaetichin 1958; Svaetichin and MacNichol 1958). L-responses are negative at all effective wavelengths and seem to be related to the luminosity of the stimulus rather than to its color. These responses are recorded in the region of the horizontal cells. The C-responses are negative (indicating hyperpolarization) at short wavelengths and positive (indicating depolarization) at long wavelengths, or vice versa. In one type of C-response the opposed maxima are in the yellow and blue, in another type in the red and green. C-responses are recorded at the level of the bipolar cells. The origin of the S-potential has not been completely solved by electrode tip-marking methods (Mac-Nichol and Svaetichin 1958; Oikawa, Ogawa, and Motokawa 1959; Tomita *et al.* 1959). The L-responses probably arise from the horizontal cells, which are very numerous and large in the fish retina (MacNichol and Svaetichin 1958). The C-response may be recorded when the electrode tip is in the Muller cells (Svaetichin *et al.* 1961, 1964). The present evidence falls short of allowing safe conclusions to be drawn concerning the role of the S-potentials in vision.

Color-coded responses from retinal ganglion cells were first found in the isolated gold-fish retina (Wagner, MacNichol, and Wolbarsht 1960). The spectral sensitivity of some "on-off" ganglion cells in the goldfish retina are biphasic, with maxima either in the red and green or yellow and blue. In other cells the "on-off" responses have the same spectral sensitivity, with a maximum in the red (Wagner, MacNichol, and Wolbarsht 1960; MacNichol, Wol-barsht, and Wagner 1961). The peaks of the spectral sensitivity curves of the color-coded ganglion cells do not coincide with the maxima of the difference spectra of the three cone pigments in the goldfish (Marks 1965). This discrepancy is to be expected if the ganglion cell responses result from interaction between the output of the cones (De Valois and Jones 1961; Jacobson 1964; MacNichol 1964; Naka and Rushton 1966). It can be shown theoretically that the outputs from the two sets of cones, each containing a different pigment, could sum algebraically to give an action spectrum which is the weighted mean of the cone contributions (Naka and Rushton 1966). Red-green ganglion cells of the goldfish have maxima at 650 and 500 nm (Wolbarsht, Wagner, and MacNichol 1961).

In the goldfish tectum three classes of color-coded units have been found: R-G with maxima at 630–651 and 497–519 nm, Y-B with maxima at 552–605 and 462 nm, and R-B with maxima at 605–651 and 462 nm (Jacobson 1964). The spectral sensitivity curves of these units are much narrower than pigment absorption curves (Jacobson 1964), very much like the narrow spectral sensitivity curves recorded from ganglion cells of the tench (Granit 1941) and carp (Witkovsky 1965). Under photopic conditions some tectal units have broad spectral sensitivity curves which fit the 620-nm pigment curve. In these units the effect of chromatic adaptation with any effective wavelength is to produce a uniform reduction of the sensitivity without any change in the wavelength of the maximum. This shows that only one pigment is involved in the response. The effect of chromatic adaptation on color-coded units depends on the wavelength of the adapting light (Wagner, MacNichol, and Wolbarsht 1960). By using monochromatic light of the appropriate wavelength to adapt one component without appreciably affecting the other, an increase in the sensitivity of the un-adapted component occurs, with a shift in the peak sensitivity toward the maximum of the cone pigment (if only one is involved).

I shall deal briefly with receptive field organization and the interactions within the receptive field. The spatial organization of receptive fields of retinal ganglion cells is a knotty problem. First, consider the observation that the geometry of a ganglion cell receptive field mapped in the usual way, by brief flashes of a small stationary light, undoubtedly changes when tested under other conditions—for example, with monochromatic light or with moving objects. Therefore, the definition of a receptive field can only be an operational one. The functional anatomy of the receptive field will vary with the conditions, as is well recognized, for example, during dark adaptation. There are also relatively minor technical difficulties such as the level of anaesthesia and correction of refractive errors.

The main problem in defining the boundary of the receptive field is that excitation may be produced by scattered light from a stimulus outside the receptive field. One may say that no sharp boundaries are likely to exist and that in "on-off" units considerable overlap of the "on" and "off" zones is usually seen. Some of the color-coded ganglion cells of the goldfish (Wagner, MacNichol, and Wolbarsht 1963) have complete overlap of the receptive fields of the opponent processes giving "on" and "off" responses. However, as is shown in Figure 1, there is often a graded change in the relative sensitivities of the two processes, with the "off" sensitivity relatively highest in the center and the "on" relatively higher in the periphery of the field or vice versa (Wagner, MacNichol, and Wolbarsht 1963). The receptive fields in the isolated retina frequently have diameters exceeding 1 mm, subtending about 20°. Therefore the large receptive fields of optic nerve fibers recorded in the intact goldfish (Jacobson and Gaze 1964) are probably not entirely due to refractive errors.

Many of these fields recorded in the optic nerve and in the tectum (Jacobson and Gaze 1964) have side-by-side "on" and "off" zones similar to the "simple" units in the cat visual cortex (Hubel and Wiesel 1959, 1962). Other receptive fields in the goldfish optic nerve are concentrically organized, with an excitatory center and an inhibitory surround. These respond to small stationary or moving objects, but not to large objects or diffuse illumination. They behave like the convexity detectors in the frog retina (Maturana *et al.* 1960; Gaze and Jacobson 1963), and respond best to a stimulus small enough to fit into the center of the receptive field, but they give reduced responses to larger objects. That is, they do not show area summation above a critical stimulus size. Some of these units are directionally selective (Jacobson and Gaze 1964). They respond to movement in one direction only, the preferred direction, not to movement in the contrary, or null, direction (Fig. 2). The response is independent of the contrast of the stimulus. Therefore it is not produced by the stimulus crossing boundaries between "on" and "off" zones in the receptive field. Barlow and Levick (1965) have made a very careful analysis of the mechanism of directionally selective units in the rabbit retina. In the rabbit retina the directional selectivity has been shown to be the property of small subunits, each subtending about 2° of the receptive field (Barlow and Levick 1963, 1965; Levick 1966).

In the goldfish, interaction between two stimuli moving in opposite directions occurs over an area larger than the area of the receptive field mapped by small stationary flashes of light. Small bar-shaped stimuli moving in opposite directions interact when separated by more than 20°. Complete nulling has been found when the two stimuli moving toward each other are separated by about 5° (Jacobson, unpublished). However, no interaction has been found when two stimuli move away from each other, even when separated by less than 5°, showing that the inhibition is directionally selective.

Interaction between two small spots of light, one which excites and one which inhibits discharges from a ganglion cell, occurs over a receptive field hundreds of microns in diameter in the isolated goldfish retina (Easter 1967). This area is much larger than the receptive field

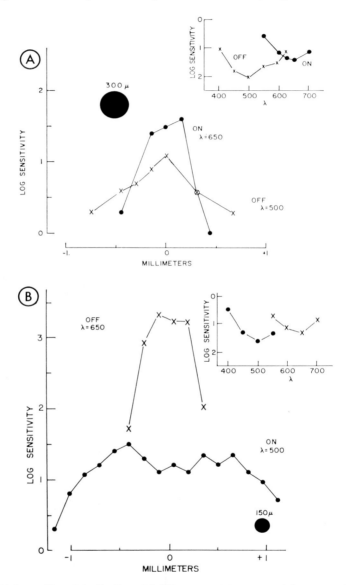

FIG. 1. Sensitivity profiles of the "on"- and "off"-component responses taken across the receptive fields of an "on"-center (*A*) and an "off"-center (*B*) color-coded ganglion cell of the goldfish retina. The large spots show the stimulus size with wavelengths in nm as indicated. Stimulus duration 0.5 sec. The spectral sensitivity curves of the "on" and "off" responses are shown in the upper right inset of *A* and *B* (from Wagner, Mac-Nichol, and Wolbarsht 1963).

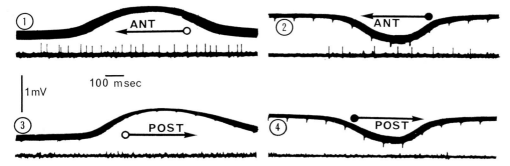

FIG. 2. Directionally selective response recorded from a single unit in the goldfish tectum. In each record the upper trace shows the passage of the stimulus as seen by a phototransistor mounted in the receptive field; the lower trace shows the response of the unit to a 2° spot of light (in 1 and 3) and a 2° black disk (in 2 and 4) moving in an anterior or posterior direction through the receptive field. The arrows indicate the direction of movement. To stationary stimuli the unit had an "on"-center with inhibitory surround. Selective response to movement in an anterior direction occurred irrespective of the contrast of the stimulus (from Jacobson and Gaze 1964).

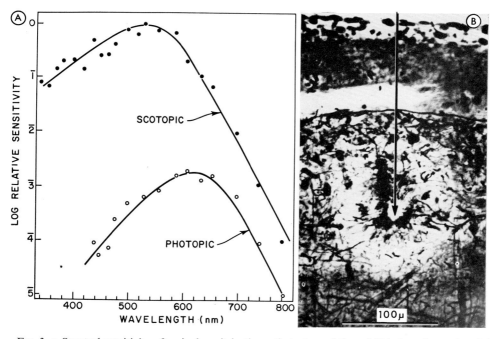

FIG. 3. *a,* Spectral sensitivity of a single unit in the optic tectum of the goldfish (equal quantum intensity spectrum). Scotopic sensitivity after 30 min dark adaptation; photopic sensitivity after adapting with white light of luminance 20 cd/m². *b,* The curves in *a* where recorded with a microelectrode from a single unit in the plexiform layer about 200 μ from the tectal surface. The arrow shows the most probable position of the unit in the center of a lesion made by brief passage of a current from the tip of the microelectrode.

of the ganglion cell. The interaction, therefore, must occur distal to the ganglion cell. The functional anatomy of these lateral interactions has not been discovered. Because techniques have not been developed for recording from the bipolar cells, their part in these lateral interactions is conjectural. It is possible that electrical interactions between bipolar cells may occur through low-resistance pathways (tight junctions) in the way in which they occur in many other tissues (Loewenstein *et al.* 1965; Penn 1966). However, the horizontal cells and amacrine cells are the most likely routes for lateral interaction in the retina. Recent studies of their anatomy (Dowling and Boycott 1965, 1966; Dowling, Brown, and Major 1966; Stell 1965; De Testa 1966) have resulted in a new appreciation of their importance.

The signals which travel up the optic nerve to the brain of the fish are the result of a great deal of information-processing in the retina. The retina deals with color, form, and movement simultaneously, and there must be a central mechanism for sorting these out. The problem is, How do the tectal cells (or cells in any visual center) distinguish between action potentials dealing with different attributes of the visual stimulus? Theoretically there are several ways this might be achieved. However the only way that it is known to occur is by segregating the information in different channels. This is clearer in the frog (Maturana *et al.* 1960) than in the goldfish (Jacobson and Gaze 1964). In the goldfish tectum, "on," "off," and "on-off" units, some of them color-coded, some directionally selective, have been recorded from the superficial layers down to about $150\,\mu$ from the surface. There is no apparent segregation of different kinds of units. At that depth a layer about 10–$20\,\mu$ thick is encountered from which only slowly adapting "on" and "off" responses are recorded (Fig. 3). These units, like dimming detectors in the frog tectum (Maturana *et al.* 1960), are segregated in this layer. These responses are not color-coded but they do show a Purkinje shift. Their scotopic spectral sensitivity curve has its maximum at 527 nm, while the photopic maximum is at 620 nm (Fig. 2). Both of these fit the Dartnall nomogram, and their shape is not altered by chromatic adaptation (Jacobson, unpublished).

We come finally to the functions of the tectum. What operations do the tectal neurons perform on the input from the retina? The brief answer is that we haven't the faintest idea.

Acknowledgment

Some of the author's work reported in this paper was supported by Grant GB 4622 from the National Science Foundation.

References

Barlow, H. B., and Levick, W. R. 1963. Are bipolar cells directionally selective? *J. Physiol. (Lond.).* 170:53–54P.

———. 1965. The mechanism of directionally selective units in rabbit's retina. *J. Physiol.* 178:477–504.

De Testa, A. S. 1966. Morphological studies on the horizontal and amacrine cells of the teleost retina. *Vision Res.* 6:51–59.

De Valois, R. L., and Jones, A. E. 1961. Single-cell analysis of the organization of the primate color-vision system. In *The visual system: Neurophysiology and psychophysics*, ed. R. Jung and H. Kornhuber, pp. 178–91. Berlin: Springer.

Dowling, J. E., and Boycott, B. B. 1965. Neural connections of the retina; fine structure of the inner plexiform layer. *Symp. Quant. Biol.* 30:393–402.

Dowling, J. E.; Brown J. E.; and, Major, D. 1966. Synapses of horizontal cells in rabbit and cat retinas. *Science* 153:1639–41.

Easter, S. S., Jr. 1967. Excitation and adaptation in the goldfish's retina: A microelectrode study. Ph.D. diss., Johns Hopkins University.

Gaze, R. M., and Jacobson, M. 1963. Convexity detectors in the frog's visual system. *J. Physiol. (Lond.)* 169:1P.

Granit, R. 1941. A relation between rod and cone substances based on photopic and scotopic spectra of *Cyprinus, Tinca, Anguilla* and *Testudo. Acta Physiol. Scand.* 2: 334–46.

Hubel, D. H., and Wiesel, T. N. 1959. Receptive fields of single neurones in the cat's striate cortex. *J. Physiol. (Lond.)* 148:574–91.

———. 1962. Receptive fields, binocular interaction and functional architecture in the cat's visual cortex. *J. Physiol. (Lond.)* 160:106–54.

Jacobson, M. 1964. Spectral sensitivity of single units in the optic tectum of the goldfish. *Quart. J. Exp. Physiol.* 49:384–94.

Jacobson, M., and Gaze, R. M. 1964. Types of visual response from single units in the optic tectum and optic nerve of the goldfish. *Quart. J. Exp. Physiol.* 49:199–209.

Levick, W. R. 1966. Receptive fields and trigger features of ganglion cells in the visual streak of the rabbit's retina. *J. Physiol. (Lond.)*. 188:285–307.

Liebman, P. A., and Entine, G. 1964. Sensitive low-light-level microspectro-photometer detection of photosensitive pigments of retinal cones. *J. Opt. Soc. Amer.* 54:1451–59.

Loewenstein, W. R.; Socolar, S. J.; Higashino, S.; Kanno, Y.; and Davidson, N. 1965. Intercellular communication: Renal, urinary bladder, sensory, and salivary gland cells. *Science* 149:295–98.

MacNichol, E. F., Jr. 1964. Retinal mechanisms of color vision. *Vision Res.* 4:119–33.

MacNichol, E. F., Jr., and Svaetichin, G. 1958. Electric responses from the isolated retinas of fishes. *Amer. J. Ophthal.* 46:26–40.

MacNichol, E. F., Jr.; Wolbarsht, M. L.; and Wagner, H. G. 1961. Electrophysiological evidence for a mechanism of color vision in the goldfish. In *Light and life*, ed. W. D. McElroy and B. Glass, pp. 795–813. Baltimore: Johns Hopkins Press.

Marks, W. B. 1963. Difference spectra of the visual pigments in single goldfish cones. Ph.D. diss., Johns Hopkins University.

———. 1965. Visual pigments of single goldfish cones. *J. Physiol. (Lond.)*. 178:14–32.

Maturana, H. R.; Lettvin, J. Y.; McCulloch, W. S.; and Pitts, W. H. 1960. Anatomy and physiology of vision in the frog (*Rana pipiens*). *J. Gen. Physiol.* 43 (Suppl.): 129–75.

Naka, K. I., and Rushton, W. A. H. 1966. An attempt to analyze colour reception by electrophysiology. *J. Physiol. (Lond.)*. 185:556–86.

Oikawa, T.; Ogawa, T.; and Motokawa, K. 1959. Origin of so-called cone action potential. *J. Neurophysiol* 22:102–11.

Penn, R. D. 1966. Ionic communication between liver cells. *J. Cell. Biol.* 29:171–74.

Stell, W. K. 1965. Correlation of retinal cytoarchitecture and ultrastructure in Golgi preparations. *Anat. Rec.* 153: 389–98.

Svaetichin, G. 1953. The cone action potential. *Acta Physiol. Scand.* 29 (Suppl. 106):565–600.

———. 1956. Spectral response curves from single cones. *Acta Physiol. Scand.* 39 (Suppl. 134):17–46.

Svaetichin, G.; Laufer, M.; Mitarai, G.; Fatehchand, R.; Vallecelle, E.; and Villegas, J. 1961. Glial control of neuronal networks and receptors. In *The visual system: Neurophysiology and psychophysics*, ed. R. Jung and H. Kornhuber, pp. 445–56. Berlin: Springer.

Svaetichin, G., and MacNichol, E. F., Jr. 1958. Retinal mechanisms for chromatic and achromatic vision. *Ann. N. Y. Acad. Sci.* 74: 385–404.

Svaetichin, G.; Negishi, K.; Fatehchand, R.; Drujan, B. D.; and Selvin de Testa, A. 1964. Nervous function based on interactions between neuronal and non-neuronal elements. In *Biology of neuroglia*, Progress in Brain Research, vol. 15, ed. E. D. P. De Robertis and R. Carrea. Amsterdam: Elsevier.

Tomita, T. 1965. Electrophysiological study of the mechanisms subserving color coding in the fish retina. *Symp. Quant. Biol.* 30: 559–66.

Tomita, T.; Murakami, M.; Sato, Y.; and Hashimoto, Y. 1959. Further study on the origin of the so-called cone action potential (S-potential): Its histological determination. *Jap. J. Physiol.* 9:63–68.

Wagner, H. G.; MacNichol, E. F., Jr.; and Wolbarsht, M. L. 1960. The response properties of single ganglion cells in the goldfish retina. *J. Gen. Physiol.* 43 (Suppl.):45–62.

———. 1963. Functional basis for "on"-center and "off"-center receptive fields in the retina. *J. Opt. Soc. Amer.* 53:60–70.

Witkovsky, P. 1965. The spectral sensitivity of retinal ganglion cells in the carp. *Vision Res.* 5:603–14.

Wolbarsht, M. L.; Wagner, H. G.; and MacNichol, E. F., Jr. 1961. The origin of "on"- and "off"-responses of retinal ganglion cells; Receptive fields of retinal ganglion cells. In *The visual system: Neurophysiology and psychophysics*, ed. R. Jung and H. Kornhuber, pp. 163–75. Berlin: Springer.

Yamada, E., and Ishikawa, T. 1965. The fine structure of the horizontal cells in some vertebrate retinae. *Symp. Quant. Biol.* 30:383–91.

3

Behavioral Analysis of Color Sensitivities in Goldfish

Dean Yager

Psychology Department
Brown University

Introduction

We have seen from Dr. Jacobson's review that much physiological information is now available about the fish visual system, especially in goldfish and carp. We know more about the discriminative capacities of retinal neurons than about the discriminative behavior of the whole fish. Despite a host of studies concerned with the color vision of fish, none actually tells us what kind of color vision a given species has. In order to pursue further the precise relations between the physiology and psychology of color vision, I have performed quantitative analyses of such capacities in goldfish. Goldfish vision should be trichromatic, like that of the normal human, because Marks (1965) has demonstrated three separate cone pigments. Furthermore, Jacobson (1964) has reported at least two opponent-type mechanisms and one photopic brightness mechanism in an analysis of ganglion cell responses in the goldfish. My aim has been the determination of trichromatic behavior in goldfish, as a test of this basic prediction from physiological data.

The most direct test of color vision would involve determination of the number of primaries required to match any spectral light in color. Trichromats need three primaries, while dichromats require only two primaries for such a match. Completely color-blind monochromats can match any light with any other by only an intensity variation. However, the problems in obtaining complete color-mixture functions in goldfish are thus far prohibitive. Therefore, I have employed more practical, if less direct, estimates of color vision capacity.

One function which can be obtained for the fish describes the minimal separation between two wavelengths that allows detection of a color difference. With brightness differences eliminated, monochromats cannot discriminate colors at all. The human dichromat's wavelength discrimination is much worse than that of normals, and the difference limen increases

25

rapidly and monotonically on both sides of the neutral point (about 500 nm for red-green blindness). However, discrimination is certainly possible from about 440 to 550 nm, so that the ability to discriminate such wavelengths provides no indication that an animal is trichromatic. Thus, the human dichromat's wavelength discrimination function is U-shaped, while the trichromat's function has two minima, and is shaped somewhat like a rounded W (Graham 1965). A complete wavelength discrimination function from a goldfish could be fruitfully compared with the human functions.

Another function which can be used to assess the type of color vision in an animal is the spectral saturation function. Spectral lights of equal brightness usually differ not only in hue but also in saturation. For example, a color-normal human looking at a stimulus of 585 nm, under daylight adaptation, sees a yellow of low saturation, while 410 nm at equal brightness gives a violet sensation of very high saturation. Estimations of degree of saturation are very difficult to make, even for a human observer. However, a monotonically related psychophysical measure of saturation is least colorimetric purity, the least amount of a spectral light that must be added to white light to make it just detectably different in color from the white alone. The higher the saturation, the less the required light. This function is usually plotted as the logarithm of the reciprocal of the least colorimetric purity, so that the top of the graph indicates high saturation.

The form of this function is strongly dependent on the specific characteristics of the color vision mechanism. If saturation is at zero for all wavelengths, then the animal is a monochromat. If the animal can discriminate most wavelengths from a white stimulus, except for one or two points in the spectrum where saturation approaches zero, then it is probably a dichromat, like the red-green– or yellow-blue–blind human. If the animal can discriminate all wavelengths from white and there are no points in the spectrum where saturation approaches zero, as with a normal human, then the animal probably has trichromatic vision (Graham 1965).

My present research is directed toward a systematic behavioral investigation of some of these functional relations in goldfish color vision. I attempt to relate the quantitative visual discrimination data to the measured physiological responses reported by other investigators. This is being done within the framework of a quantitative theory of color vision, a form of the Hering opponent-process model (Hering 1964). In experiments completed, I have determined the spectral brightness sensitivity function for the goldfish, which is a necessary first step, and a spectral saturation discrimination function, both under the same conditions of adaptation and viewing.

Procedure

Experiment 1—Spectral Sensitivity

The fish were trained to press transparent Plexiglas targets for food reinforcement, and then were given a choice between an illuminated, reinforced target and a nonilluminated, nonreinforced target. An "observing" response on a third target initiated a trial. The eyes were kept in a constant light-adapted state. In order to find the stimulus energy of a given wavelength required for 75 per cent choice of the illuminated target, a modified method of constant stimuli was used, with 50 trials at each energy level. For each wavelength employed, a graphic representation of log energy versus per cent correct responses was made, and the energy required for 75 per cent correct responding was estimated from the graph. These threshold energy values were plotted as a function of wavelength.

Experiment 2—Spectral Saturation

Conditions were the same as in the spectral sensitivity experiment, except that now there was a constant amount of white light on each stimulus patch. When the fish pressed the observing target, monochromatic light was added to the white light on one stimulus patch, and additional white light was added to the other. The fish was rewarded with food for pressing the target illuminated with a mixture of white and monochromatic light. The psychometric functions for the determination of the energies of spectral lights required for 75 per cent correct responding in this experiment were similar to those obtained in the spectral sensitivity experiment. These chromatic threshold energy values were converted to luminance units by the equation

$$L_{0_\lambda} = \frac{E_{0_\lambda}}{E_{t_\lambda}} , \tag{1}$$

where E_{t_λ} is the threshold energy from experiment 1, E_{0_λ} is the chromatic threshold energy in experiment 2, and L_0 is the luminance of the chromatic threshold stimulus in units of threshold energy. The same operations were carried out for the diluting light, w. Then the ratio

$$\frac{L_w + L_\lambda}{L_\lambda} \tag{2}$$

was computed for each wavelength. This is the reciprocal of the least colorimetric purity required for detection of a saturation difference, which is the usual way of expressing saturation discrimination. The logarithm of this ratio was plotted as a function of wavelength.

Results

Experiment 1

Spectral sensitivity must be related, by some function, to the spectral absorption curves of the visual pigments found in the retina. The light absorbed by these pigments in some way triggers neural responses which are combined at some point in the visual system to produce "brightness," or at least some perceptual quality which enables the fish (or human) to make a discrimination. Recently, Liebman and Entine (1964) and Marks (1965) have succeeded in recording difference spectra from individual cones in goldfish retinas. The following discussion will attempt to relate the spectral sensitivity functions obtained in the present experiment to these cone photopigments. Pigment nomograms (Dartnall 1953) were used in this analysis rather than the measured difference spectra (Marks 1965) because of the variability of the microspectrophotometric data and the possibility that photoproducts distorted the difference spectra obtained by measuring absorption before and after light exposure.

To be compared with the absorption spectra of visual pigments, the sensitivity data have been corrected for preretinal absorptions on the basis of Burkhardt's (1966) measures. Also, the retinal sensitivities have been expressed in terms of an equal quantum intensity spectrum. Figure 1 is a plot of relative spectral sensitivity for an equal quantum intensity spectrum at the retina, for Fish G6, G7, and G8. In this graph, the abscissa is a frequency, rather than wavelength, scale.

There are two models that can be used to relate spectral sensitivity to photopigment absorptions. One of these is the envelope model, which assumes that the threshold at any wavelength is determined by the single most sensitive mechanism at that wavelength. The other assumes that all mechanisms contribute to the threshold response in proportion to their respective separate sensitivities. The latter is the additive model, which, unlike the envelope model, also applies to suprathreshold spectral luminances. It was decided to attempt to relate pigment absorptions to spectral sensitivity by applying the simple additive model in the present analysis. (A recent experiment by Boynton, Ikeda, and Stiles [1964] questions the validity of using such a model, because events at threshold are more complicated than the simple additive model suggests. However, this model may be used as a first approximation.)

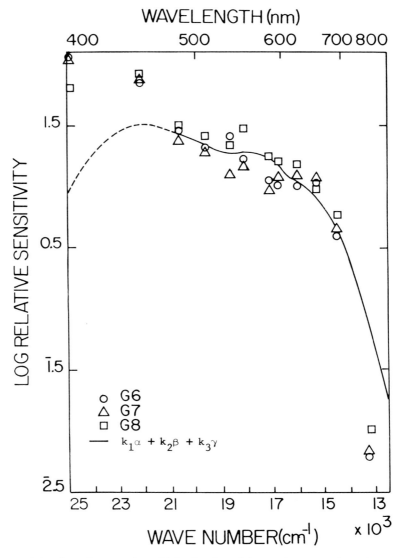

FIG. 1. *Symbols*, photopic spectral sensitivity for three fish, equal quantum intensity spectrum at the retina. *Solid line*, best-fitting photopigment summation function.

This model assumes that

$$B_\lambda = f(k_1 a_\lambda + k_2 \beta_\lambda + k_3 \gamma_\lambda) , \qquad (3)$$

where B = brightness; a, β, and γ are percentage absorption functions for three selective photopigments; and k_1, k_2, and k_3 are factors which express the spectral absorptions of the three photopigments relative to each other.

Now, for any measure of equal brightness at different wavelengths, λ and λ',

$$B_\lambda = B_{\lambda'} \rightarrow k_1 a_\lambda + k_2 \beta_\lambda + k_3 \gamma_\lambda = k_1 a_{\lambda'} + k_2 \beta_{\lambda'} + k_3 \gamma_{\lambda'} . \qquad (4)$$

Thus to find the relative heights of the three functions, we need to find k_1, k_2, and k_3, such that B is constant for all λ. The spectral sensitivity curve obtained in the present experiment can be treated as a measure of the number of quanta needed at each wavelength to produce a constant (threshold) brightness. Then, k_1, k_2, and k_3 are just those factors that give

$$S_\lambda = k_1 a_\lambda + k_2 \beta_\lambda + k_3 \gamma_\lambda , \qquad (5)$$

where S is the behavioral measure of relative sensitivity. Although no exact fit can be expected because of intersubject variability, the deviations may be minimized by seeking a least-squares fit to the data. This was done using the data of all three subjects for sensitivity measures from 484 through 690 nm; the factors obtained were $k_1 = 0.25$, $k_2 = 0.14$, $k_3 = 0.09$.

The sensitivity function calculated by equation (5) using the estimated k factors is also shown in Figure 1 along with the behavioral data. The photopigment summation function describes a smooth curve which falls fairly close to the median measurements for the three S's. The close agreement is neither surprising nor particularly important, since the k's were chosen to minimize the differences. It will be seen, however, in accounting for the saturation function, that these particular k values may indeed represent biological parameters in the goldfish retina.

The sensitivity values measured at 401 and 453 nm clearly depart from the theoretical curve. Three reasons for such departure can be cited.

(*a*) As already noted, there is considerable uncertainty about the shape of the pigment absorption curves in this region of the spectrum; they may rise at short wavelengths, as does that of "cyanopsin" (Wald, Brown, and Smith 1953).

(*b*) Ocular media, as well as the extraocular media comprising the fish tank, water, and Plexiglas probe, may fluoresce when irradiated by short wavelengths of light. This fluorescence would distort the sensitivity data (Hosoya 1929).

(*c*) These same materials also scatter shortwave light; in human experiments, this can have the effect of significantly raising shortwave foveal sensitivity, due to scatter to more sensitive retinal areas. A control function for a human observer obtained with the present apparatus shows distortions at short wavelengths similar to those in the fish function.

Experiment 2

The psychometric functions for the determination of the energy required for 75 per cent correct choice, when the fish were responding to mixtures of spectral and broad-band lights, were similar to those obtained in the spectral sensitivity experiment. These energy values were converted to luminance units by equation (1) and the reciprocal of least colorimetric purity calculated for each wavelength by expression (2).

Figure 2 is a plot of log $(L_w + L_\lambda)/L_\lambda$ for each of the three fish used in this experiment. Each function was computed individually for each fish whose own threshold energy values were used. It was obvious that saturation discrimination for all three fish is maximally sensitive at the spectral extremes, and that there is a third maximum in the midspectral region between about 510 and 535 nm. There is a well-defined minimum at around 600 nm, and a shallower one around 490–500 nm. None of the monochromatic lights used in this experi-

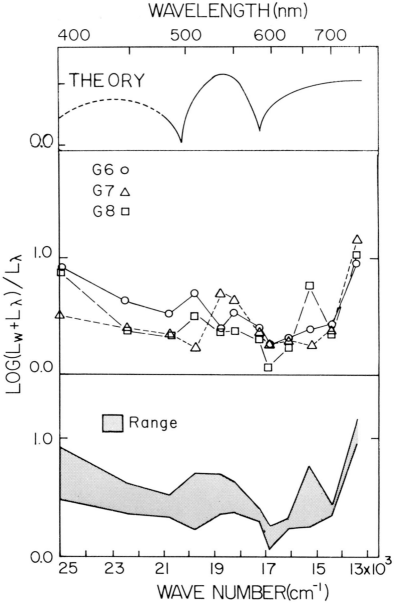

Fig. 2. *Top,* theoretical saturation discrimination function from the opponent-colors theory. *Bottom,* spectral saturation discrimination functions for three fish.

ment were confused by any fish with a broad-band tungsten light. The evidence suggests that all spectral wavelengths elicit color responses that differ from the response to the broad-band tungsten distribution, and that goldfish vision is trichromatic.

Spectral saturation must also be related to the spectral absorption curves of retinal visual pigments. A quantitative theory that can be used to generate a saturation discrimination function is the opponent-process theory of Hering, as developed quantitatively by Hurvich and Jameson (Jameson and Hurvich 1955; Hurvich and Jameson 1957). This theory assumes that for a trichromatic visual system, there are two independent, paired chromatic response processes which are determined by positive and negative interactions among three fundamental processes α, β, γ, and the positive component of the achromatic visual response (both brightness and whiteness) is determined by an addition of the responses α, β, γ. The specific equations relating α, β, γ, to produce opponent chromatic response are specified for hypothetical photopigment absorptions for a human in the Hurvich-Jameson analysis.

In choosing particular equations to relate the measured photopigment absorptions and opponent neural responses for the fish, it was decided to use the simplest expressions that would produce two opponent systems, and which would, at the same time, produce minima in the saturation function at positions roughly corresponding to those found in the behavioral function. If a, b, c, d, are names for chromatic responses for the fish, and W is the achromatic response, then

$$a_\lambda - b_\lambda = k_2\beta_\lambda - k_1a_\lambda , \tag{6}$$

$$c_\lambda - d_\lambda = k_2\beta_\lambda - k_3\gamma_\lambda , \tag{7}$$

$$W_\lambda = k_1a_\lambda + k_2\beta_\lambda + k_3\gamma_\lambda , \tag{8}$$

where k_1a, $k_2\beta$, $k_3\gamma$ are the best-fitting photochemical absorptions for the spectral sensitivity function.

Jameson and Hurvich (1955) have shown that saturation discrimination is accurately predicted by the ratio of total chromatic response to achromatic response at each wavelength. This function, based on the expression

$$K\left(\frac{|a_\lambda - b_\lambda| + |c_\lambda - d_\lambda|}{W_\lambda}\right), \tag{9}$$

has been computed for the goldfish.

Rewritten on the basis of equations (6), (7), and (8), we have

$$K\left(\frac{|k_2\beta_\lambda - k_1a_\lambda| + |k_2\beta_\lambda - k_3\gamma_\lambda|}{k_1a_\lambda + k_2\beta_\lambda + k_3\gamma_\lambda}\right). \tag{10}$$

This function is also shown in a logarithmic plot in Figure 2.

It is obvious that the opponent-process theoretical function bears a close relation to the behavioral function. Two minima are clearly present and correspond closely to the behavioral minima. The fact that the relative heights of the two minima are in reversed order in the two functions may be due, in part, to the use of relatively low color-temperature comparison and diluting lights. A further possible reason for the deviations that occur may be in the choice of the interaction equations. The general expression for interaction of the receptor responses for each of the visual response processes is

$$\text{visual response} = \pm C_1(k_1a) \pm C_2(k_2\beta) \pm C_3(k_3\gamma) . \tag{11}$$

For simplicity, only values of unity or zero were chosen for C in the expressions for the three opponent processes; hence, this symbol does not appear in the equations for visual responses (equations [6]–[8]). The C values could be manipulated to produce a better fit.

Two a priori considerations lean toward the opponent-process theory as a better model of the visual system than that of the Young-Helmholtz theory:

First, Hurvich and Jameson (1957) have had a good deal of success in accounting for several human visual functions with the use of this model.

Second, opponent-type chromatically coded responses have been discovered at several different levels of the fish visual system.

It should be emphasized that the photopigment coefficients used in the saturation formula were the same ones determined in the spectral sensitivity experiment. The opponent-process formulation for saturation discrimination may be tested by obtaining spectral sensitivity and spectral saturation functions under conditions of strong chromatic adaptation. The changes necessary in the coefficients k_1, k_2, k_3 to account for the new spectral sensitivity curve will lead to consistent predictions about changes in shape of the saturation functions. This will, of course, include shifts in the locations of minima.

From the visual response functions of equations (6), (7), and (8), a theoretical wavelength discrimination function may also be computed, according to the formula of Hurvich and Jameson (1957). Wavelength discrimination depends on both hue and saturation differences. Spectral saturation and hue coefficients may be calculated, and variations in wavelength discrimination derived, as proportional to the sum of the rates of change of the two coefficient functions. The form of this function is specific to the stimulus conditions used in the present study. This awaits an experimental test, although Yarczower and Bitterman (1965) have obtained a wavelength discrimination function for the goldfish which is qualitatively similar to the predicted function (Yager 1967).

Furthermore, the visual response functions in equations (6), (7), and (8) create strong expectations about the specific forms of retinal and tectal single-cell response functions under the present conditions of adaptation and stimulation. Although the stimulating and adapting conditions were very different, electrophysiological data that have been reported (Svaetichin 1956; MacNichol, Wolbarsht, and Wagner 1961; Jacobson 1964) unquestionably show qualitative similarities to the theoretical response functions (Yager 1967).

Summary

Goldfish have been shown to be able to discriminate monochromatic spectral lights from white light at many points in the spectrum. This confirms the prediction, from electrophysiological considerations, that the goldfish visual system should give some chromatic response at every visible wavelength. Wavelength-coded processes in the goldfish retina and optic tectum also imply that goldfish vision is mediated by an opponent-process system. An analysis and treatment of photopigment responses in accordance with opponent-process postulates predict a saturation discrimination function that is quite similar to the behaviorally measured function. The theoretical visual response functions also show a remarkable qualitative similarity to measured graded potentials and spectral response functions from individual ganglion cells in the fish visual system.

References

Boynton, R.; Ikeda, M.; and Stiles, W. 1964. Interaction among chromatic mechanisms. *Vision Res.* 4:87–117.

Burkhardt, D. 1966. The goldfish electroretinogram: Relation between photopic spectral sensitivity functions and cone absorption spectra. *Vision Res.* 6:517–32.

Dartnall, H. 1953. The interpretation of spectral sensitivity curves. *Brit. Med. Bull.* 9:24–30.

Graham, C. H. 1965. *Vision and visual perception.* New York: John Wiley and Sons.

Hering, E. 1964. *Outlines of a theory of the light sense.* Translated by L. Hurvich and D. Jameson. Cambridge: Harvard University Press.

Hosoya, Y. 1929. Fluoreszenz der einzelnen Augenmedian und Sichtbarkeit des ultraviolette Gebiete des Spektrums. *Tohoku J. Exp. Med.* 13:510–23.

Hurvich, L., and Jameson, D. 1957. An opponent-process theory of color vision. *Psychol. Rev.* 64:384–404.

Jacobson, M. 1964. Spectral sensitivity of single units in the optic tectum of the goldfish. *Quart. J. Exp. Physiol.* 49:384–93.

Jameson, D., and Hurvich, L. 1955. Some quantitative aspects of an opponent-colors theory. I. Chromatic responses and spectral saturation. *J. Opt. Soc. Amer.* 45:546-52.

Liebman, P., and Entine, G. 1964. Sensitive low-light-level microspectrophotometer: Detection of photosensitive pigments of retinal cones. *J. Opt. Soc. Amer.* 54:1451–59.

MacNichol, E.; Wolbarsht, M.; and Wagner, H. 1961. Electrophysiological evidence for a mechanism of color vision in the goldfish. In *Light and life,* ed. W. D. McElroy and B. Glass. Baltimore: Johns Hopkins Press.

Marks, W. B. 1965. Visual pigments of single goldfish cones. *J. Physiol.* 178:14–32.

Svaetichin, G. 1956. Spectral response curves from single cones. *Acta Physiol. Scand.* 39 (Suppl. 134): 17–46.

Wald, G.; Brown, P.; and Smith, P. 1953. Cyanopsin, a new pigment of cone vision. *Science* 118:505–8.

Yager, D. 1967. Behavioral measures and theoretical analysis of spectral sensitivity and spectral saturation in the goldfish, *Carassius auratus. Vision Res.* 7:707–27.

Yarczower, M., and Bitterman, M. 1965. Stimulus-generalization in the goldfish. In *Stimulus generalization,* ed. D. Mostofsky. Stanford, California: Stanford University Press.

4

Shape Discrimination in the Goldfish

N. S. Sutherland

Department of Psychology
University of Sussex

Introduction

One of the most important unsolved problems in psychology is that of pattern recognition. One aspect of this problem is how animals discriminate between visually presented shapes. Sutherland (1963) has carried out a series of behavioral studies in which animals are trained to discriminate between two shapes and are subsequently tested for transfer to other shapes. By presenting new pairs without differential reward, it is possible to discover which of the new shapes are classified as similar to one or another of the training shapes. Such experiments enable us to make inferences about which features of the shapes animals actually use to distinguish them. We will illustrate below how such inferences can be made.

On the basis of work conducted mainly with the octopus, Sutherland (1957, 1960) suggested a possible mechanism for shape recognition. This mechanism computed the total vertical extent of a shape at each point on the horizontal axis, and the total horizontal extent along the vertical axis. However, further studies (Sutherland, Mackintosh, and Mackintosh 1963) revealed that this theory was inadequate. For example, it predicts (falsely) that the two shapes shown in Figure 1 could not be distinguished, since the shapes have the same horizontal and vertical extents both of black and of white at each point on the two axes. Since this theory was proposed, we have arrived at a much clearer idea of what types of mechanisms must be involved in shape recognition. The clarification of our ideas stems partly from analyzing records of single-unit activity obtained by microelectrode recording in the visual system, and partly from advances in pattern recognition by machine. The purpose of this paper is to adumbrate this new theoretical approach to the problem of shape recognition in animals, and to review some recent experimental results obtained from goldfish in the light of the theory.

35

Theoretical Approach

Hubel and Wiesel (1962, 1965) have described units in the cat's visual cortex which respond selectively to specific local features within a particular part of the visual display. The same types of feature detectors are replicated over all parts of the input picture. Some of the features detected by such neurons include: (*a*) a light bar against a dark background, lying in a particular orientation; (*b*) a horizontal edge, dark above and bright below; (*c*) an edge in a particular orientation, regardless of which side is dark; (*d*) an edge in a given direction which terminates at a fixed point; and (*e*) an edge in a given direction which has a discontinuity at a particular point, i.e., it either terminates at that point or continues from it in a different direction. In the cat brain, different features are extracted at several different levels, and the output from feature detectors at one level is probably the input to feature detectors at the next higher level.

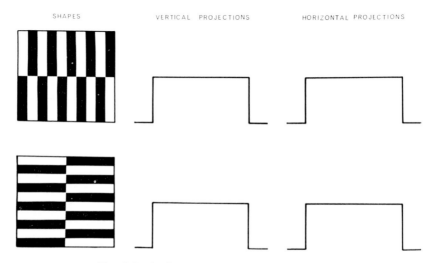

FIG. 1. Reduplicated rectangles and their projections

At each level of visual analysis, a topological map of the picture is preserved. Features having a given spatial relationship to one another in the input picture are detected by units whose relative positions preserve this relationship. Although the picture is therefore dismembered into local features at the early levels of analysis, it can always be reassembled at a higher level. For example, a filled-in black square would stimulate four units (among others) detecting "stopped edges": two horizontal edges with opposite brightness relations, and two vertical edges with the left-right direction of black and white reversed. Sufficient information is contained in the firing of these units to determine not only the direction of the edges, but that each edge ends at the same point where another begins.

Feature detectors of the types found by Hubel and Wiesel cannot in themselves account for the behavioral phenomena of shape recognition. If the nervous system simply kept a record of which units were activated when a particular shape was input, there would be no recognition of a shape when its properties were altered. For example, goldfish that have been trained to discriminate shapes using one part of the retina can recognize without further training the same shapes presented to a different part of the retina (Cronly-Dillon, Sutherland, and Wolfe 1966). Again, goldfish trained to recognize the orientation of a rectangle transfer well to rectangles in the same orientation when their linear dimensions are doubled or halved (Mackintosh and Sutherland 1963). In both instances, the new shapes would fire feature-detector units in new positions; they might well fire not a single unit in common with those fired by the training shapes. In order to account for such perceptual equivalence when the properties of a shape are changed, we must postulate that the brain stores a much more abstract description of an input shape than would be achieved by simply recording the individual units fired.

To explicate what we mean by storing information at a more abstract level, let us consider how a black square can be represented by an abstract description of its local features. Such a figure could be specified by the sequence:

$$N(x)_{e=n}E(x)_{s=e}S(x)_{w=s}W(x)_{n=w} \ .$$

The last symbol is to be taken as preceding the first symbol. Capital letters stand for edge detectors sensitive to edges running in a particular direction, with brighter regions to the north, east, south, and west, respectively. The variable x specifies length and can take any value. The subscript letters indicate the coordinates of the east edge of the north horizontal line, the north edge of the east horizontal line, etc.; since the subscript "e" in $N(x)_e$ defines a different point from the same subscript in $_eS(x)$, these variables can have different values except where an *equals* sign appears between a pair. If the description of an input square were stored in this form, various types of transfer could be mediated. Since the stored description is free from position on the retina, transfer from one retinal locus to another would occur. Since (x) is not specified, transfer to different-sized squares could take place. To the extent to which some jitter is allowed in the definition of line orientation (N, E, S,W), transfer would also be possible to small rotations of a square, and to slightly distorted squares. Furthermore, if we allow N, E, S, or W to stand for any kind of contour (formed either from a line or from a boundary) then we would obtain generalization from filled-in to outline figures, and to shapes having changed brightness relationships with their background.

In what follows, we shall refer to the mechanism that extracts local features as the "processor" and to the mechanism for inducing and storing descriptive rules as the "store."

There are many reasons for supposing that visual shape recognition in higher animals is mediated by a mechanism of the type suggested. First, feature detectors have been found by microelectrode studies in all species investigated so far. Given that the input is decomposed into local features, it is hard to see how patterns with changing properties can be recognized unless we postulate a store which works somewhat after the fashion outlined. Second, several computer scientists, e.g., Clowes (1967), working on the problem of pattern recognition by machine have independently adopted mechanisms similar to the one outlined. One alternative mechanism can certainly be ruled out; namely, template analysis performed on the whole shape. For example, the tendency of many animals to confuse oblique rectangles oriented at 45° and 135° to the horizontal is incompatible with a template model, which could not simultaneously match both shapes. The confusion between mirror-image shapes can be explained if the information placed in the store is coded in a form that does not record the direction of left-right differences. For instance, an L shape could be stored as the sequence:

$$V(2x)_{s=ew}H(x),$$

where V is a vertical bar, H a horizontal bar, and "ew" refers to either end of the horizontal bar, but does not specify which end. The theory suggested above appears to be the only candidate that comes near to meeting the known facts about pattern recognition.

If a man views a complex natural scene for one-tenth of a second, he will be able to identify the scene as, for example, a forest or beach, but he can provide very few details about it. Yet the physiological evidence makes it likely that the nervous system processes every part of the picture. Moreover, Julesz (1961) has performed a behavioral experiment which suggests that far more processing goes on in humans than is normally available to control the response. He presented an array of random dots to one eye, and simultaneously presented to the other eye an identical array, except that in the second array a central square area of points was shifted laterally with respect to the same part of the first eye's array. When the two images are binocularly fused, the central square is seen displaced in depth. It is impossible to see any difference between the two patterns if they are presented side by side and viewed with both eyes. Yet Julesz' experiment proves that information about the location of individual picture points is being processed and raises the question why the information cannot be used to recognize the two pictures as different. The answer must lie in the type of rule formulated in the store to describe the input picture. Only when an input picture can be matched to a descriptive rule is it recognized, and it is recognized only as an instance of that rule. In recognizing a forest scene we match the pattern of local features extracted from the picture to a stored description of forest scenes. Since the details of how the match was achieved are not available to determine the response, the viewer may be able to say very little about the details of the scene. To describe the details, he must match each of them to a separate rule.

Sutherland and Williams (1968) have recently demonstrated that even rats can form high-level rules to describe shapes. Rats were trained to respond differentially to a regular checkerboard made up of 16 alternating black and white squares, and to an irregular one in which a black and a white square were interchanged. The animals transferred without further training to new irregular checkerboard patterns. If we simply count correspondence of elements, some of these new irregular patterns were nearer to the original regular pattern than to the irregular one. Again, template-matching cannot account for this type of result. The animals also transferred to regular and irregular checkerboards containing 36 and 64 elements. In terms of our model, the rats had stored a rule describing a regular checkerboard irrespective of the number of elements present.

If the model we are suggesting is correct, the visual system could take advantage of the redundancy of the environment through evolutionary selection of the types of local feature detectors and of built-in biases in the types of rule that will be formulated. Objects are bounded and connected, hence the advantage of coding information in terms of local features. There could (in theory) be feature detectors which fired if certain points scattered at random over the retina were black and the remainder white; since it normally does not help in recognizing objects to correlate points separated in space in this way, we can dispense with feature detectors of this kind. This achieves an economy of brain hardware, at the expense of making it difficult or impossible to recognize random dot patterns in contrived laboratory experiments.

Although the theory we have outlined may be a plausible account of pattern recognition in higher animals and man, it should be stressed that almost all the details remain to be filled in. We do not know the physiological locus of the store—it could be in the inferotemporal cortex in primates, since this area receives efferents from the visual cortex and since lesions there interfere with complex pattern recognition while leaving acuity and brightness discrimination almost unimpaired. We do not yet know the full range of feature detectors in any species, nor do we know their relative frequencies, We know little or nothing about the process which examines the output from feature detectors and formulates a rule for storage. Finally, we know nothing about the retrieval process whereby a patterned input is matched with a stored rule.

To solve these problems will require work of three different kinds. First, further micro-electrode work on the visual system is needed in order to spell out the details of the feature detectors and the relative frequencies of different types of detector in different species. This is not an easy problem since our sampling will be biased if it proves more difficult to record from some types of unit than from others. In our existing state of knowledge it seems un-likely that microelectrode recording will throw much light on the organization of the store, since we neither know with certainty where to look for it nor have much idea what to look for. However, selective placement of lesions might help in the identification of the locus of the store. Second, we need to know how different species actually do classify shapes. This in-formation, put together with the results of microelectrode work, could help us interpret the consequences of having different types or frequencies of receptive units. An example of this approach will be given below (cf. also Ingle, in this volume, who has successfully exploited this approach in studying motion detection in goldfish). Behavioral studies could also tell us something about the type of rule that can be formed by the store and about the details of the retrieval process. Third, in order to interpret the behavioral data, we must construct rigorous models of the processes postulated and must simulate different models by computer. The possible systems are likely to be so complex that we would be unable to infer how a given model would actually behave except by extensive simulation. If we found differences in the ways different species classify shapes, then we could construct models exhibiting these differ-ences and use the models to predict further behavioral differences, to be confirmed by new tests.

The remainder of this paper summarizes some unpublished results of experiments on shape recognition in the goldfish and attempts to interpret them within the framework of the theory just outlined. The interpretations will necessarily be tentative—to achieve more certainty we need many more results of both a behavioral and a physiological nature than are available at present.

There are three reasons for choosing goldfish as a subject for this type of work. First, it is a convenient experimental animal, being cheap, robust, and easy to maintain, and it learns shape discriminations quickly and reliably. Second, it is phylogenetically very different from the other main species on which studies of shape discrimination have been made (octopuses, rats, and pigeons). Third, several workers (cf. Jacobsen, this volume) are currently investi-gating the visual system of goldfish with microelectrodes, although so far the receptive fields found appear to be related to movement detection rather than to pattern detection.

Experimental Methods

Figure 2 depicts the training situation we have used with goldfish. The experiments are conducted in the subjects' home tanks, which measure 45 × 25 × 25 cm. At the start of each trial, the goldfish is driven behind the black detention screen (*Det*) and the circular aperture is blocked by a sliding black door. The shapes to be discriminated are exposed at the far end of the tank against a white Perspex discrimination screen (*Dis*) from which projects a parti-tion (*P*) dividing the two shapes. Each shape has a small trough projecting from its center. The trough attached to the positive shape is baited with a food pellet and that in front of the negative shape is baited with a small pebble. All animals are pretrained to go through the opening in the detention screen when the door is raised and to swim for food reward to the positive shape presented alone. During training, the shapes are baited while the fish is behind the detention screen, the door is raised, and the fish swims to one shape or the other. A response is recorded when the goldfish snaps at the trough. A modified correction procedure is used: on trials on which a fish chooses wrongly, it is driven back behind the detention screen and rerun until it makes a correct choice. Only the first error within a trial is counted. During training the position of the positive and negative shapes is varied in a semirandom order. To make sure that animals are discriminating on the basis of the shapes themselves and

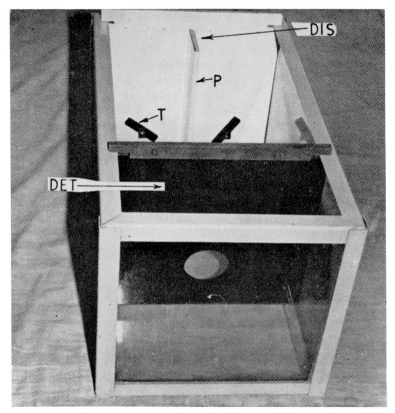

FIG. 2. The training situation

not on the basis of a difference between the pebble and the food bait, control tests are always conducted at the end of training with both shapes baited with food. These tests are interspersed with retraining trials on which only the positive shape is baited with food. If as many correct choices are made on tests trials as on training trials, we may conclude that performance is being controlled by differences in the shapes. In eight experiments run with this apparatus, involving over 150 fish, there has never been any significant difference in performance on test trials and interspersed training trials.

   In all the experiments to be described, transfer tests were run at the end of training. In transfer tests, two shapes are presented, at least one of which differs from the original training shapes; both transfer shapes are baited with food so that the animal gets a reward whichever one it chooses. In any one experiment about 20 or 30 different pairs of transfer shapes were used and each animal received at least 10 tests with each pair. Within any one group of animals trained on the same pair of training shapes (*A* and *B*), half the animals were trained with *A* positive, the remainder with *B* positive. Performance on transfer to a given pair of shapes (*X* and *Y*) is determined in the following way. We find the number of trials on which animals trained with *A* positive take *X*, and the number of trials on which animals trained with *B* positive take *Y*. This figure represents how often animals responded to *X* in the way they were trained to respond to *A*. If this figure is significantly above chance, we can infer that, of the two transfer shapes, *X* is more readily classified as like *A* (and unlike *B*) than *Y*. If the figure is significantly below chance, we can infer that *Y* is more readily classified as like *A* (and unlike *B*) than is *X*. In giving the results of transfer tests we will not present significance levels, but wherever it is stated that transfer occurred it means that there was a significant difference ($p < .05$) in the way fish responded to the two transfer shapes. Wherever it is stated that there was more transfer to one pair of shapes than to another, it means that the difference in responding to the two pairs was significant beyond the .05 level.

The apparatus leads to fast and efficient learning, presumably because the shapes stand out clearly from their backgrounds and the response is made as directly as possible to the shape to be discriminated. On the discriminations we have so far used in training, goldfish take between 30 and 200 trials to reach a criterion of 18 out of 20 correct responses in succession. They continue to perform over extended series of further training trials at an accuracy between 80 per cent and 100 per cent correct, depending upon the difficulty of the discrimination. It is interesting that even in developing such a simple situation we ran into various snags.

1. We discovered that goldfish would learn to swim quickly to the positive shape only if they were swimming away from the experimenter. If the experimenter stands behind the discrimination shapes so that the fish has to swim toward him, the goldfish never learns to swim reliably to the positive shape. When the experimenter stands behind the detention chamber, the fish learns to swim to a single positive shape (within 15 sec of the door being raised) in 50 to 100 trials.

2. The goldfish would not learn to take the bait from a trough which had a flat top with a small depression holding the food. In order to get them to take the bait whenever they snapped, we had to bevel the top of the trough downward and toward the fish. Beveling the top of the trough had two effects—it made the food directly visible to the fish, and if they hit the feeding trough with their snouts they were forced up toward the food so that they had no difficulty in picking it up.

3. Fish could not readily learn to swim through the circular opening in the detention screen if a transparent door was used. Swimming through was extinguished in the intertrial interval since they banged their snouts against the transparent door. Fish also could not learn to swim through the opening if the detention screen was the same color as the discrimination screen—presumably it was difficult for them to detect when the door was raised since under these conditions the hole was about the same brightness as its surround.

4. The fish learned much more readily with black shapes on a white background than with white shapes on a black background (Mackintosh and Sutherland 1963). This is probably because the bait shows up much more readily against a black trough than against a white trough. It is possible, however, that this difference in the discriminability of black and white shapes reflects something more fundamental about goldfish vision. In our training situation

goldfish usually approach the shapes from slightly below. Now, for a fish, objects in the upper half of the visual field will normally be silhouetted against the light. It is possible, therefore, that in the lower hemiretina there are more receptive units for detecting dark objects against a light background than for detecting light objects against a dark background. In an unpublished experiment, Cronly-Dillon and Sutherland trained goldfish with either the medial or lateral optic nerve brachium cut so that the fish were using either their lower or upper visual field. The goldfish were trained with black and white shapes, and our hypothesis was that fish using only their upper visual field would be relatively impaired on white shapes, while those using only their lower visual field would be impaired on black shapes. The results did not confirm the hypothesis, since we could not detect any differential impairment of discrimination of black and white shapes consequent on cutting the medial or lateral brachium.

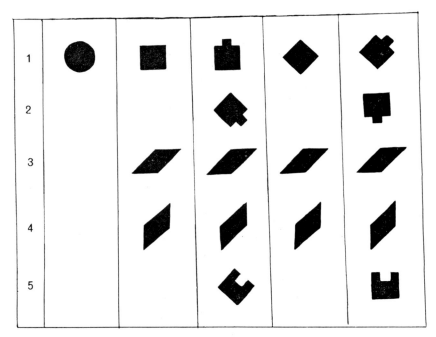

Fig. 3. Experiment 1. The training shapes are shown in row 1; the remainder of the figure illustrates some of the transfer shapes used.

However, if differences in the relative frequencies of different types of receptive unit could be established over different parts of the visual field, the technique used could help to establish the function of different types of units and would be a useful supplement to the comparative technique discussed below.

Experiment 1

Sutherland (1959) trained octopuses to discriminate between circles and squares and circles and diamonds (the diamond being a 45° rotated square). When these animals were subsequently retrained, substituting a diamond for the square and vice versa, they took as long to learn the new discrimination as to learn the original one. Octopuses therefore have no tendency to classify together a square and its 45° rotation. In terms of the theory outlined above, the rule stored to describe a square cannot be matched to the input from a diamond.

It was thought worthwhile to repeat this experiment on goldfish, with a further variation. If the shapes in the first row of Figure 3 are inspected, there appears to the human observer to be a greater similarity between the square with a knob on it and the diamond with a knob on it than between the square and the diamond. This suggests that the presence of the knob might also mediate transfer for animals from square to diamond. In other words, the rule formed to describe a square with a knob on it can be at least partially matched by an input from a diamond with a knob on it.

In order to test this possibility, Bowman and Sutherland (1968*a*) conducted the following experiment. Four groups of goldfish were trained to discriminate between the circle and the other four shapes drawn in the first row of Figure 3; different groups were trained with each of the four shapes. All subjects received 140 training trials, and all had met a criterion of 18 correct responses out of 20 successive trials by the end of training, There was no difference in the learning rates of the four different groups. Animals averaged 188 per cent correct responses over the last 20 trials of training. After training, 29 sets of transfer tests were given with new pairs of shapes—most of these pairs included the original circle as one member. During the retraining trials on the original discrimination, given in alternation with transfer tests, the animals averaged 94 per cent correct responding. The results of transfer tests will not be given in detail here, but we shall present a summary of the main conclusions.

1. The result previously obtained on octopuses was replicated with the goldfish. When a square was substituted for the diamond or a diamond for the original square, performance was chance (47 per cent correct—counting as a correct response choice of the circle by animals trained with circle positive, choice of the other shape by animals trained with circle negative).

2. When the square with knob was substituted for the diamond with knob or vice versa good transfer was obtained (75 per cent correct), provided the knob remained in the upper half of the shape. If, however, the square and diamond with knobs were interchanged and the knob appeared in the lower half of the shape (Fig. 3, row 2) there was no transfer.

3. Several further transfer tests revealed that all animals were discriminating between the shapes in terms of differences in their top halves. For example, when an upright isosceles triangle and an inverted isosceles triangle were presented, animals trained with the square treated the inverted triangle as like the square, whereas animals trained on the diamond responded to the upright triangle (which has a point at the top) as they had been trained to respond to the diamond. A whole series of further transfer tests both in this experiment and in other experiments showed that goldfish tend to base their responses on differences in the upper halves of the shapes rather than on differences in their lower halves. It might be thought that this effect is a function of our training situation, but the same finding has been obtained by Hemmings (1965) using other training situations. He found that different species of tropical fish learned visual discriminations in terms of the top halves of the shapes both when the shapes to be discriminated were cut-out plaques and the response was pushing the positive plaque with the nose, and when the shapes were apertures in a screen through which the fish had to learn to swim.

The tendency to learn about only part of a shape rather than the whole is not uncommon in discrimination experiments on animals (Sutherland 1961). Rats learn in terms of the bottoms of shapes rather than the tops, both in the Lashley jumping stand and in a Grice-type apparatus (Sutherland 1961*b*). If only we could crossbreed rats and goldfish we might produce an animal that learned about the whole shape.

4. The main differentiating characteristic of the square learned by the goldfish was the

presence of a long horizontal edge at the top. There was good transfer when the parallelogram shown in row 3 of Figure 3 was presented with a circle, but performance was chance when the parallelogram shown in row 4 was substituted for the square. Animals trained with the diamond appear to have learned both that there was a point at the top and that there were oblique lines in the top half of the shape. Although transfer occurred from the diamond to the parallelogram shown in Figure 3, row 3, transfer was better to the parallelogram in row 4, which contains only one oblique line in the top half but does contain a north-facing point.

5. As shown above, the animals trained with the shapes containing a knob had detected its presence. This conclusion is further supported by the fact that animals trained on the square with a knob did better on a square with a knob when the knob was presented in three other positions (east, west, and south) than they did when it was omitted altogether. The animals had also detected other features of the diamond and square with knobs. Those trained with diamond-knob showed transfer to both parallelograms, and again they showed more transfer to the row 4 parallelogram than to the row 3. The animals trained with square-knob seem to have learned that there was a short horizontal line at the top of the shape. When presented with a horizontal and a vertical rectangle, they treated the vertical rectangle in the way they had learned to respond to the square-knob, whereas animals trained on the square without a knob treated the horizontal rectangle as like the original square.

One interesting feature of the results is the importance of the point at the top for animals trained on the diamond. To a human observer the diamond appears to be a pointed figure, and the square a figure lacking points. Yet geometrically, if the diamond contains points facing north, south, east, and west, the square contains points facing the four intermediate compass positions (northwest, etc.). This seems to be equally true for goldfish, since a shape with points facing northwest, northeast, etc., is not treated as a square when these points are not right angles, whereas any figure containing points made up by joining two lines other than a horizontal and a vertical line is treated to some extent as a diamond by animals trained on the diamond. There appears therefore to be a completely different rule written into the store for a right angle made by a junction of horizontal and vertical lines than for all other angles.

A second interesting feature of the results is the fact that the knob does mediate transfer to 45° rotations of the original shape. The knob must be coded in the store in a different way from the way in which straight lines are coded, since the orientation of straight lines is critical for transfer (there is no transfer between square and diamond) whereas the orientation of the knob is not critical. It may be that the knob is coded by a rule which marks it simply as a discontinuity in a straight line. It would be interesting to know, for example, whether, after training with square-knob or diamond-knob, transfer would occur to the two shapes shown in Figure 3, row 5, where the shapes are rotated and the knob is changed to an indentation. Unfortunately, transfer tests were not performed with these shapes in the experiment reported, though we are at the moment undertaking further work on this problem.

Experiment 2

The training shapes used in the next experiment are shown in row 1 of Figure 4. Three groups of animals were trained, one on each pair of shapes. The shapes were chosen with no particular hypothesis in mind except that we wanted to investigate further the discrimination of points by goldfish. Rate of learning was significantly slower than in the first experiment, and all subjects were given 200 training trials. All fish had met the criterion by the end of training and responded with an average accuracy of 95 per cent correct over the last 10 trials of training. They continued to respond at this level of accuracy throughout the retraining trials given with transfer tests.

Again the most interesting part of the experiment was the outcome of the transfer tests. Only a few examples of the 20 tests will be reported here (for more details see Bowman and Sutherland 1968*b*).

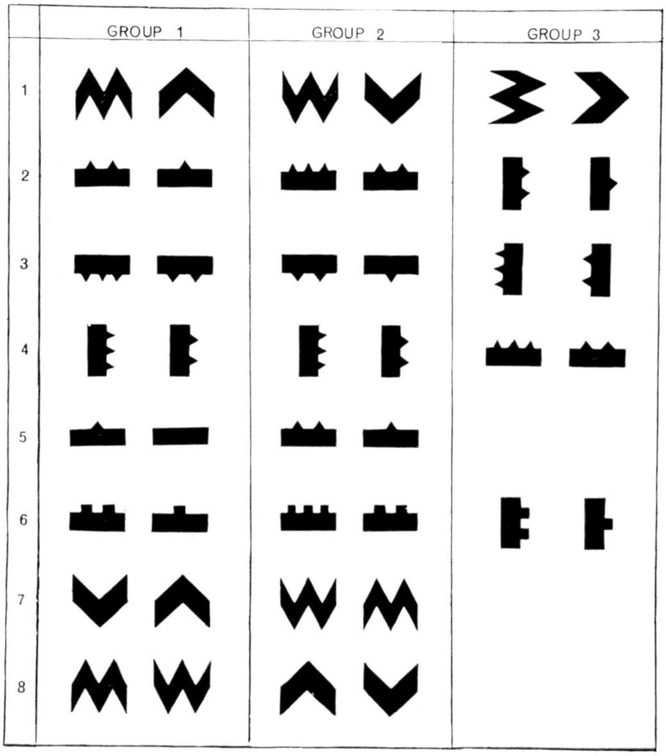

Fig. 4. Experiment 2

The main finding was that animals of Groups I and II learned the discrimination in terms of the difference in the number of points at the tops of the figures, while Group III learned in terms of the different number of points at the sides. Thus transfer by Groups I and II was very good to pairs of shapes of the type shown in row 2 of Figure 3—animals treated the left-hand member of the transfer pairs as like the original **M** or **W** shape on 86 per cent of transfer trials. Transfer to new shapes bearing the same number of points facing downward as the originals (row 3) was poor and not significantly above chance (56 per cent correct). Both groups, however, showed reasonably good transfer to shapes of the kind shown in row 4, having a different number of points at the side of the shape (76 per cent correct). This is reminiscent of one of the findings of experiment 1—altering the direction in which a point is facing has much less effect on transfer performance than altering contour slope. The reason performance was so poor when points were facing downward was presumably that the subject had difficulty in detecting the presence of the points when they were in this orientation. Similar results were obtained with Group III—they performed well when transfer shapes differed in the number of points at the side (rows 2 and 3, 80 per cent correct), equally well when the points faced the top (row 4) and not so well (67 per cent correct) when the points were at the bottom of the shape.

One further finding is of considerable interest. Although animals had learned that the W shapes contained more points than the V shapes, they gave no evidence of having learned the exact number of points in each. For example, animals treated the left-hand member of the pairs shown in row 5 as like the original M and W shapes (75 per cent) although it has the same number of points at the top as the original Λ or V shape. They were influenced not by the absolute number of points but invariably treated the shape with *more* points as like the original M or W shape. This finding occurred in many other transfer tests and animals were able to discriminate well between shapes having four and three points at the top (75 per cent correct), treating the shape with four points at the top as like the original W, although that has only three points at the top. When shapes with knobs on them were substituted for shapes with points there was still good transfer, though it was less than with shapes with the same number of points (80 per cent for the shapes in row 6 as against 85 per cent for the shapes in row 1).

These findings were also checked in experiments with Groups I and II in which one or another of the original shapes was presented with a 180° rotation of itself (rows 7 and 8). Transfer was good where the original shape differed from its rotation in terms of number of points at the top in the same direction it differed from the other training shape (row 7). Yet performance was at chance level (56 per cent) when rotating a shape produced a difference in the opposite direction to the original difference in number of points at the top (row 8).

These findings confirm one of the results of the previous experiment. Points are readily detected by goldfish and used in shape discrimination. Whatever rule is formed to describe an input shape with points can be matched by a new input shape having points in a different direction. The rules formed do not specify the exact number of points carried by a shape; they specify only that a shape has many points or few.

Experiment 3

The third experiment to be summarized here was carried out long before the other two, though the results still have not been published elsewhere. It is of interest because it illustrates the sort of inferences that can be drawn by working across several species. Rats, octopuses, and goldfish were trained in situations as nearly comparable as possible to discriminate between the same pairs of shapes. All three species were trained on the two pairs of shapes shown in Figure 5 (row 1), one group within each species (Group H) being trained with the horizontal parallelogram, the other (Group V) with the vertical parallelogram. Only 100 training trials were given and at the end of training performance averaged 85 per cent correct. Group V learned slightly but not significantly faster than Group H, and their performance during retraining trials was significantly better—presumably the presence of a point at the top of the vertical parallelogram had made the discrimination easier than when both shapes contained a straight line at the top.

After training, transfer tests were carried out with all species. In addition to simultaneous transfer tests in which two shapes were presented at once, successive tests were run in which only one shape was presented at a time, and the experimenter recorded whether the animal selected it or went to the other side of the apparatus where no shape was present. This technique makes it easier to rank-order transfer shapes in terms of how far each was treated in the same way as one or the other of the originals. Rather than present the detailed data from transfer tests we will summarize the main conclusions that emerge and give an indication of how they were arrived at.

For the goldfish, the most important differences between the square and the parallelograms are that the horizontal parallelogram has points facing east and west, the vertical parallelogram has a point at the top, and the square does not have points. Goldfish transferred from the training parallelogram to all figures presented that had points lying in roughly the appropriate directions, including both an X and a diamond. The presence of oblique contour was not on its own sufficient to mediate transfer from the parallelogram, nor was the presence of points if they faced at 90° to the direction of the points in the original parallelogram. For example, Group H did not transfer to the rotated parallelogram shown in row 2 of Figure 5, and Group V actually treated the row 2 parallelogram as like the original square —presumably because it has a horizontal line at the top. Again, although both groups tended to classify horizontal and vertical rectangles as like the original square, Group H treated the vertical rectangle as more like the square than the horizontal, whereas Group V responded more often to the horizontal than to the vertical rectangle in the same way as to

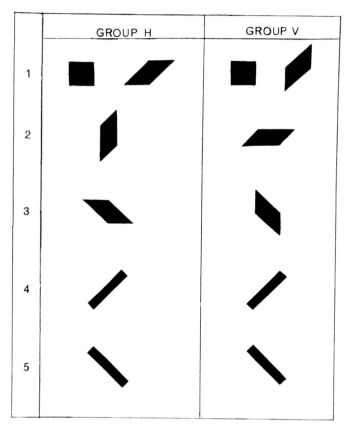

Fig. 5. Experiment 3

the original square. This was presumably because, for Group H, a horizontal rectangle can be treated as having points at east and west (like the original parallelogram) while for Group V it is the vertical rectangle that has pointlike features in the same directions as the points on the original parallelogram. Finally, the goldfish had detected the orientation of the oblique lines in the parallelogram; transfer was not perfect to a mirror-image parallelogram (Fig. 5, row 3), and there was better transfer to an oblique rectangle with outlines running in the same direction as the oblique contours of the original parallelogram (row 4) than to an oblique rectangle with contours at 180° to those of the original parallelogram (row 5).

The main differences between the rats and the goldfish were as follows. The rats' behavior in transfer tests was controlled by features at the bottom of the shapes rather than at the top. The presence of points facing in the same directions as those of the original parallelogram did not mediate transfer from the parallelogram—for instance, both diamonds and horizontal and vertical rectangles were treated as like the original square, not like the original parallelogram. The most important feature of the parallelogram for rats was the presence in the lower half of oblique contours running *in the same direction* as the oblique contours of the training parallelogram. Thus the obliques in row 4 were treated by rats as like the parallelogram, whereas those in row 5 were responded to in the way animals had learned to respond to the square.

Octopuses differed from both rats and goldfish. They relied most heavily on the general orientation of the parallelogram. Group H treated shapes elongated along the horizontal axis or either oblique axis as like the original parallelogram; Group V transferred from the original parallelogram to shapes elongated along the vertical axis or either oblique axis. For the octopus, it did not matter whether a shape was elongated along the oblique axis of the original parallelogram or the mirror-image axis. For example, octopuses transferred completely to mirror-image parallelograms (row 3) and showed no difference in amount of transfer to the oblique rectangles shown in rows 4 and 5.

The findings may be summarized and interpreted as follows. Rats do not confuse mirror-image shapes, octopuses totally confuse them, and goldfish have a tendency to do so. In terms of the model outlined above, rats store rules which specify whether a feature is at the east or at the west of another feature; octopuses store a rule which does not differentiate east and west; goldfish store a rule that is most readily matched if the original east-west relations are preserved but can be matched when they are reversed. Rats rely more heavily on contour orientation than either goldfish or octopuses. Octopuses rely more heavily on the orientation of the whole figure than either goldfish or rats.

It is possible that the visual processor in the rat contains predominantly edge detectors, whereas octopuses have predominantly bar detectors, and goldfish have both in equal proportions. The horizontal parallelograms would fire bar detectors in the horizontal and oblique axes, and if octopuses used predominantly bar detectors this would explain why they treat rectangles in the appropriate orientation as like the original parallelogram, whereas rats and goldfish, relying less heavily on this type of detector, treat horizontal and vertical rectangles as like the square, since they lack the oblique contours detected by edge detectors.

We are suggesting that some of the differences in the way these species discriminate between the same pairs of shapes can be attributed to differences in the *feature* detectors used, while others should be attributed to the way in which *rules* are formed and stored. To test these hypotheses we need to know the distribution of different types of receptive units in the visual system in each species.

Conclusion

Whatever the correct model of shape recognition, it must ultimately be able to account for behavioral findings. We have shown that goldfish do not in general recognize a rotation of a shape as the same as the original shape. The presence of a feature such as a point or a knob may, however, mediate transfer to different rotations. Goldfish appear to detect readily the presence of points in a shape, and to recognize differences in the relative number of points present in two shapes. Goldfish differ from rats in that they rely more heavily on points and less heavily on orientation of contours; they differ from octopuses in the reverse direction. These differences may be due to different proportions of bar and edge detectors being present in the three species. The species also differ in the extent to which they classify a shape as the same as its own mirror image. This difference is more likely to be due to differences in the rules that are formed in the store.

At the beginning of this paper we outlined a theory of shape recognition which we believe is the only plausible theory in the light of our present knowledge. Although the general outlines of the theory may be correct, the theory as so far developed is still vague and the details need filling in. The behavioral experiments described in this paper show how we can start putting some flesh on the bones of the theory. One of the main difficulties at the moment is to know whether to attribute a particular behavioral finding to the way in which the processor works or to the way in which the store works. This difficulty could be overcome if we had more information on the neurophysiology of the receptive units in the visual systems of different species.

Acknowledgment

The work reported here forms part of a project on "stimulus analyzing mechanisms" supported by the American Office of Naval Research (Contract N62558-4791).

References

Bowman, R., and Sutherland, N. S. 1968. Discrimination of circles and squares with and without knobs by goldfish. In preparation.

———. 1968. Discrimination of "W" and "V" shapes by goldfish. *Quart. J. Exp. Psychol.* In press.

Clowes, M. B. 1967. Perception, picture processing and computers. In *Machine intelligence*, ed. N. L. Collins and D. Michie, 1:181–97. Edinburgh: Oliver & Boyd.

Cronly-Dillon, J. R.; Sutherland, N. S.; and Wolfe, J. B. 1966. Intraretinal transfer of a learned visual shape discrimination in goldfish after section and regeneration of the optic nerve brachia. *Exp. Neurol.* 15:455–62.

Hemmings, G. 1965. Pretraining and transfer in shape discrimination. Ph.D. diss., University of Hull.

Hubel, D. H., and Wiesel, T. N. 1962. Receptive fields, binocular interaction and functional architecture in the cat's visual cortex. *J. Physiol. (Lond.)* 160:106–54.

———. 1965. Receptive fields and functional architecture in two non-striate visual areas (18 and 19) of the cat. *J. Neurophysiol.* 28: 229–89.

Julesz, B. 1961. Binocular depth perception and pattern recognition. In *Information theory*, ed. C. Cherry, pp. 212–21. London: Butterworth.

Mackintosh, J., and Sutherland, N. S. 1965. Visual discrimination by goldfish: The orientation of rectangles. *Anim. Behav.* 11:135–41.

Sutherland, N. S. 1957. Visual discrimination of orientation by *Octopus*. *Nature* 179:11–13.

———. 1959. Visual discrimination of shape by *Octopus*. Circles and squares, and circles and triangles. *Quart. J. Exp. Psychol.* 11:24–32.

———. 1960. Theories of shape discrimination in *Octopus*. *Nature* 186:840–44.

———. 1961*a*. The methods and findings of experiments on the visual discrimination of shape by animals. *Quart. J. Exp. Psychol.*, Monogr. 1, pp. 1–68.

———. 1961*b*. Visual discrimination of horizontal and vertical rectangles by rats on a new discrimination training apparatus. *Quart. J. Exp. Psychol.* 13:117–21.

———. 1963. Shape discrimination and receptive fields. *Nature* 197:118–22.

Sutherland, N. S.; Mackintosh, J.; and Mackintosh, N. J. 1963. The visual discrimination of reduplicated patterns by *Octopus*. *Anim. Behav.* 11:106–10.

Sutherland, N. S., and Williams, C. 1968. Discrimination of checkerboard patterns by rats. *Quart. J. Exp. Psychol.* In press.

5

Spatial Dimensions of Vision in Fish

David Ingle

Psychiatry Service
Boston City Hospital

Introduction

The visual system of the teleost fish serves to maintain a conformity between the movements of the organism and his spatial awareness. The positions of objects in space are related to the position of the fish by means of the retinal-tectal projection map, which is itself set in register with the motor system. The impingement of a particular image upon the retina is directly translated into the spatial coordinates of a sensorimotor system, which informs the fish which direction to move in or which to avoid. Through motion-sensitive cells in the retina, the fish is continually informed of his progress, as he moves through a realm of surfaces, edges, colors, and shadows. Within this dynamic spatial framework the motives, memories, and sensations compete for decisive motor commitment. Clearly the coding of position and direction is a fundamental problem for students of the visual system, and one which students of memory and motivation as well must eventually encounter.

Speaking broadly, there are two ways by which one can describe visual processes: by a *mechanistic* account of afferent integration, beginning with the retinal receptors and ascending stepwise into the central nervous system, or by a *teleological* approach that begins instead at the end, by analyzing visually guided responses. The second approach requires a modest explanation, since some puritanical behaviorists seem to regard any flirtation with teleology as a most incriminating sin. However, I shall attempt to demonstrate both pragmatic and theoretical justifications for my "backwards" approach to the functions of the visual system of fishes.

Although the physiologist can measure the input-output functions of single visual neurons with great virtuosity, he can only guess as to the manner in which the central nervous system classifies these trains of impulses. By describing visual inputs in terms of their motor outcomes, we hope to provide biologically relevant categories of perception. In distinguishing two visual objects as "biteable" vs. "frightening" we indicate something about the particular motivational or motor systems activated by our disparate inputs. By using feeding as a standardized behavioral criterion, we can look for the optimal releasing stimulus, under the assumption that visual integrations by afferent neurons somehow detect these particular attributes. A behavioral account of such optimal inputs for various activities—fighting, nest building, approaching a mate—can tell the electrophysiologist what to look for. Furthermore, success in matching visual features with particular motor organizations provides clues as to the kind of specificity we should expect from central neural systems.

The principle of "response classification" of visual inputs is well illustrated by a recent study of rabbit ganglion cells by Oyster and Barlow (1967). For this species, many retinal units respond selectively to small spots of light moved across the field in particular directions. The distribution of those directions giving maximal responses among a population of units clusters about four axes: up, down, front, and back. These axes are identical to the directions that objects would be displaced by contractions of the four rectus muscles. The authors therefore suggest that each group of cells sensitive to a particular direction of movement might constitute the arm of a servomechanism that operates to center the eye upon a moving object. Similar considerations about the movement of the whole organism can help us to interpret data from discrimination experiments with fish, as I now hope to demonstrate.

An Experiment on Motion Detection

The study of movement perception by fish provides a good entrée into problems of stimulus classification. The parameters of stimulus presentation may be studied by traditional training procedures, and by using natural behavior as well. Fish share with many other animals a dramatic sensitivity to those movements within their visual world that denote food or danger. Electrophysiological studies of several vertebrate species have revealed the existence of directional motion detectors within the retina, so that a comparative neuropsychology of movement perception is very much on the horizon. Studies on goldfish by Jacobson and Gaze (1964) and by Cronly-Dillon (1964) have agreed that the majority of such directionally sensitive units respond best to spots moving along the horizontal axis. Of these units, the majority respond to nasalward, rather than to temporalward, movements. I have carried out a behavioral study with goldfish in order to test the obvious suggestion that these subjects should detect forward-moving spots more easily than those moving in a backward direction.

In this study cardiac deceleration provided a quantitative index of sensitivity to motion, during a shock-motivated classical conditioning procedure. Goldfish about 20 cm in length were placed in a small sponge-lined chamber, which was set within a 50-gallon training aquarium (see Fig. 1). The tank was internally covered with gray plastic sheeting, in which a window was cut at a distance of 20 cm directly lateral to one eye. The window subtended a width of 24° of visual angle, and was 18° high. A white disk revolved outside the aquarium in such a way that black spots of 2° diameter moved one at a time horizontally across the window. The disk was under control of a reversible, variable-speed Bodine motor.

The relative sensitivity of the subject to nasal and temporal directions of movement was determined by measuring the cardiac rate during the 10-sec interval of stimulus movement. Subjects were exposed to alternating presentations of the two directions, and on each trial the 10-sec CS was followed by a brief shock of 1- to 2-volt a.c. across the caudal regions of the body. When comparisons of successive trials were made, all subjects that became conditioned to the movement CS showed a definite asymmetry of response, favoring one particular direction of movement.

When a single black spot moved through the window at 12°/sec, all six subjects responded more strongly when the stimulus moved nasally. The prediction was thus fulfilled, using stimulation parameters similar to those used in the two electrophysiological studies. However, two other groups of subjects showed just the opposite effect when other parameters were used. When the spot moved at only 3°/sec, all six fish showed a stronger response to the temporally moving stimulus. The reduction of movement velocity therefore has revealed the existence of a second and unexpected mechanism for movement detection.

Velocity of movement is not the only variable which determines the optimal direction of movement. Those six subjects trained to respond to a multiple-spotted stimulus (see Fig. 1) moving at 12°/sec also showed greater cardiac deceleration as the stimulus moved in the

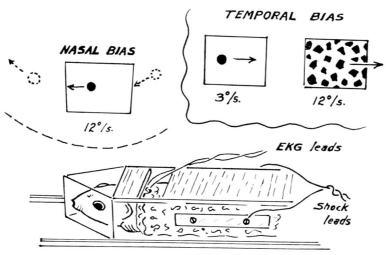

FIG. 1. Apparatus for cardiac conditioning to moving stimuli. Rotating disk moves spots behind window in side of aquarium. Inset top right shows stimulus variations used with second and third groups.

temporal direction. If we try to account for these results in terms of only *two* motion detecting processes, how may we fit the temporally biased stimuli into a common category that excludes the fast-moving single spot? The subjective impressions of the human observer may provide a clue: the single fast-moving spot seems to jump from place to place, whereas the other stimuli appear to flow with a more diffuse motion. This account recalls MacKay's (1961) hypothetical distinction between detectors of "velocity" and of "position change" in the human visual system.

We can make this somewhat abstract notion more concrete by identifying the two processes with actual responses that fish perform under guidance of moving stimuli. We may imagine that fish use the "change of position" analysis as they orient toward moving prey. Certainly angelfish or mouthbreeders, as the author has observed, wheel into striking position with a rapid movement as food enters the lateral visual field. The position of the food within the visual field apparently informs them of the required response so that they end up accurately pointing at the food object, ready to track it down. Probably one or two brief appearances of an object are sufficient to elicit an accurate orienting response, since the fast-moving mouthbreeders perform well even in stroboscopic light flashing at a rate of 3/sec.

However, as the fish dart toward the sinking food pellet, they invariably misjudge its position and snap too high, when illumined by this slower frequency of flickering light. At a rate of 8–10/sec they appear to catch food as accurately as during steady illumination. If we assume that horizontally moving prey is tracked by the same process, then it appears that a continuous visual feedback based on the velocity variable is necessary for the subject to aim his final lunge and snap. As the fish bears down upon his food, he will monitor the rate of *temporal* motion relative to his eye, so we might expect this mechanism to show greater acuity for the temporal direction. Our hypothesis agrees by analogy with the known facts about control of human eye movement: an initial saccad is triggered by a change in position (Rashbass 1961), while continuous tracking depends upon appreciation of the velocity variable (Young and Stark 1963).

But why should the random-spotted stimulus reveal such directional bias in the fish visual system, since it cannot be perceived as a moving *object?* We suggest—without direct evidence, as yet—that fish can regulate their swimming velocity by means of visual feedback resulting from their own swimming motions. For example, a fish moving against the current could judge his rate of forward progress only by visual cues—i.e., by monitoring the rate of temporalward movement of the entire surround. In this case, the movement of any single object independently of the surround would prove a misleading reference point. The multiple-spotted stimulus, then, constitutes a *surface* in motion, and has a functional correspondence with the visual framework (weeds, stones, etc.) that moves as a unit. We might also suggest that fish can judge distances of stationary surfaces during rapid approach by monitoring the temporal flow-gradients and comparing these with his own velocity. In either instance, the surface motion-detection system should be biased for temporal directions, just as our conditioning experiment has indicated.

We might test our hypothesis by placing a fish in an alley flanked by movable surround, which could be moved in either direction so as to provide an abnormal correlation between the fish's swimming velocity and the rate of temporal displacement of the environment. We would expect a forward-moving environment (e.g., at half the fish's velocity) to induce a compensatory increase in speed, even though the *relative* displacement is still temporalward. Furthermore, we would expect that a multiple-spotted surface would be more effective in modifying the subject's swimming speed than one covered with a few isolated spots, even though the cardiac-conditioning criterion shows the latter stimulus as the more effective.

Our notion that various movement stimuli may have different orders of effectiveness depending upon the kind of behavioral response criterion will not astonish the ethologist, but it implies a degree of stimulus-response specificity not generally assumed by experimental psychologists. If the categories of movement detection can be more exactly specified, the electrophysiologist should reexamine the kinds of units in retina and tectum with a better notion of the relevant parameters. While this has not yet been attempted for the fish, it is notable that, for the rabbit, Barlow, Hill, and Levick (1964) discriminate between ganglion cells with small fields, which are sensitive to slow movements, and those with larger fields, which specialize in detecting faster movements.

An Experiment on the Coding of Visual Direction

I now proceed to a different kind of experiment, which is concerned with the coding of so-called mirror-image shapes. When an organism views such a pair of shapes, for example, arrowheads pointing left and right, he can distinguish them only by their respective orientations. Such a discrimination could be based upon "local sign" of the retinal impingements if the shape were large enough; i.e., for the left-pointing arrowhead, the tail would fall in the middle of the field with the point falling in the left field. On the other hand, if the same arrowhead were easily identified when falling consecutively on disparate retinal loci, we would infer that "relative direction" was perceived independently of the retinal position.

A series of experiments by Mello (1965a, b, 1966) in which pigeons were tested for interocular transfer of mirror-image shape discriminations produced results that challenge our assumptions about how visual directions are coded. Pigeons trained monocularly to peck at a key decorated with a 45° oblique line and to refrain from pecking when a 135° oblique was projected tended to peck at the "wrong" stimulus when tested via the second untrained eye alone. This paradoxical "interocular reversal" phenomenon has been replicated with several other shapes as well. These experiments demonstrate that the pigeon does not view such shapes primarily as "left-right" decisions, since a leftward arrowhead seen by one eye is taken as equivalent to a rightward arrowhead viewed by the opposite eye. On the other hand, these pigeons did show "front-back equivalence" between opposite eyes, if we allow that shapes pointing "toward the midline" are viewed as pointing "forward" in the third dimension.

I have carried out similar tests of interocular transfer with goldfish, in order to replicate earlier observations (Ingle 1965) that this species can show the expected "left-right equivalence" of mirror-image discriminations. Because these results were in apparent contradiction to the pigeon data, it seemed valuable to explore any differences in the procedures that might provide a clue as to the coding processes underlying transfer of such discriminations. Large goldfish were trained to make successive discriminations by the shock-avoidance technique of McCleary (1960). Fish learned to swim forward from a starting box into an identical goal box on the introduction of the positive stimulus, but to withhold such a response in the presence of the negative (mirror-image) shape. Following stable discriminatory performance, subjects were given six transfer trials via the opposite, untrained eye in a predetermined sequence. Following a retraining session, fish were tested once more and transfer performance evaluated on the basis of these twelve unreinforced test trials.

The transfer tests following training on oblique-line and arrowhead discriminations transferred according to the left-right type of equivalence. As Figure 2 illustrates, a forward-pointing arrowhead viewed by the right eye is taken as the equivalent of a backward-pointing arrowhead when placed on the left side. Although these stimuli do not show "front-back" equivalence, they *are* equivalent when moved around into the frontal plane and compared in respect to their left-right dimensions.

It appeared from this remarkably consistent outcome that goldfish and pigeons organize their visual space in quite different ways. However, by using a third kind of mirror-image discrimination (see Fig. 3) it was possible to convert goldfish quite readily into pigeons. When sideward T's were used as stimuli, all six fish transferred according to the "front-back" mode of equivalence. It is notable that these latter stimuli subtended about 15° of visual angle, while the former two shapes subtended about 10° of arc. In order to test the possibility that the intrafield separation of the two "halves" of the stimulus was a critical determinant of the transfer results, a fourth discrimination was employed. By using a stimulus consisting of a red plus green pair of squares set apart at 22° (see Fig. 3) the front vs. back distinction was further enhanced. Transfer tests did reveal interhemispheric equivalence of the "front-back" type.

We suggest that enlargement of the stimulus alters the coding principle by enhancing the "local sign" of the left and right parts, while weakening the figural "gestalt." With the larger figures, the commissures relay more information about the absolute spatial positions of the two parts. Certainly, for a lateral-eyed animal (such as fish or pigeon) it is reasonable that separate positions of retinal impingement should denote "front" vs. "back." Nevertheless, with smaller shapes the figure is taken in as a unit and is analyzed in terms of the relative rather than the absolute position of the parts. Although the physiological basis for either

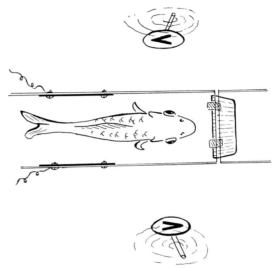

FIG. 2. An "equivalent" pair of shapes, as judged by interocular transfer tests following monocular training on "forward" vs. "backward" arrowheads. This kind of transfer equivalence is called "left-right." During a conditioned avoidance response, the subject swims forward through the door into the identical goal box.

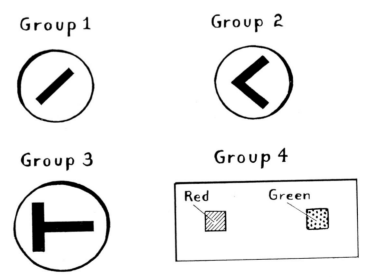

FIG. 3. Stimuli used for each of four mirror-image discriminations

type of coding must remain speculative, the present data contradict the simplistic notion that the internal representation of visual directions is always related to the retinal-tectal projection mapping. That is to say, the two opposite modes of transfer for mirror-image shapes cannot both be based upon the assumption of a point-to-point equivalence between the two tectal maps.

This notion of dual coding of directions can be made more concrete through the following hypothesis. I suggest that the retinotectal projection map provides a substrate for orienting movements to objects at particular positions. This hypothesis identifies the discriminatory process underlying "front-back" equivalence with that mechanism by which *orientation* is guided. On the other hand, the "left-right" transfer mechanism is assumed to depend upon a process of object *identification*, or shape recognition. This kind of distinction is implicit in the kind of interpretation that Harris (1965) has given to the dramatic "visual" readjustments that Kohler has claimed for human subjects who have worn inverting or reversing prisms for several weeks. The plasticity of spatial location, according to Harris, is confined to the *orientation* process—an object on the left now elicits an orienting movement to the right and seems (in some sense) to *be* on the right. Yet objects *within* a particular place, for example letters, are still seen in their reversed orientation. Although it would be bold to suggest that spatial vision, or shape recognition, is closely comparable for fish and for philosopher, it seems necessary to distinguish between "spatial direction" and "configurational direction" throughout the vertebrate phylogeny.

We may perform a hypothetical experiment in order to illustrate the predictive value of our principle of "response categorization." If the mirror-image transfer paradigm were extended to moving stimuli, such as we employed during the first set of experiments, how would a fish equate directions of motion between the two eyes? If we regard the single fast-moving spot as a releaser for a food-tracking mechanism, then the turning movements involved in following the nasalward motion via one eye will predict a temporalward motion as the object crosses across the vertical meridian into the field of the second eye. If spot movements are categorized in terms of their common response outcomes, a nasally-moving spot seen by one eye should be equivalent to a temporally-moving spot on the opposite side, as indicated by tests of interocular transfer. However, we make just the opposite prediction for the multiple spot stimulus. Because reafferent movement of the environment produced by the subject's own forward movements is temporalward for each eye, a forward-moving surface seen via one eye should be equivalent in the test situation to a forward-moving surface on the opposite side.

How far dare we pursue our view that "response-typologies" can be directly matched with categories of visual perception? It seems likely that various "shape-analyzing" mechanisms also have preferred relationships with emotional or motor systems. For example, I have found that goldfish prefer to snap at small, bite-sized circles rather than at squares or triangles of the same size. It would be useful to know whether fish actually identify "food" within the lateral field, or whether they make the evaluation only after centering the object within the anterior position. If fish making food discriminations do not, in fact, learn to inhibit the primary orientation to the non-food object, we are forced to predict that shape discriminations within the lateral field should be inferior to those within the nasal field. Although there is no good evidence on this question, my unpublished research indicates that goldfish do readily learn discriminations between circles and squares subtending 4° within the lateral field.

It is possible that new kinds of visuomotor coding enter into the perception within the "microspace" just in front of the fish's nose, in contrast to the "macrospace" within the lateral fields. During consummatory behaviors—fighting, feeding, nest-building—fish make continual adjustments to position, shape, velocity, and orientation of objects. These finer movements—twisting, pulling, darting forward, biting, etc.—are continually modified in accord with visual, tactile, or gustatory feedback. For these reasons, the electrophysiologist should examine the possibility that coding mechanisms are differently distributed between anterior and posterior tectal regions. Certainly, the work of Akert (1949) indicates that efferent mechanisms differ between the two regions. Stimulation of the anterior tectum of the trout causes smooth, convergent eye movements, while activation of more posterior areas elicits conjugate movements of both eyes away from the stimulated side (the so-called visual grasp reflex).

From stimulation studies, we might infer that control of visual orientation or visual avoidance is largely unilateral in respect to the initial motor command. Indeed, stimulation and lesion experiments on goldfish in our laboratory indicate that visual approach (orientation) depends on crossed tectofugal pathways, while the faster visual avoidance (tail flip) depends upon a descending ipsilateral route. The work of Savage and of Regestein reported in this symposium shows that the effects of unilateral forebrain or hypothalamic lesions on visually mediated avoidance behavior are strikingly lateralized. However, we suspect that the more subtle movements during consummatory behavior, guided by visual stimuli in the frontal field, must be bilaterally controlled at all times. These activities demand, as it were, the commitment of the whole animal. It is tempting to attribute the fact that goldfish can easily acquire opposing color or shape discriminations in the lateral fields simultaneously via opposite eyes (Ingle 1968) to the essential laterality of avoidance learning when the stimulus appears only on one side. It is notable that neither Schulte (1957) nor Shapiro (1965), using food-approach procedures with shape discriminations, could train fish to "dissociate" visual memories with respect to the eye in use. It seems quite possible that certain commissures within the teleost fish, like the corpus callosum of mammals (Whitteridge 1965), are primarily concerned with visual integration about the vertical meridian. A more refined consideration of the responses associated with binocular usage in fish will certainly enrich our imagination in designing experiments to determine the function of the inter-hemispheric commissures.

Conclusion

From the evidence that we have culled from experiments on the visual behavior of goldfish, it is clear that such terms as "movement" or "visual direction" are inherently ambiguous and require differentiation into more refined categories. We suggest that consideration of the natural functions of the teleost visual system will assist in categorization of retinal and tectal mechanisms. Furthermore, the attempt to conceive "response classifications" in respect to visual-discrimination capacities of fish has led to some specific hypotheses that can be tested by the psychologist and the electrophysiologist. We suspect that the science of neuropsychology should follow the lead of molecular biology or immunology and search for specificities among the sensory and motor organizations underlying behavior. In some sense, the stimulus is a "key" which fits the motoric "lock." By describing the optimal stimuli releasing orienting and consummatory responses, we should be able to delineate the neural representations of our lock-and-key model, and take an important step toward unlocking the still forbidden mysteries of neural plasticity.

Acknowledgment

The work described in this article was supported by Research Grant MH 11555 from the National Institute of Mental Health and by an award from the Medical Foundation of Boston, Massachusetts.

References

Akert, K. 1949. *Helv. Physiol. Pharmaocl. Acta* 7:112.
Barlow, H. B.; Hill, R. M.; and Levick, W. R. 1964. *J. Physiol. (Lond.)* 173:377.
Cronly-Dillon, J. R. 1964. *Nature* 208:214.
Harris, S. C. 1965. *Psychol. Rev.* 72:419.
Ingle, D. J. 1965. *Perspect. Biol. Med.* 8:241.
———. 1968. *Brain, behavior, and evolution*, 1:58–85.
Jacobson, M., and Gaze, R. M. 1964. *Quart. J. Exp. Physiol.* 49:199.
McCleary, R. A. 1960. *J. Comp. Physiol. Psychol.* 53:311.
MacKay, D. M. 1961. In *Sensory communications*, ed. W. R. Rosenblith. Cambridge, Mass.: MIT Press.
Mello, N. K. 1965a. *Science* 148:252.
———. 1965b. *Proc. Amer. Psychol. Assoc.* 1:137.
———. 1966. *Physiol. and Behav.* 1:292.
Oyster, C. W., and Barlow, H. B. 1967. *Science* 155:841–42.
Rashbass, C. 1961. *J. Physiol. (Lond.)* 159:326.
Schulte, A. 1957. *Z. Vergl. Physiol.* 39:432.
Shapiro, S. M. 1965. *Amer. J. Psychol.* 78:21.
Whitteridge, D. 1965. In *Functions of the corpus callosum*, ed. E. G. Ettlinger. London: J. & A. Churchill.
Young, L., and Stark, L. 1963. *I.E.E.E. Trans. Human Factors Electr.* HFE-4 (#1), p. 38.

6

Vision in Fish: The Origins of the Visual Frame for Action in Vertebrates

Colwyn Trevarthen

Center for Cognitive Studies
Harvard University

Introduction

Comparative anatomy teaches us to see a common vertebrate body plan, and any two vertebrates are found to have homologous features which are part of this plan. Special details of form which at first seem obvious exceptions to this turn out to be related to the common plan. The brains of vertebrates, for example, have evolved great differences in size and in the proportions of their parts. Nevertheless one general morphological scheme, reflecting a common law of growth and differentiation among nerve cells, is impressed upon the whole series.

Is the same conservation of a basic design, expressing a single underlying principle of functional organization, to be found also in vertebrate behavior? If so, then vision, a modality of reception in which vertebrates as a group excel from very early in their history, will have a mechanism in primitive forms which is to some extent fundamental—a ground plan for all subsequently evolved forms. The general anatomies of the eyes and of the muscles associated with them are, indeed, remarkably uniform in vertebrates from lamprey to man. There is encouragement in this for the hope that the central neural mechanisms also share basic principles of design and function.

In this paper I am hunting for general principles in the visual behavior and in the anatomy and physiology of the visual brain of fish. I am looking for a simpler standard or prototype of vision which will serve as a tool in the analysis of vision in the mammals and in man. Other work has brought to my attention two more specific aspects of this quest which might be regarded as uncharted territories where knowledge of the visual mechanism of fish as simpler vertebrates could be usefully applied if we had possession of it.

First, we observe that mammals, including primates, can withstand surgical separation of the cerebral hemispheres with almost no disruption of general visuomotor coordination.

61

The two separated telencephalic and diencephalic visual perception and memory mechanisms of a split brain act collaboratively in control of many complex patterns of action—taking part harmoniously with only very rare dissensions (Myers, Sperry, and McCurdy 1962; Black and Myers 1965; Trevarthen 1965). This corroborates an increasing body of data from anatomical, physiological, and ablation studies which indicates that integrative processes in subhemispheric parts of the brain of a mammal are essential background to the more labile and selective control of visual awareness within the cortex. Could this be due to the retention of a basic visuomotor mechanism in the midbrain, one homologous with the visual brain of primitive vertebrates?

Second, there is the puzzle of the beginnings of vision in the early stages of human growth. Here we are confronted with a bewildering complexity of processes. In attempting to sort out neotenic, recapitulatory, or specialized larval adaptations, there is a need for a clearer view of the ground plan of the vertebrate brain. Many of the strange steps in the course of infant development may receive explanation only in terms of a process which must integrate complex and new forebrain processes within the old vertebrate brain plan. This is a far more momentous metamorphosis than that between the aquatic and the land vertebrates.

The behavior of fish is neither simple nor automatic. Even though they lack a cerebral cortex, fish show elements of behavior which require explanation in terms of changing anticipatory adjustments within the nervous system to fit standard consequences of acts. In simpler forms of fish, visual function is closely tied to the activity of locomotion, but the higher teleosts show the beginning of a more selective, more "voluntary" adjustment of visual contact with surrounding visibles. Anatomically the mechanism for all these acts in the visual frame is essentially subhemispheric, with the main links in the mesencephalon. Clearly the visual spatial frame for orientations and displacements of the body and its parts is well established in the midbrain of fish. Presumably this is also true for the foundations of visuomotor integrations in all vertebrates.

The Peripheral Visual Apparatus of a Fish and the Optical Field

The optics of a fish's eye is simpler than that of the eye of any vertebrate living in air (Fig. 1). The visual field is a projection of points in the outside world through a nodal point at the center of the spherical lens. The latter is unchanging in shape and is the only element of refractive index different from that of the surrounding water. When relaxed the eye is focused for near distances; accommodation for distant points is accomplished by muscular retraction of the lens inward toward the temporal (posterior) retina.

Each eye admits light from a field of nearly 190°, the iris being tilted to allow rays at about 95° to the optic axis to gain entry to the lens and to reach the border of the retina. Every species of fish shows its own adaptive iris form which molds the contours of the visual field, and the pupil is frequently irregular in outline to favor particular sectors of the visual field. The optic axis at rest and the margins of the field are such that each retina receives a projection of a region of space in a particular correspondence with the body axis, and this, too, varies from species to species. (For further information on the eyes of fish, see Walls 1942.)

I have satisfied myself that this is a precisely regulated correspondence in one species by carefully measuring the visual fields of three goldfish.[1] The three individuals gave results in very close agreement. The field is shown in Figure 1.

Possession of two eyes does not merely double the visual field. Most fish possess a binocular field in which each point is projected simultaneously to both retinas. In general, the binocular field of a fish is wide in front of the mouth and there are frequently enlargements dorsal and ventral to this anteriorly. As Figure 1 shows, these enlargements are present, but small, in the goldfish. Behind there is usually a blind segment, about 20° wide, which is occupied by the trunk and tail when the fish is not swimming.

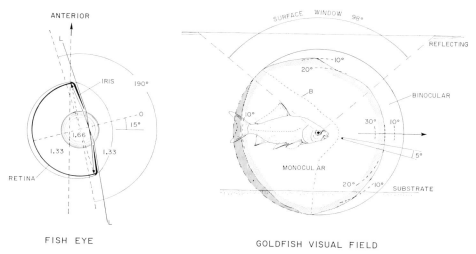

FIG. 1. *Left*, the eye of a fish seen in horizontal section. The numbers indicate the approximate refractive indices of lens material and surrounding media. *Right*, the visual field of a goldfish with eyes oriented in the midline position. *B*, approximate edge of the binocular field in the midplane.

This, then, is the extent of the static visual field, limiting physically the range of visual discriminations as long as there are no motor adjustments. For each eye only one narrow depth zone is well focused on the retina at any instant. The two retinas receive different images of the surroundings by projection through two points separated by the interocular distance. The parallax differences between these two projections for the binocular part of the field are potential bases for detection of depth relations for the control of movement.

Transformations Produced by Movements of the Eye

Displacement of points in space relative to the eyes produces orderly transformations of the visual images and greatly multiplies the information held momentarily in the visual array. Retraction of the lens, rotations of the eyes relative to the head, and translations and

---

[1] The fish were anesthetized with MS222 and placed with the eye centered at the point of intersection of the 2 axes of rotation of a theodolite-like apparatus. The eye was turned along each meridian until the entrance pupil could be seen as a narrow black slit through a small telescope. The extreme border of the visual field was plotted at 10° intervals around its perimeter.

rotations of the two together with the head put active control over these transformations within the command of the nervous system.

As the fish approaches an object, the retractor lentis muscle may be relaxed to optimize the definition of the image. As the eye moves forward, visual features flow over the retina, the whole pattern expanding from a point at the rear end of the axis of movement (Fig. 2). The angular displacement of near points over the hemispherical retina exceeds that of far points. Thus a motor parallax effect, a potential cue to depth, is produced in each eye. For points at the same distance from the eye the depth disparity of image motion is greatest in the direction normal to the line of displacement of the eye. Since the eye of a fish faces laterally, a large part of the retina carries rapidly moving images during forward locomotion (see Fig. 2). Rotation of the eye around its center affects all rays to the same degree. If rotation and translation are combined there is a displacement of the stable node for the expanding pattern of retinal images.

These lawful effects are produced automatically by the normal movements of an active fish.

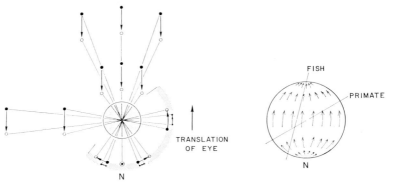

FIG. 2. Displacements of the retinal images produced by movement of eye relative to the surrounding world. At right, a comparison of displacement figures in fish and primate when the eye, in normal orientation, is displaced by forward locomotion. *N*, the expansion node of the visual array.

Establishment of a Standard Postural Frame for Choice of Motor Displacements—Stabilization of the Eye

In the normal animal, adjustments of posture act to maintain a standard relationship between the gravitational field and the organized receptor fields of all modalities. It must be supposed that the elaborate and precise neural regulation of the resting body orientation in all vertebrates is a necessary foundation for behavior.

Fish are convenient subjects for experimental study of postural regulations, and many classical investigations have been performed with them. They move perpetually to maintain their orientation in the water in accustomed relation to gravity and light, or to some secondary reference such as the substrate, the water surface, the flow of water, or the position of floating plants. Free-floating orientation is generally a product of precisely regulated adjustments made simultaneously to gravity and to direction of light from the sun (von Holst 1950*a*, *b*; Mittelstaedt 1964). Information about displacements of the body relative to gravitation is also obtained from proprioceptors and from the semicircular canals, which respond to accelerations. Reflex regulations of eye movements, as well as body and limb movements, in response to stimulation of these receptors, tend to counteract or reverse motions affecting vision (Lowenstein and Sand 1940*a, b;* Lowenstein 1950). These reflexes are important in regulating locomotor activity.

Maintenance of standard orientation of the visual field to gravity and to light, by assuring correspondence of retinal effects with regular features of the environment, greatly simplifies the analytic operations required for visual control of more complex behavior. The six eye muscles which rotate each eye in the head were perhaps primitively concerned only with this maintenance of a basic spatial position vis-à-vis physical fields shared with other objects, animate and inanimate.

MAXIMUM EYE-MOVEMENTS — GOLDFISH

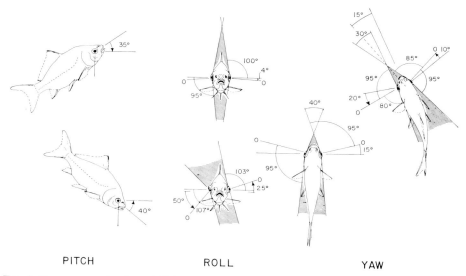

PITCH   ROLL   YAW

Fig. 3. Eye movements of a goldfish, based on measurements made with a spinal fish; *O*, optical axis of eye.

The oblique muscles of fish rotate the eyes over large angles and are capable of making almost complete compensation for pitch changes as the fish swims up or down. The movements actually made have not been described. In the goldfish, the compensatory movements for roll are about twice as large for the upward-moving eye which, therefore, may remain normally oriented when the body tilts to one side, while the lower eye is directed partially down. Lateral turning movements of the head are, as we shall see, accompanied by complete compensatory rotations of the eyes only if the movement is imposed upon the fish by an external force. Goldfish make small and unequal fore-and-aft movements of the eyes, responding with the trailing eye when passively turned to one side relative to the medium in the labyrinth or to the visual field. The movements are closely similar in amplitude to those reported by Harris (1965) for the dogfish when the fish is rotated passively from side to side. Reflex displacements of the eyes of a spinal goldfish subjected to passive rotations are shown in Figure 3.

Orientation—The Neuronal Basis Is a Map of Behavioral Space

From within a standard postural frame of reference, a fish may orient to a particular event in the visual field. A movement is made which is of appropriate size to avoid an obstacle, to bring a piece of food close to the mouth, to keep up with a school, to solicit a mate, or to increase the distance from a threat by the quickest route. What is the possible neuronal basis for the space-dependent aspect of these behaviors, which results in each locus in the visual field being pinpointed in a map of possible orientation movements?

Orientation requires detection of an event at a particular place relative to the body. A visual event may elicit activity in a particular group of retinal ganglion cells which, in turn, send optic fibers to the brain. The same event at another place may excite an indistinguishable pattern of ganglion cell discharge, but in a different bundle of nerves. Information for determination of an orientation movement must be contained in the group of fibers excited, and this information must be kept intact until the requisite integrative correspondence has been set up between the visual pattern and a congruent motor pattern. In other words, there must be a central neuronal topography in some form corresponding to the topography of motor activity within the visual field.

The first evidence for an orderly projection of retina to brain came from anatomical studies of Ströer (1939). Behavioral evidence of correspondence between tectal loci and visual-field loci was obtained by Sperry (1944). There have recently become available a large number of maps of the visual projection obtained by anatomical techniques and by microelectrode recording of activity evoked by retinal stimulation. The tectal maps in a number of fish are described by Schwassmann in this volume. Accurate maps of the greater part of the projections onto the optic tectum of a dozen species of vertebrates in different groups are now available.

There is a remarkable consistency in the layout of these maps. When they are plotted in the usual way, in terms of the coordinates of the optical system of the eye, this is not obvious, but if replotted in terms of the body-centered space within which the animal judges his movements, they are all essentially the same. I have chosen the maps from two extremely different forms, a fish with the eyes facing outward, and the cat, where there is almost complete frontality of vision, to illustrate this point (Fig. 4). This is a most strikingly visible anatomical correlate of a behavioral control system common to all vertebrates (Fig. 5).

On each lobe of the optic tectum is a map of points in the opposite half of the visual space surrounding the body. The vertical meridian parallel with the axis of the body lies along the anterodorsal region, with one-half of the binocular visual field extending outward from this to a variable distance in different species. In every case the central region, in front of the head, where all the most important behavioral commitments are made when the animal is fully oriented, occupies the anterior end of the optic lobe. For example, when a fish sights a piece of food in the periphery, it is brought to the center and seized by the mouth. This movement also brings an image of the food object in nerve cell activity along the side of the tectum to the anterior region near the junction of the midbrain and dorsal thalamus, a focal point in morphogenesis where ingrowing optic fibers segregate to pass to a number of different visual areas, of which the optic tectum is by far the largest.

Spatial Reference in the Binocular Field—Stereopsis

The central binocular field, near the midplane of the body, presents some problems. If one makes the assumption that the tectal map is specified as a map of the two mirror

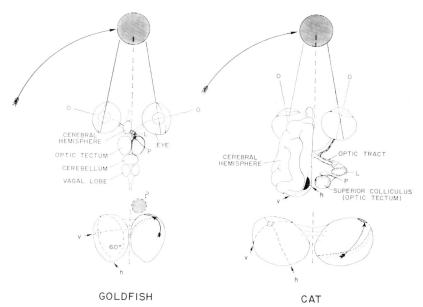

CEREBRAL HEMISPHERE
OPTIC TECTUM
CEREBELLUM
VAGAL LOBE
O
L
P
EYE

GOLDFISH

CEREBRAL HEMISPHERE
O
O
OPTIC TRACT
L
P
SUPERIOR COLLICULUS (OPTIC TECTUM)
v
h

CAT

FIG. 4. Retinotectal projections in cat and goldfish. Data for the cat obtained from Apter (1945). The goldfish map is based on measurements made by Schwassmann and Kruger (1965) and by Jacobson and Gaze (1964). *O*, optical axis; *L*, lateral geniculate area of posterior dorsal thalamus; *P*, pretectum; *v* and *h*, vertical and horizontal meridians of the visual field on optic coordinates. The central behavioral field and its probable representation in the C.N.S. are crosshatched (the projection of retinal central area on cortex in cat is black). The border of the binocular field is indicated on the right tectum in each case by a dotted line with shading on the monocular side.

BEHAVIORAL SPACE

CENTRAL

LATERAL   LATERAL

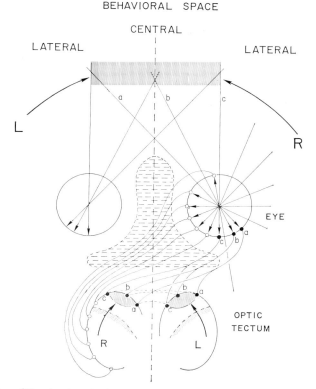

L   R

a   b   c

EYE

R   L

OPTIC TECTUM

FIG. 5. The plan of the visual projection in vertebrates, from the space around the body to the retina and thence to the optic tectum.

halves of a behavioral space divided at the same midplane, then for each eye a point in the visual field to the nasal side of the plane through the center of the eye and parallel with the body axis could be classed as either to the right or to the left of straight ahead (Fig. 5). If the directions of the lines of sight to such an ambiguous point can be compared in the brain, the ambiguity would be resolved, and both left-right locations and distance away from the head would be measured. Given that this can be done, the next question is, Where does such comparison occur? According to all anatomical and neurophysiological studies available, the optic nerves of each eye of a fish are completely crossed. Do fibers pass at a later stage within the brain from each eye to both sides of the tectum, or does the transfer occur through intertectal commissures specifically associated with the interocular corridor of behavioral space? These alternatives are illustrated in Figure 5.

The mapping of the binocular field of the frog by Gaze and Jacobson (1962*a*) indicates that in this animal there are two different zones within the binocular field. Points lateral to the body are mapped onto both tecti at asymmetric loci; points within the central area in front of the head are doubly mapped at the anterior pole of each tectum. In the latter area, visual excitation passes from each eye to the contralateral tectal surface and thence across the midline to homotopic points in the ipsilateral tectum, apparently through commissures in the ventral tegmentum (Gaze and Jacobson 1962*b*).

Thus the frog possesses a neuronal basis for judging both orientation and distance of off-center points by intertectal comparison and for judging the distance of a straight-ahead object simultaneously in each tectum. At present it is not possible to be sure if fish with well-developed binocular vision have the same kind of double map. The frog makes very slight eye movements and shows no convergence. It is possible that those fish which make clear convergence movements to fixate near objects may eliminate the spatial ambiguity in the binocular field by adjusting the orientation of the two eyes to center the image of any object attended to on central areas or foveae.

It should be noted that present anatomical and neurophysiological data leave uncertain where the binocular field in the brain of a fish is represented. It is not established that this field, where the most critical identity discriminations must be performed, is completely represented in the optic tectum. The published maps for the goldfish (Jacobson and Gaze 1964; Schwassmann and Kruger 1965) do not extend far enough to decide this, though they do suggest that the binocular area is not extensive on the surface of the tectum. The map published by Jacobson and Gaze was made from measurements made with the eye in air. Although it shows measurements to 90° for the optic axis, the map is, in fact, no more extensive than that of Schwassmann and Kruger and covers an area equivalent to about 70° from the axis for the eyes in water. Optic fibers pass to pretectal and diencephalic centers as well as to the tectum and either or both of these could be specifically concerned with analysis of information within the frontal binocular field. An anatomical study by Burns and Goodman (1967) suggests that this is the case for the alligator.

Eye Movements, Scanning, and the Evolution of Selective Regarding

With each movement of the eyes in the head, the retina is moved within the body-centered visual frame to receive different samples of it. Eye movements have a variety of functions. As we have seen, the simplest, and apparently the most primitive, merely compensate for tilt and drifts of the body. If the body position is changed passively, the visual frame is kept approximately constant.

More interesting are spontaneous recentering movements which result in preferential sampling of parts of the visual space to establish touch points or guidelines for controlled motor activity. From these eye movements some fish appear to have evolved complex exploratory rotations by means of which a complex visual world may be sampled by a retina with a specialized region of high resolution, an area centralis or fovea. In mammals this evolution is quite clear.

Fish present a wide variety of independent eye movements of the second type. An excellent recent analysis of dogfish eye movements made by Harris (1965) lays a foundation for comparative investigations. He found that a dogfish has complete oculogyric compensation for passive displacement of the head and eyes, but that, when locomotion is in progress, the sinusoidal undulations produce side-to-side motions of the head which are only *partially* compensated for by out-of-phase movements of the eyes. The automatic labyrinthine compensation is countered by influences from the spinal cord. The result is that a pair of vertical planes about 3 ft on either side of the head are stabilized by alternate side-to-side fixation. As the head rotates to the right, the right eye remains directed at a vertical line 3 ft to the right; meanwhile the left eye moves with the head, shifting fixation a step forward. Thus the fish progresses by stepping, as it were, from one line of fixation to the other as it wags its head from side to side. Harris has pointed out how this would provide a basis for a fixed visual frame by which the dogfish (which, like a bird, must move forward to keep aloft) can maintain a regulated height above the sea bottom.

A dogfish turns by reversing one step in its undulatory rhythm, resetting the integrated patterns of muscle contraction to produce a double pull to one side, and the eyes manifest this change of direction slightly ahead of the body. The net result is that the eyes make a step in the direction of the turn $\frac{1}{8}$ sec before the turn is made. This anticipatory saccadic eye movement presumably helps in maintaining the visual frame in spite of the changed direction of movement.

The eye muscles act in conjunction with the trunk muscles, and, when the fish is at rest on the bottom of the tank, rhythmic eye movements with the same period as normal locomotor rhythms attest a latent central excitatory state—the foundation for swimming.

My own cursory observations of three teleosts lead to the conclusion that out of these anticipatory eye movements, which form a low threshold component of locomotor patterns, a wide variety of "voluntary" eye movements have been evolved. Teleosts have perfected refined locomotor agility and, along with a control of their specific gravity, freeing them of dependence on constant forward progression, have a complex range of mechanisms for slow or fast, brief movements in almost any direction. Many of the less-specialized teleosts progress, when not alarmed or excited, by a succession of evenly spaced strokes of pectoral fins and tail, making either short forward spurts or else sudden turns through 10 or more degrees. The visual effect of these movements, in frequency, speed, and magnitude, would be much the same as that of an average oculomotor saccade in a human subject. It is possible that vertebrate visual function which aims to keep intact a consistent frame for action is highly dependent upon discontinuous displacements of the image over the retina, produced by locomotor or oculomotor saccades and resulting in spatial-sampling rates of the order of from one to three per second.

Apart from the locomotor displacements, teleosts show spontaneous eye movements in the head to different degrees. Apparently, voluntary eye movements, serving eventually to establish a highly specific exploratory selection within the visual frame, have been evolved from the "protovoluntary" type of anticipatory eye displacements seen in the dogfish. Goldfish move their eyes little, but do show conjugated rotations associated with locomotion, make anticipatory reorientations before each turn of locomotion, and exhibit spontaneous rhythmic shifts of the eyes when at rest. Although certain cichlids like *Tilapia* move their eyes little more than the goldfish, the marbled cichlid, *Astronotus ocellatus* (or "Oscar"), has conspicuously bulging eyes which move constantly in an obviously alert way. Film analysis of this activity showed that the orientation shifts of the eyes may be timed in conjunction with the delicate rhythmic motions of the pectoral fins, which are constantly active when the fish is slowly drifting, or even when it is stationary, treading water. Each subtle change in the position of the fish is preceded by a saccadic eye movement, and a full-scale turn is accompanied by several anticipatory shifts of the eyes. It is most important, however, that many redirections of the eyes, though they may be related to pectoral fin rhythms, are not followed through by locomotor displacements. They are tentative environmental-sampling reorientations of the visual distance receptors, changing the visual input to the brain. Such reorientations are susceptible to modification by alerting stimuli which are inspected visually before any other move is made. Inspection movements may be monocular in some fish which fixate or track off-center stimuli with one eye or the other separately.

Of course, a shift of gaze of an eye which lacks a central area, or fovea, and corresponding adaptations of the central visual mechanism in the brain, would merely extend the range of vision in one direction. When two eyes with homogeneous retinas move together, the area covered by vision is displaced, and any binocular field is likewise displaced relative to the body. When there is a differentiated area of higher resolution or specialized analyzing properties, eye movements serve to make more critical selective samples of the visual environment independently of head or body displacements. Walls (1942) has emphasized the relationship between voluntary eye movements and the presence of foveae in fish. It is also interesting that fish with well-developed voluntary eye movements appear both more "alert" and more discriminating in their responses and generally less dependent upon constant locomotor activity. Goldfish move almost incessantly; Oscars glide or rest stationary, but sample the visual environment constantly, then make a well-chosen and agile response to some highly specific event in the visual field. Likewise, the highly foveate sea horses and blennies of shallow coasts and tide pools mostly sit and watch in their well-lit and highly populated environment. The coral fish and other plectognaths of clear tropical waters cruise slowly, but perform large and frequent eye movements, converging immediately on close objects, to which they direct themselves with agile reorientations of the body.

In the variety of visuomotor adaptations outlined we may detect the evolution of a visual process which depends increasingly upon highly regulated movements of the eyes. The purposive and discriminating actions of any one of the "more intelligent" fish show that a visual perceptual frame is built up and kept intact by these movements.

Before attempting to understand how this perception of the visual world might be produced by what we know of the neuromotor apparatus which a fish possesses, let us bring together in a greatly simplified overview the range of visual behaviors of fish. For our purpose it will be necessary to emphasize the close relationship between visual process and regulated movements of the body and its parts.

An Attempt to Classify Visuomotor Integrations—A Search for Principles of Organization

We know little of how a visual search or a learned choice between visual objects is performed by the brain, but certain predictions about the mechanism can be made on the basis of the way behavior is organized. Unfortunately, relevant detailed features of behavior, which potentially could be measured, are as yet imperfectly described.

Compared to the more highly evolved land vertebrates, fish behave in a rather automatic way, with many stereotyped movements involved in their feeding and social behavior. It is possible to give an inventory of the main kinds of actions performed by fish in general, with particular attention to those which are partially or wholly dependent upon visual control, or which in some other way are productive of significant changes in vision.

1. Certain muscular movements cause no change in the environment, but serve to adjust or modulate the intake of information by the organism from the environment (Horn 1965). Such are the movements of the lens of the eye and of the eye in the head, to which we have given some attention. These muscles are incapable of changing anything in the environment except if they are seen by another organism capable of responding to them.

2. All *locomotor movements* produce visual effects. As oculomotor and locomotor movements are coordinated in regular ways, the displacement of visual images produced during locomotion is, as has been described, lawful and informative. At the same time, information from other modalities changes in more or less predictable ways with locomotion. There are thus associative rules linking effects in one modality with effects in another. These rules are of great importance in determining the search behavior of an animal. Vision is a sense capable of giving precise information about the temporal and spatial distribution of objects within a few feet of a fish. Other modalities, such as olfaction or gustation, are less discriminating spatially but may serve to announce the proximity of a biologically significant source—such as food. A moving object may cause stimulation of lateral line organs which are capable of giving information about its size and approximate location. This modality and the physics of the operation of its receptors are described by Pumphrey (1950). The visual searching behavior which may be observed following excitation of another modality is a reflection of the rules of association between effects in this modality and effects in vision which are under locomotor control. This kind of behavior is described as "anticipatory" (Sherrington 1906) or "appetitive" (Craig 1918; Lorenz 1937), or as a component of the orientation response (Sokolov 1960).

3. *"Consummatory" actions* are affirmed and guided immediately by mechanically determined contact afference (Sherrington 1906; Craig 1918; Lorenz 1937; Hinde 1953). They almost always result in displacement of specific objects in the environment by the movements of the organism. The environment is changed in a direction which is generally favorable to the acting organism. As an example, feeding illustrates the association between a particular mechanical organ and its muscles and receptors, on the one hand, and a guiding sense by means of which it is set in operation. In fish, the mouth forms the most important organ for acting on the environment, though some specific actions may be performed by fins, tail, or body as a whole, especially when there are morphological adaptations of the organ concerned to this end.

4. *Communicating movements* are adapted to produce changes in the behavior of other individuals (Marler and Hamilton 1966; Marler 1967). They modulate the visual receptor functions in another nervous system. Many of the adaptive responses of fish are guided by visual signals produced by other individuals. Signals, consisting of visible patterns of characteristic form or color on part of the body and generally in association with particular movements of this part, determine activity in a predator, combat with a rival, aggregation of a school, or courtship and breeding behavior with a mate. Visuomotor links of this kind have been studied in great detail for several different species and they have furnished classical

material for ethology (see Tinbergen 1951; Hinde 1966). Important characteristics may be summarized as follows:

a) Since the signal produced, if visual, is generally not visible to the sender or actor and cannot be monitored directly, and because even if it were so received its significance could not be the same, there is need for automatization of the presentation, except where the consequences can be read in the actions of the partner. If not, a program must be determined independently. Hence the often remarkably elaborate ritualized movement patterns of communicating behavior. Sometimes special conspicuous and mobile structures are evolved whose main purpose is communication.

b) These patterns of activity are, in most cases, clearly derived in evolution from segments of more generalized activity such as locomotion, feeding, respiratory movement, or gill cleaning. They are produced, however, as detached segments of no ultimate function in adjusting the organism's relationship to the inanimate environment.

c) The precision of communication and its effectiveness in optimizing the associative behavior of two or more individuals depend upon selective sensitivity on the part of the receiver to signals of definite description. Furthermore, where the task as a whole requires a long description, as in coordination of mating and its orientation to a specific nest location, the end is attained by successive approximations. Apparently the nervous system of fish is incapable of elaborating such a specific complex description as a whole and adapting it to a particular circumstance. The same end is achieved, at least in a majority of cases, by a causal chain of actions and reactions between the partners. The sign stimulus produced by an individual acts as a marker for a step in the behavior of the partner.

d) In the perfectly executed sequence, the introduction of signs and the formation of responses to them form a unidirectional succession leading automatically to the highly specific consummatory acts which require that the protagonists be in particular states at the same time. However, careful analysis of some of the more elaborate sequences has shown that the ideal chain is arrived at with many false starts and retracing of steps (Baerends, Brouwer, and Waterbolk 1955; Barlow 1962). To ensure eventual coordination there must be repeated use of alternative action patterns until, by elimination, a workable approximation to the sequence is attained. Learning plays a clear role in the perfection of coordination in certain cases.

From this survey we may draw out three distinct classes of visuomotor processes. Fundamental is the controlled sampling of a changing visual world which allows a fish to navigate and make selective adjustments in a complex array of objects. This demands a continuous assessment by the central nervous system of self-produced transformations in the visual array and the derivation of invariants defining fixed features in the environment. As Gibson (1966) has emphasized vision must be both proprioceptive and exteroceptive to perform this feat.

Second, against the background of a visual space of static objects sampled in this way, motor effects due to the movements of other animals are sharply defined by the visual system. Presumably this detection is performed by visual mechanisms which also function in the monitoring of self-produced displacements of elements in the visual array.

Third, special visual effects that are distinguished from all others of the last kind serve as signals between individuals. They are produced by specific motor activity and the visibility of each seems to depend upon both the visible symbol and the movement pattern to which it is attached.

Figure 6. We will consider briefly three kinds of active adjustment which could bend the integrative process and so change the course of behavior. Adjustments which might occur (1) among the sensory analyzers so that sensory information is "processed" differently, (2) in the intermediary system itself to change the general state of sensorimotor adjustment, or (3) close to the units of motor expression. We should note, again, that two kinds of motor regulation are possible: those whose only role is to focus or aim effects on the receptors, and others which are direct actions on the environment likely to change it in some way. Our first task in looking into the visual mechanism in more detail is to try to obtain a good account of what we mean by a visual analyzer. This turns out to be a rather complicated and difficult problem, but something which must be solved before the integration of acts and vision can be understood.

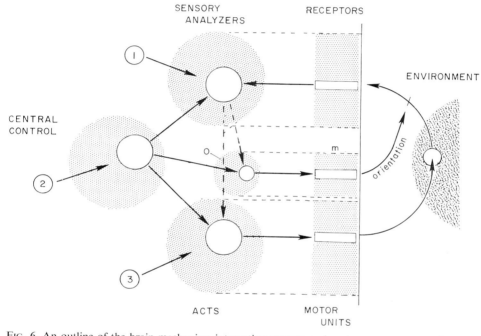

Fig. 6. An outline of the brain mechanism integrating sensory and motor processes; *o* and *m* are the neural and motor mechanisms, respectively, of orientation adjustments (for example, by eye movements).

Analysis of the Visual Image—Static or Dynamic?

The adjustments of behavior cannot go beyond the limits of sensitivity nor beyond the capacity of the nervous system to distinguish dimensions of environmental change. With the aid of microelectrode recordings from single visual units, much progress has been made in recent years in the description of elementary visual analyzers. These are elements of highly specific morphological and functional organization which respond selectively to particular configurations or transformations in the retinal image (see Jacobson, this volume). It now seems possible to envisage each organism as possessing a population of feature detectors in terms of which the visual field is analyzed and coded in nerve cell activity (see Sutherland, this volume).

At present only comparatively simple analyzer fields have been detected in single unit recordings from retinal ganglion cells or tectal cells of fish. In the goldfish rather irregular fields ranging from 10° to more than 40° were found to be sensitive to dimming or brightening, to movement of small spots of light or darkness across boundaries of excitatory and inhibitory zones, or to the direction of movement of a stimulus (Jacobson and Gaze 1964; Jacobson, this volume). Most of the last kind were responsive to movement of the stimulus in a direction parallel to the horizontal and from posterior to anterior. There are as yet no reports of the types of visual unit to be found in the histologically complex, multilayered tecta of a fish such as *Blennius* or *Astronotus* with highly evolved visual functions and well-developed "voluntary" eye movements.

The efficiency of visual locomotor guidance and of visual discrimination in goldfish, and their precise visual orientation to specific small moving targets, suggests that a fair differentiation of visual analysis must take place in spite of the apparent poverty of form analyzers in retina and tectum. It is possible that the visual system is organized to measure visuospatial configurations with the aid of the standard transformations produced by locomotion. Since fish do see effects resulting from their own movements, it is likely, as Ingle (1965, and this volume) has suggested, that, with rather simple static feature analyzers and a population of velocity detectors especially sensitive to motion in the horizontal direction, they are able to distinguish motionless objects from the dynamic effects generated by their own locomotion.

This suggests a fascinating converse, that highly elaborated visual feature analysis, especially for static contours or "standing edges" (Maturana *et al.* 1960) of specific orientation, has evolved in animals such as the frog or the octopus which show reduction and refinement of locomotor activity. The same may be true for the higher teleosts. Comparative data from different animals with different locomotor habits are not yet sufficient to pass judgment on this, but the contrast in the neuronal organization of the visual projections of the frog and the goldfish is suggestive. Mammalian vision must depend upon fine differentiation of contour features over a fixed retinal image or a succession of static images. Although our own detection of spatial relations and their transformations during locomotor displacement is remarkably precise in twilight or in the far periphery of vision, these distinctions, which are so important to locomotion, are at the very fringe of consciousness and are quite different from the elaborations of fully conscious perception. It is as if there were two levels of visual process—a more primitive one generated during locomotion, and a more refined and discriminating one dependent on discontinuous sampling.

With these considerations in mind, it seems prudent, in interpreting visual discrimination tests designed to explore how fish see differences between stimuli, to take into account the ways in which the visual image on the retina is transformed by active movements of the eye to the subject relative to the stimuli. For example, horizontal eye movements, either rotations or translations, favor detection of vertical contours. This direction of eye movement is by far the most common in the normal progression of the fish. Translations of the eyes, as in locomotion, produce parallax transformations, including expansions of textures and separation of contours (Fig. 2).

It has been shown that goldfish easily distinguish between vertical and horizontal rectangles baited at the center, but that the same rectangles inclined at 45° to the horizontal and with opposite slopes are distinguished with difficulty (Mackintosh and Sutherland 1963). This finding establishes that vertical and horizontal dimensions are measured preferentially by the visual system of the goldfish, just as they are by some other animals as Sutherland (1963) has concluded. However, the precise way the system makes the measurement may depend, for example, upon detection of relative horizontal or relative vertical displacement of edges during locomotor approach to the center of the stimulus, and not upon dimensions of a static image (Sutherland and Muntz 1959).

Furthermore, before attempting to explain visual pattern recognition in terms of separate analyzers for local features in small areas of the visual field, consideration should also be given to the spatial plan of the whole visual field and possible key-and-lock fits between certain stimulus features and the structure of this large-scale visual analyzer.

For example, in the experiments of Mackintosh and Sutherland, the stimuli (black rectangles on white, or white rectangles on black) were presented at the start of each trial some inches away from the fish at the ends of two parallel compartments on either side of a partition. In the center of each stimulus was a small cup containing a pellet of food or a pebble of the same appearance. After approaching the chosen side to snap at the reward, the goldfish were oriented with the stimuli in a specific relationship to the vertical binocular field in front of the mouth. Obviously the vertical and horizontal rectangles would have given very different visual stimulation in this segment of the field and the diagonal rectangles would have been poorly differentiated. The visual field as a whole may function as a large kind of detection field operating like the oval analyzers proposed by Sutherland to account for the performance of the octopus and other animals in discrimination of shapes (Sutherland 1963).

To summarize: vision in primitive vertebrates such as the elasmobranchs and the more primitive teleosts is, in all probability, highly dependent upon patterns of motion within the visual image, especially those which result from locomotor activity. Self-mobile objects are also highly visible to the system at this stage of evolution. Furthermore, the primitive visual frame for action in a fish is, we have seen, bisymmetric, with a central region which has an anatomically distinct representation in the central nervous system. The general structure of this frame is also considered to be highly important for the analysis of effects in the retinal images of events in the world surrounding the body. We conclude that a mosaic of geometrically organized analyzer templates for recognition of local visual features may be a further elaboration of the visual apparatus associated with refinement and specialization of patterns of motor activity. These considerations have important implications for studies of electrical activity in the visual system by unit analysis. We feel that the data available at present fit this hypothesis of visual evolution in vertebrates well.

Adjustment of Analyzers

It is evident that some choice among visual functions must take place at some point in the nervous system when behavior changes spontaneously with respect to visual stimuli. Sutherland has emphasized the importance of the process of analysis selection to learning. In a series of generalization experiments it has been shown that different animals have different visual analyzing capacity, and that the experience of each individual conditions his use of the analyzers at his disposal (see Sutherland, this volume).

How is this selection of analyzers obtained? There are two distinct possibilities. One involves motor adjustments which change the relationship between receptor elements of fixed function and the pattern of environmental events ("orientation" in Fig. 6). A second, covert form of adjustment, occurring entirely within the central nervous system, may be more important to learning. In this case, changes in overt behavior are consequent upon an alteration of the logic of sensory analysis itself ([1] or [2] in Fig. 6).

We have given attention to the motor adjustments of visual function which fish make. It has been emphasized that though many fish are continually engaged in some form of locomotion, some highly visual teleosts are frequently immobile, except for rapid saccadic reorientations of the eyes which serve to sample the visual field. Some appear to make highly selective, "intelligent," voluntary visual adjustments in this way in association with refined locomotor movements.

With regard to the second kind of adjustment, there is no direct evidence in vertebrates for a *completely internal* neural adjustment of analysis capacity, though many attempts have been made to explore centrifugal attention-changing mechanisms, and there are indications of selective facilitation of particular modalities or fields of receptors (Horn 1965). Recently a remarkable example of the modulation of a visual analyzer unit by a gravity receptor in an invertebrate has been described by Wiersma and Yamaguchi (1966). They found that certain units in the optic tract of the crayfish respond to light in the upward-facing quadrant of the visual field, regardless of the position of the eye in space. Presumably statocyst fibers, which are found passing in a centrifugal direction in the optic tract, adjust the access of receptor cells to this "space constant" unit so that the receptor field remains in fixed orientation relative to gravity.

It is possible that centrifugal fibers adjust retinal systems of analysis in vertebrates in a similar manner (Granit 1959). Arey (1916) found that pigment cells in the retina of one eye in some fish could be caused to move by stimulation of the other eye. This may be a mechanism for interocular regulation, at the retinal level, to maintain a constancy of brightness perception. However, it seems more likely that in vertebrates in general, the greater part of any adjustments which take the form of selection of sensory analyzers would take place more centrally. For fish there is evidence that the cells of the deeper layers of the optic tectum, adjacent to the tegmentum, are modified by centrifugal influences in the course of conditioning (see Prosser, this volume).

Selection of Acts—Response to Stimulus, Release, or Intrinsic Determination

In the artificially constrained circumstances of a random-alternation choice experiment, a pattern of consummatory action which changes little in form becomes attached by learning to one stimulus and a second stimulus is shunned. At least this is how it appears to superficial observation. However, a fish may potentially orient a number of quite different forms of action with reference to an event or an object appearing at one point in the visual field. Each of the spatially equivalent responses results here in a characteristic set of re-afferent signals. For example, a displacement of the locus of the stimulus in the visual field will faithfully reflect the displacements of the eyes by orienting and locomotor movements (Fig. 7). Presumably, choice of one of these patterns of approach or avoidance by the brain depends upon a change in the intermediary functions which link the visual projection with the motor mechanism, so that both act and template for reafference are changed.

The determination of the form of the visuomotor link and the pattern of activity produced may, in some states of the organism, depend little on the characteristics of a visual stimulus. Recognition of a cue or a context is then broad and uncritical. Thus, a "food-taking" activity may be triggered by almost any small visual object if a hungry fish is already alerted to food by an appropriate olfactory cue. In this kind of adjustment visceral factors and information from other modalities must influence or modulate the visuomotor link to change the "motivation" for the act and, thus, the probability of its occurrence. A broad range of stimuli may trigger a form of action if the preparatory state for this form of action is near the threshold of spontaneous appearance.

What are the characteristics of this mechanism which chooses, releases, or motivates action in a particular direction? The original formulation of the concept of "innate releasing mechanisms" (Tinbergen 1951) may be misleading, as Hinde (1966), for example, has pointed out. The responses in question are neither strictly innate nor are they simply "released" by a stimulus. However the main point is clear. Animals often show relatively stereotyped patterns of activity which are specifically sensitive to certain patterns of stimulation.

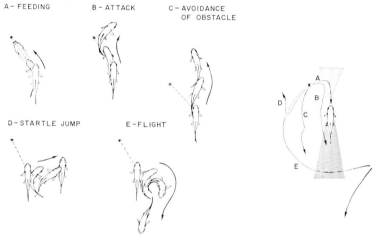

FIG. 7. Each pattern of motor adjustment produces characteristic visual displacements and specific reafference of potential use in control of the act.

Many of these patterns are clearly "activated" by changes in the environment, or because of the action of hormones produced within the body of the animal in response to such changes. As in the case of appetitive action-patterns of daily occurrence such as feeding, the seasonal and more elaborate patterns of mating or nesting are frequently modifiable by stimulation or abolition of function in parts of the hypothalamus and neighboring structures (von Holst and von Saint Paul 1963). Local regions in this area of the brain appear to be differentiated for the regulations of different classes and forms of motor integration which have varying dependency on afferent control. Haldane (1956) has suggested that the so-called higher centers of Tinbergen coordinating complex innate response patterns may, in fact, be in the very ancient parts of the central nervous system, associated with the hypothalamus. These "centers" are ultimately concerned with adjustments of bodily state and so with both internal and external aspects of the process of keeping this state well regulated. So the selector of alternative patterns of action may well be, also, an autonomic state selector.

On the whole, it appears to be rare in fish or other vertebrates for a spontaneous act to be so autonomous in its execution and so independent in its consequences that the place of its inception is located in one segment of the lower neuromotor apparatus. This kind of unit motor activity does occur in local reflex adjustment where an immediately effective act is triggered by stimulation in an associated sensory field. It is more general for complex spontaneous behavior to take the form of total patterns which must be set up in a mechanism integrating the whole motor system, or in more anterior parts of the nervous system which are higher up the integrative hierarchy. The setting-up process would necessarily include internal, so-called autonomic adjustments, permitting the body to change in anticipation of the consequences of carrying out the chosen plan of action. Where, as in fish, a limited number of stereotyped action patterns are easily recognized, this is an indication of intrinsically organized and well-insulated neural mechanisms of action control somewhere in the upper nervous system, and of well-ordered lines of communication to the motor mechanisms of the lower nervous system.

The Special Nature of Visual Information and Associations between Vision and Other Modalities of Reception in the Definition of Contexts for Behavior

Patterns of visuomotor integration reflect the nature of the information in the visual sensory frame. This frame is both exteroceptive, for events distant from the body, and proprioceptive, since it gives report of any motor act which displaces the eyes. For the majority of acts which are regulated in some degree by vision, the visual image gives information for guiding approaches or withdrawals from contact with events in the environment—the space outside the body. A proportion of visual effects calls for quick recognition of an object and substitution of one behavior for another, so these effects act as primary motivational signals, as, for example, when something seen evokes sudden flight or attack.

Other sensory modalities provide physically different frames for behavior, and the integrative adjustments made in the nervous system with reference to them are correspondingly of different kinds. In the course of behavior, the modalities must be associated in complementary roles by these adjustments which act in conjunction with morphological restraints. In some cases, for example, excitation in one modality (say, olfaction) will come first in association with one pattern of behavior and predispose another modality (say, gustation or vision) to activity of a particular kind and so cause a change of behavior.

The intermodality relationships are of two main kinds. First, in the case of *spatial control*, a particular shape of response may be elicited in much the same form by stimuli of a variety of other modalities as well as by a number of different visual stimuli. Each act is made within many intersecting sensory fields upon which its spatial regulation depends. The mechanism of motor control, therefore, must be in a form which accepts convergent influence from the neural fields of different sensory projections, all mapped in parallel onto it. Furthermore, exteroceptors offering information about the spatial distribution of objects and events around the body, and also the proprioceptors informing the nervous system of relative positions and displacements of body parts, must share the same spatial reference frame or context if behavior is to remain well integrated. An object detected by several modalities can be given certain identity and location only if the various afferent measures are reduced to the same spatial scale with the same reference origin. Any move defined with respect to the position of an object relative to the body will be accompanied by a proprioceptive description of the movement which, to be useful in regulation of movement, must again be made with reference to this origin and this spatial scale.

Second, the adaptations of body form and of the receptor structures, as well as those of skeletomuscular systems, determine certain *serial relationships* between complementary modalities and within each modality. Thus, for example, a definition of a goal by vision may precede, or accompany, other sensations arising out of locomotion to that goal. Food first apprehended by olfaction elicits exploratory movements, then locomotor orientation to the visual cue—with closing of the mouth comes confirmation from taste and touch. Visual orientation within a specific "home" terrain requires some serial ordering of impressions in an overall spatial and temporal scheme.

Processes within the nervous system, of which we are essentially ignorant, must ensure appropriate timing of changes in sensory analysis and of the release of specific motor patterns. From anticipatory changes in one modality due to influences from another would arise the behavioral phenomena of selective attention. This would gain greatly in predictive capacity if retention of what was predicted permitted its modification according to the actual results each time it was followed through to consummation.

In sum, vision would appear to be the main sense for precise *orientation and timing* of movements in the majority of fish, supplanted by olfaction, lateral line sense, or acoustic or electrical location only when there is insufficient light. For most fish vision also serves as an *alerting* channel, often giving first information for a new action sequence. In the neural regulation of fish behavior by vision there are, therefore, two main kinds of adjustment in the C.N.S. One is for *control of spatial relations* and governs the link between events in a visual topographic field and a topography of motor displacements, primarily locomotor. The other is for *choice of consummatory acts* which are committed in the central part of the topographic field. This second kind of adjustment is concerned with definition or recognition of objects which have attributes that are significant to the internal state of the organism, and also with picking out a specific pattern of consummatory response which "uses" the object to the advantage of the organism. As learning proceeds, visual perceptions are drawn in, as it were, out of the spatial frame for orientation, and brought within the central visual function to define new objects of behavioral commitment.

Different Varieties of Change in Visuomotor Behavior

The above outline of some of the most important general features of visuomotor integration makes clear how closely interwoven motor and sensory processes must be. First, it is likely that analysis of visual events by the nervous system is primitively dependent upon regulated motor patterns transforming the visual image. Second, some selection of receptor analyzers of stimuli is by motor control of the sampling of environmental effects. Third, spontaneous selection of patterned acts must generally include some predictive tuning of sensory channels as well as autonomic adjustments. Therefore, of the three arrows in Figure 6 "inflecting" the process of integration at different levels, a "central adjustment" arrow (2) seems to be the most significant, because only a central change would permit simultaneous reformulation of sensory analysis, choice of pattern of action, and autonomic adjustment. There is, however, one important qualification; because sensorimotor control has the properties of a control loop, a change at any point would *ultimately* alter the whole balance. The question here is one of the completeness of the schema for action formulated within the brain, and the answer might be obtained by observing for each act how much and at what stage motor activity is actually adjusted to input from the periphery. In other words one would expect different kinds of behavior change depending upon the locus of adaptation near the receptors, in the patterning of acts or somewhere in between, such that both sensory analyzers and mechanisms of motor control are selected simultaneously.

Let us consider a familiar sample of fish behavior from this point of view. It is possible to formulate an explanation for the learning by the goldfish in a left-right choice apparatus by assuming that what the fish sees at the time the food or a pebble is taken into the mouth may be combined with what had been seen during locomotion from the choice point. This means that learning to predict which way to turn at the choice point requires that the events at the end of the trial, in the small visual field round the goal, become involved in changing the responses to effects in the larger visual space, which is the frame for the approach movements in subsequent trials. To learn, the fish does not store effects of a fixed retinal impression made at one moment, but takes in a self-generated dynamic sample while swimming to the food, and analyzes and stores this. The relevant cue, then, is not just a set of lines or corners at some orientation, but is rather a particular display of expanding contours and areas embedded in the total visual space and regulated by the fish's own motion.

If this is so, the fish must discriminate stimuli differently from a rat on the jumping stand. Before making his leap, a rat may scan for specific stimulus features with rotations of head and eyes, movements which do not produce large relative displacements of elements in the visual field. But the goldfish may have no alternative to the type of analysis which uses motion cues. The overtraining reversal experiments of Mackintosh *et al.* (1966) show that, in fact, while rats and other animals show the ability to reverse a well-learned visual discrimination more easily than one which has just been learned to criterion, goldfish do not. These authors concluded that attachment of stimulus analysis to response is stronger in the goldfish than in the rat. Surely this amounts to saying that the way a goldfish retains the ability to discriminate the visual cues is more dependent on the locomotor pattern of response. Close observation of the movements and latencies of adjustments or reorientations in goldfish when they are learning such a discrimination should be sufficient to establish this point.

According to the reafference principle, every spontaneous act is accompanied by a preparatory adjustment of receptor processes anticipating significant features of the reafferent signal. The effect of learning could be obtained in such a system by substitution of activity patterns; e.g., exploratory scanning behavior for commitment of the consummatory act. The reafferent pattern for a rewarded orientation response becomes incorporated in the nervous system as the predictive template for the positive stimulus. According to this view, learned connections between stimulus and response are selected from spontaneously produced sensorimotor couples and not forged in some way where no link existed before, across some hitherto unstructured matrix.

To recapitulate, learning by change of sensory receptivity alone, or by selection among reafference-regulated units of activity, would result distinctively in different behaviors. The first would result in an "aroused" animal in immediate orientation to chosen features only when the receptors are stimulated by an appropriate pattern, because the analyzers identifying this pattern have been potentiated or, in Sutherland's terms, "switched in" to give it preferential control of activity. The second would produce an appropriate search behavior following specific arousal of the appetitive phase of response.

Distribution in the Nervous System of the Spatial Control of Acts

Before considering the anatomy of nerve cell systems in the primitive brain to see what can be elucidated more directly about the mechanism of visuomotor integration in fish, we will describe the gross localization of motor control by visual processes in the fish central nervous system, as it has been exposed by experimental analysis.

Two important principles have been established. First, it may be shown that, while the logic of motor control is widely distributed within the nervous system so that isolated portions may have an autonomous functional integrity, the various levels are coordinated in a hierarchical system, and there is a control superimposed over the spinal cord from the special sensory fields of the anterior parts of the brain. Second, the topography of the visual field mapped on the surface of the tectum in the brain is a topography of integrated motor adjustments of the body as a whole.

Our summary of fish behavior shows that, compared with other vertebrates, fish possess limited means of acting on the environment. Almost all their responses are based upon locomotor adjustment. In primitive forms locomotion is a steady forward progression with occasional turning movements, and depends upon rather simple undulations of the trunk; but in many teleosts motor agility has reached a high level of perfection and small displacements may be made quickly and accurately in any direction.

However complex the repertoire of controlled movements becomes, the formulation of activities within locomotion means that most neural adjustments of fish are made with respect to the bisymmetric space of locomotor orientations. Every act is incorporated within a unified locomotor pattern.

A spinal dogfish makes well-coordinated swimming movements involving all but a very small proportion of the muscles of the body. The coordination is largely due to propagation of activity in central neuronal networks which alone ensure smooth sequential and reciprocating activity flowing from anterior to posterior body segments, even when the peripheral nerves from the associated sensory zones are almost all interrupted. However, a minimum of input is required to maintain rhythmical activity. This may come from any one of several segmental sensory nerves. The motor pattern may be modified by stimulation in various ways and it is automatically adjusted so that, from the start, the movement is oriented in relation to the distribution of afference within the segmental proprioceptive or touch fields (Gray and Sand 1963*a*, *b;* Lissman 1946*a*, *b*).

Similarly, a goldfish with the central nervous system divided anterior to the medulla shows organized swimming movements in the trunk which are intrinsically regulated by a rhythm propagated from medulla to cord, to which movements of all fins are associated. When all the afferent nerves are intact, the swimming movements may become differentiated into separate patterns. For example, the movements of pectoral fins and tail are often independently organized (von Holst 1935*a*, *b*, 1939). Thus, as in the dogfish, the largely autonomous central mechanism for sustaining the rhythmical activity of locomotion is modulated and differentiated according to the symmetry of sensory input within a number of sensory modalities.

The brain in the head portion of a spinal fish produces rhythmic patterns of movement in eyes, jaws, and gill arches. Spontaneous side-to-side movements of the eyes are suggestive of those eye movements associated with locomotor activity. In fact, the rotations of the eye may be loosely coupled with swimming movements of the trunk, in spite of the complete separation of brain and spinal cord, through nerves from stretch receptors (Harris 1965).

Electrophysiological methods have shown that there is an entry at the tectum to a map of orientation movements coordinating the visual field and the motor system. Coincident with the retinotectal map of visual points around the body is a map of points from which orientation movements addressing this same space may be stimulated artificially. This has been shown by Akert (1949*a*, *b*), who excited points on the surface of the tecta of the trout with electrical stimulation to produce movements of eyes and fins and body. When one side of the tectum was stimulated the movements approximated the orienting adjustments made normally by the fish to face the eyes toward the locus in the opposite half of visual space which projects to this same side of the tectum. Convergence movements were obtained when points on the anterior end of the tecta corresponding to the anterior middle part of the visual field were stimulated. A more complete exploration by Apter with the cat similarly produced two coincident maps, one of the visual half-field to the superior colliculus surface (Apter 1945), and the other of points in the colliculus to oculomotor orientations in the same half-field (Apter 1946).

Although it is not possible to identify the tectal cells stimulated in these experiments with motor integrating cells—they may merely have had fairly direct and orderly access to such cells—these effects show that a systematic reflex mechanism of visuomotor integration passes from retina to tectum and thence to integrated motor mechanisms for each locus in visual space. The unit visuomotor correspondences are distributed on the tectal surface in a bisymmetric map preserving topographic relations. Akert noted that, unlike responses to visual stimuli, the orienting adjustments were resistant to habituation, and he compared the motor phenomena to the stereotyped orientation elicited by Hess with electrodes implanted in the diencephalon of cats (Hess 1943).

An Outline of the Anatomy of Visuomotor Integration in a Primitive Vertebrate

The most comprehensive, functionally oriented account of the organization of the basic vertebrate brain is that given by Herrick in *The Brain of the Tiger Salamander* (1948). Herrick intended to make a detailed analysis of nerve cell morphology and connections in a brain which would serve as representative for the vertebrates as a whole. He describes the primitive vertebrate nervous system in the following terms. (Fig. 8 is based on figures selected from Herrick's work to illustrate this account.)

Neurone cell bodies are primitively located in a central gray region surrounding the axial cavity of the nervous system. Outside this is a white cortex of nerve fibers of all kinds. Cells in the central gray send processes of two kinds branching into the surrounding alba. Dendrites extend in distinctive patterns, to spread over wide areas, or are concentrated densely in particular layers or clusters within the alba. Axons may pass a short distance before branching and terminating among dendrites and cell bodies, or they extend for long distances in the alba to terminate in one or more remote parts of the C.N.S. The fibrous feltwork or neuropil contains short axons and their collaterals and the terminal arborizations of long axons interwoven among dendritic trees to which they form selective connections. The whole forms one immensely complex synaptic field, the bulk of which is situated in the alba. In certain regions, however, the cells of the gray are surrounded by a dense mesh of periventricular neuropil.

Within the neuropil various anatomical differentiations occur which, presumably, potentiate certain integrative relationships within the synaptic field. Where many long axons pass in the same general direction they are grouped together to form clearly visible tracts. Within the neuropil are zones where there is a highly organized distribution of dendrites and converging axons expressing a connectional affinity between certain neurone groups. In later differentiation, both in ontogeny and in the evolution of more complex vertebrate brains, cell clusters (nuclei) are formed by the outward migration of cell bodies into the neuropil. In this way, cells giving rise to local clusters of dendrites and axons come to lie closer to the site of synaptic integration. In many cases the cell body itself becomes specialized as part of the local synaptic field.

Motoneurones and associated parts of the neuropil differentiate into two ventral columns. The dorsal parts of the embryonic neural tube receive terminations from the dorsal afferent nerves and the dorsal part of the neuropil becomes specialized for processing of sensory information. Long efferent tracts leave the neuropil to descend between alba and central gray toward the motor apparatus; ascending tracts pass in more superficial and dorsal regions of the neuropil.

The primary motor column (of Coghill) extends anteriorly on each side as a prolongation of the motor column of the spinal cord. It terminates in the ventral mesencephalon in a field of supreme importance in the integration of motor control. Herrick describes this "ventrolateral peduncular neuropil" as the "chief central motor pool of the skeletal muscles." Efferent fibers pass from it in the medial longitudinal fasciculus to activate the musculature of the trunk, and also through the oculomotor nerve to the muscles of the eye.

With the development of highly specialized organs of special sense at the anterior ends of the body (eyes, olfactory organ, taste and touch systems of the head, inner ear and

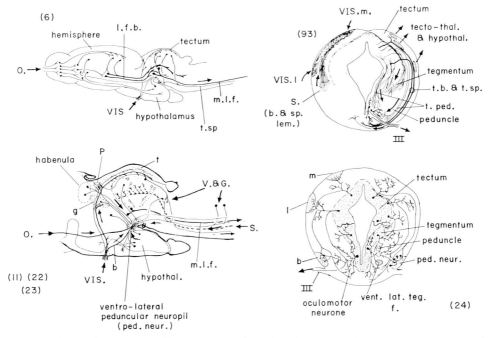

FIG. 8. Anatomical patterns of importance in visual function in the primitive vertebrate brain; redrawn from illustrations in Herrick (1948), *The Brain of the Tiger Salamander*. The numbers refer to the original figures from which anatomical details were drawn. Afferent channels: *O*, olfactory; *VIS*, visual; *VIS.l.* and *VIS.m.*, lateral and medial optic tracts; *S*, somesthetic; *b. & sp.lem.*, bulbar and spinal lemnisci; *V & G*, visceral and gustatory. Areas where visual afferents terminate: *t*, tectum; *p*, pretectum; *g*, lateral geniculate or posterior dorsal thalamus. Branches of optic tract: *b*, basal; *l*, lateral; *m*, medial. Links toward motor system: *l.f.b.*, lateral forebrain bundle; *m.l.f.*, medial longitudinal fasciculus; *t.sp.*, tectospinal; *t.b.*, tectobulbar; *t.ped.*, tectopeduncular; *vent.lat.teg.f*, ventrolateral tegmental fasciculus; *III*, oculomotor nerve. The two figures on right show diagrammatic sections through the midbrain of the salamander with afferent paths and terminations at left, and efferent paths at right. The central gray with cell bodies is dotted.

labyrinth, lateral line organs of head and body) the neuropil of the sensory zone becomes differentiated into a series of paired centers for sensory analytic functions. These provide comparative material in fishes which show a wide variety of ecological specializations of sensory equipment and corresponding anatomical differences. Herrick and others have devoted much attention to describing the complex paired sensory lobes of various fishes. The high development of olfactory sense is reflected in enlargement of the olfactory lobes; highly visual fish have greatly enlarged optic tecta in the dorsal midbrain, and likewise there are externally visible swellings associated with high development of gustatory, vestibular, or tactile sense for the anterior parts of the body.

Each sensory lobe is produced by the proliferation of the neuropil in a region where axons from receptor structures of a particular modality converge and form dense connections. Whenever a modality is well developed the neuropil of the corresponding lobes shows clear differentiation of concentric laminae. This is particularly evident in the case of the optic lobes of fishes (Leghissa 1955; Schwassmann, this volume).

Fibers from the retina terminate in five main locations within the mesencephalon and diencephalon. Herrick suggests that this comparatively wide dispersal of fibers from one peripheral source is primarily determined by the numerous types of motor responses under visual control. It also reflects the fact that optic nerve fibers arise from neurones which are at least two steps of integration removed from the receptor cells.

The great majority of the visual fibers spread within the superficial layers of the optic tectum on each side and make contact with dendrites of several outer layers of neuropil. Optic nerve fibers also pass by way of the basal optic tract to the ventrolateral peduncular area of the midbrain, making connections which effect activation of the bulbar and spinal motor apparatus (via the medial longitudinal fasciculus), and also of the oculomotor neurones.

En route to the tectum, the optic tracts give rise to fibers to three regions of the diencephalon—ventrally to the preoptic area of the hypothalamus to influence hypophysical endocrine activity, and dorsally to the posterior dorsal thalamus (the precursor of the lateral geniculate bodies), and to the pretectal area just in front of the posterior commissure. Both of the latter regions are close to the point where the optic tract branches at the anterior end of the tectum to form the medial and lateral tracts. The distribution of fibers suggests a coincidence of a morphogenetic field influencing growth of nerve cell processes and the final topographic representation of the visual field illustrated in Figures 4 and 5. The central behavioral field appears to be represented in a critical region at the junction of midbrain and diencephalon where optic nerve fibers segregate.

The optic tectum is a complex integrative tissue which both sends and receives many fibers. The main outflow is by the tectobulbar and tectospinal tracts to the medulla and spinal cord. Important fiber tracts pass directly on through the posterior commissure to nuclei of the medial longitudinal fasciculus and thence to the motor system of the trunk musculature, and to the oculomotor nuclei. Other fibers terminate in the adjacent ventrolateral peduncular area so that there are numerous alternative paths from tectum to ventral and ventrolateral neuropil of the midbrain.

Herrick's account contains suggestions that these connections are grouped according to the area of their origin from the tectum. In view of the marked topographic organization of the visual projection onto the tectum, and of the consistent organization of this projection with respect to oriented behavioral acts, these different connections suggest an orderly mapping from tectal field onto the motor system as it is represented in the ventral half of the midbrain. Herrick points out that localization of function in the tectum of the sala-mander is determined more by what is going on in the efferent side of the arc than in the afferent side. In drawings of the arrangement of descending axons from the tectum to the dendrites of the ventral cells, including the oculomotor cells, preferential connections are indicated between loci in the tectal section and specific areas of these dendritic fields (see Fig. 8).

Tectal cells also send axons to the hypothalamus and ventral thalamus and, by way of the brachia of the superior colliculi, to the geniculate neuropil of the dorsal thalamus. Within the ventral thalamus are activated further cells which give rise to fibers following the medial longitudinal fasciculus.

The diencephalic visual areas (pretectum and geniculate area) are linked by two-way connections to form a closely integrated system. Each one of these regions which receives visual input also receives input from other sources. The afferent fibers to the tectum include fibers from striatum and habenula in anterior parts, and a large system of ascending fibers in the spinal and bulbar leminisci which carry tactile, proprioceptive, visceral-gustatory, vestibular, and lateral line influences to the neuropil within which optic nerves terminate. Olfactory fibers have no direct influence on the tectum but may attain the tectal neuropil by way of the habenula.

Visceral-gustatory stimulation must play a critical role in conditioning of food-taking behavior to visual stimuli. The visceral-gustatory system has a particularly large projection to the ventrolateral peduncular neuropil. This latter region also receives fibers from the ol-factory system and the hypothalamus directly, and all ascending afferent influences may be relayed to it by way of connections from the dorsal thalamus.

In this bewilderingly complex system of interconnections there appear certain orderly groupings of function, and it is possible to outline a number of main regions or centers and links of visuomotor integration and the influences which "inflect" their function.

The most direct mapping of the neural representation of visual space onto the motor apparatus is via the tectobulbar and tectospinal projection to the motor system of bulb and cord which, as we have seen, is organized intrinsically to produce orderly locomotor pat-terns. A parallel system passes by way of visual projection fields to the ventral neuropil of the midbrain and thence by the medial lateral fasciculus to this same bulbar and spinal motor system. Presumably the second system is more flexible and is essential to both appetitive be-havior and the plastic adjustments shown in learning. Herrick refers to experimental work showing that lesions of the ventral midbrain tegmentum and medial lateral fasciculus, can lead to massive reduction in motor initiative. There is much supportive information avail-able now (Sprague, Chambers, and Stellar 1961).

It is of interest that the most important auxiliary influences to the tectal neuropil con-sist of axons from cells which receive excitation from dorsal roots of spinal cord and bulb with no particular input from olfactory visceral or gustatory systems. This suggests that modulation of visual analytic activity in the tectal neuropil is concerned with adjustments to general locomotor performance. In contrast, the ventrolateral peduncular neuropil, which is such an important way station in the output of the tectum and other parts of the visual analysis apparatus, is richly innervated by axons of the olfactory, gustatory, and visceral systems and from the hypothalamus, where presumably regulation of internal state is centralized. Herrick reasons from anatomical characteristics of this relatively superficial neuropil that it is a "more sensitive medium for strictly individual adjustments (conditioning) than the deeper neuropil." He admits that there is no experimental evidence for this hypothesis but suggests that it is "supported by the fact that in higher animals cerebral cortex develops within this layer and apparently by neurobiotactic influence emanating from it."

Herrick summarizes his conclusions concerning visual excitation of motor activity by way of the integrating mechanism of the ventral midbrain in the following words (Herrick 1948, pp. 37–38).

> In the structural setup before us it may be inferred that the first result of a retinal excitation is the activation of the entire tectum, pretectal nucleus, and dorsal thalamus through the thick myelinated fibers of the optic nerve and tract and also of the ventrolateral neuropil of the peduncle through the basal optic tract. This is presumably a generalized nonspecific effect, and it will come to motor expression, first, through the basal tract, for this is the shortest path. The resting state is changed to a state of excitation in both the peduncular gray and the peripheral musculature with which it is connected. This is immediately followed by volleys from the tectum, pretectal nucleus, and thalamus through the myelinated tecto- and thalemopeduncular tracts; and this may contribute a spatial factor determined by the position of the exciting object in the visual field and the sector of the tectum upon which this local stimulus is projected. The first overt movement, accordingly, is an orientation of the body and the eyeballs with reference to the source of stimulus. After an appreciable time the smaller fibers from the retina deliver their volleys, and the small fibers of the correlating tracts are activated. These deliver to the peduncle, not unmixed or purely visual impulses but discharges, fired or inhibited, as the case may be by the existing excitatory state of the correlating apparatus; and this, in its turn, is determined by numberless nonvisual features of the total situation, present and past.

The mechanism we have described here is in all essentials that of a fish. However, the visual system in the midbrain is proportionately better developed in many fish than it is in the salamander, and there are differences in other visual structures, as is clear from Schwassmann's account in this volume. Though there is no clear-cut correlation between the known system of anatomy and the conclusions we have come to from a discussion of behavioral organization in fish, the two general schemes do correspond in important ways as, if they are correct, they must do in the final analysis.

There is apparently no single localizable structure corresponding to the central integrative mechanism of Figure 7. However, within the neuropil, between sensory analytic and motor analytic zones, there are many parallel systems through which both sides, sensory and motor, may be adjusted. Appropriate patterning of activity among units within the intermediary mechanism of the ventrolateral peduncular neuropil, for example, would at one and the same time alter preparatory sets to motor action and also the receptivity or "processing" of visual stimuli. Up and down the central nervous system intermediary cells with dendritic and axonal trees of specified form could thus act collectively as a selector mechanism ensuring, by the balance of activity among them, a correspondence between reafferent "expectancy" and the form of action initiated. The simplest case to consider may be that of an oculomotor neurone, a cell with close affinities to the cells of the neighboring tegmental neuropil, but which discharges to produce a pattern of muscle contractions which modifies the visual display in a specific direction (see Fig. 8).

Conclusions

Ethologists have made detailed descriptions of the complex behavior of many fish, especially of their social behavior. Learning experiments have shown the capacity of fish to distinguish the visual orientations, forms, textures, and colors of objects. There is a large body of anatomical knowledge about the fish brain. Neurophysiologists studying fish have made classic studies of the organization of the vertebrate motor system and of several receptor mechanisms; and now unit analysis is being applied to the visual apparatus of fish at several levels. Yet we do not have a clear picture of the fish brain, and we are far from knowing how fish see. The body of knowledge we have seems disjointed and confusing. Part of the trouble is certainly incompleteness of knowledge, but it could also be that there is a fundamental flaw in an approach which tends to split the sensory and motor processes apart. It is not impossible that a synthesis might be achieved by another approach which would, at the same time, have application in other groups and so fill in the comparative perspective.

Vision, though among the more complex regulatory functions of the brain, has the apparent advantage of being describable at the receptor end with greater physical precision than can be achieved for the majority of other senses. This is especially true with respect to the effects of movements of the receptor organs, though these effects are often overlooked.

The simplest forms of fish possess good image-forming eyes, are highly locomotor, and rotate their eyes in their heads by a muscular servomechanism which serves to stabilize the relationship of the retina to the visual world against certain common perturbations. The more complex forms are less continuously locomotor but have relatively more developed visual parts of their brains and better formed eyes. We conclude from our brief survey of visual mechanisms in fish that there are several stages in an evolutionary progression of visuomotor functions, which may be outlined as follows.

Hypothetical Evolution of Vision in Fish

Stage I: Vision by Locomotor Scanning

Vision in the simplest, most primitive fish gives a spatial frame for the adjustment of locomotor movements and for the location and crude identification of self-mobile prey. Eye movements at this stage of evolution are simple; spontaneous rotations are always associated with locomotor rhythms. Olfaction is highly developed in many of the most primitive fish and may be the main discriminatory sense in most of them, leaving vision a secondary role. Example: dogfish.

Stage II: Vision Includes Simple Oculomotor Scanning

Locomotion at this stage is more subtle, but these are fish which are still almost continuously locomotive. Some of the eye movements are, however, spontaneous sampling movements free of locomotor commitment. Example: goldfish.

Stage III: Highly Selective Oculomotor Sampling—Specialized Locomotion

Fish with highly discriminatory visual behavior show refined locomotion. Many highly evolved fish also have complex visual social communication. They all show well-developed voluntary eye movements, including, in some cases, individual fixation movements of the two eyes. Examples: cichlids, blennies, plectognaths.

Along with the trend to more complex visuomotor adaptations go development of retinal specializations and elaborations of the anatomy of the central visual receiving areas, including, we believe, progressive evolution of units capable of elementary form analyses which may detect near stationary visual features.

The close interdependency in the behavior of fish between motor capacity and visual receptivity which we have emphasized seems to us to be strong evidence of a visual process which is neither sensory nor motor but a synthesis of the two. The pattern of spontaneous behavior in any individual is an expression of some patterned activity in the nervous system which pushes the animal to act in certain ways, and also to process or attend to particular forms of stimulation. We have reviewed experiments which demonstrate that an actively moving fish is differently receptive to visual stimulation than is an inactive one. We believe that many puzzling complexities of behavior become somewhat less inexplicable with the assumption that active visual function depends upon the integration within the brain of some description of the visual consequences of an act as that act is carried out. The elaborate adjustments of eye position relative to the body would ensure standardization of the effects of acts in the projected visual image.

In other words, we believe that fish show evidence in their behavior of a perception process by means of which is constituted in their brains a changing model of the world within which they act. This is much the same point of view as Young (1964) has advanced, with more detailed support, to explain the behavior of the octopus. Young acknowledges a debt to the theoretical approach of Kenneth Craik (1943)—a notion of a model of the world as the foundation for the control of behavior by the brain. Craik's work is an indispensable introduction to this point of view.

If we allow that there is a perception process in behavior, even in the case of fish, can we meet the challenge if asked to locate the mechanism of this model-building in the brain? This is obviously not easy, but we can go nowhere without it.

The brain does not have any one governing center which could have the "ideas immanent in nervous activity" of McCulloch—but there is a population of neurones which could be the matrix of which models are built.

There is in the brains of all vertebrates an extensive intermediate system of neurones with dendrites to the sensory analyzing fields and axons extended toward the mechanisms wherein acts are integrated. Elements of this system could be the logical members of a population out of which a set is selected to constitute some kind of neurone committee of proposed action. First to be defined is the spatial frame of action, because each act has a spatial context. The same space is common to several modalities simultaneously and so a spatial adjustment would be defined within the brain in a way that would bring the appropriate modalities together. An act would be made within a multimodal frame of adjustments in sensory analyzer mechanisms. It is clear that, if the central process is such an integrated adjustment in a neural representation of behavioral space, vision, for example, would involve more of the brain than is held by any classical conception. No one believes that vision is in the retina. It is not even safe to conclude that it is in the midbrain tectum or some diencephalic center. The hypothalamus and tegmentum and many other structures must play a part in any adjustment of vision, not as external influences, but as indispensable components. For this reason neurophysiologists recording from units in immobilized or anesthetized fish are in some danger of only scratching the surface, an essential surface, but only the surface, nevertheless.

Finally, three areas of inquiry seem to me to be worthy of special attention, and immediately accessible to available techniques.

1. It is important to determine if the topographic order in the map on the midbrain roof of fish is an indispensable component of the visual space-controlling mechanism. Both motor and sensory relationships to this topography should be considered in any study of it.

Does the projection change when the relative orientation of eyes to body is changed voluntarily?

2. What is the significance of regional specialization in the visual system? Is it possible to map in the brain a neural representation of the central field, and how does it differ from the lateral fields on either side? Are some behavioral adjustments confined to the central field and its neural substrate to the extent that it would be justifiable to distinguish two kinds of vision in fish, peripheral and central?

3. Eye movements, their role in vision, and their evolution clearly deserve closer study, and the neural link between tectal map and the oculomotor neurones would appear to be of special interest as a system of visuomotor integration of a relatively simple kind.

References

Akert, K. 1949a. Experimenteller Beitrag betr. die zentrale Netzhaut-Repräsentation im Tectum Opticum. *Schweiz. Arch. Neurol. Psychiat.* 64:1–16.

———. 1949b. Der visuelle Greifreflex. *Helv. Physiol. Acta* 7:112–34.

Apter, J. T. 1945. Projection of the retina on the superior colliculus of cats. *J. Neurophysiol.* 8:123–34.

———. 1946. Eye movements following strychninization of the superior colliculus of cats. *J. Neurophysol.* 9:73–86.

Arey, L. B. 1916. The function of efferent fibers of the optic nerve of fishes. *J. Comp. Neurol.* 26:213–45.

Baerends, G. P.; Brouwer, R.; and Waterbolk, H. Tj. 1955. Ethnological studies on *Lebistes reticulatus* (Peters): I. An analysis of the male courtship pattern. *Behaviour* 8:249–334.

Barlow, G. W. 1962. Ethology of the Asian teleost *Badis badis:* IV. Sexual behavior. *Copeia* 2:346–60.

Black, P., and Myers, R. E. 1965. A neurological investigation of eye-hand control in the chimpanzee. In *Functions of the corpus callosum*, ed. E. G. Ettlinger. Ciba Foundation Study Group, no. 20, pp. 47–59. London: J. & A. Churchill, Ltd.

Burns, A. H., and Goodman, D. C. 1967. Retino-fugal projection of *Caiman sclerops. Exp. Neurol.* 18:105–15.

Coghill, G. E. 1929. *Anatomy and the problem of behaviour.* Cambridge: Cambridge University Press.

Craig, W. 1918. Appetites and aversions as constituents of instincts. *Biol. Bull.* 34:91–107.

Craik, K. J. W. 1943. *The nature of explanation.* Cambridge: Cambridge University Press.

Gaze, R. M., and Jacobson, M. 1962a. The projection of the binocular visual field on the optic tecta of the frog. *Quart. J. Exp. Physiol.* 47:273–80.

———. 1962b. The path from the retina to the ipsilateral optic tectum of the frog. *J. Physiol. (Lond.)* 165:73–74.

Gibson, J. J. 1966. *The senses considered as perceptual systems.* Boston: Houghton Mifflin.

Granit, R. 1959. Neural activity in the retina. In *Handbook of Physiology*, ed. J. Field. Section I: Neurophysiology, vol. 1, pp. 693–712. Washington, D.C.: American Physiological Society.

Gray, J. 1950. The role of peripheral sense organs during locomotion in the vertebrates. In *Physiological mechanisms in animal behaviour.* Society for Experimental Biology Symposium no. 4, pp. 112–26. Cambridge: Cambridge University Press.

Gray, J., and Sand, A. 1936a. The locomotory rhythm of the dogfish (*Scyllium canicula*). *J. Exp. Biol.* 13:200–209.

————. 1936b. Spinal reflexes in the dogfish (*Scyllium canicula*). *J. Exp. Biol.* 13:210–18.

Haldane, J. B. S. 1956. Les aspects physiochemiques des instincts In: *L'Instinct dans le comportement des animaux et de l'homme*. Paris: Masson.

Harris, A. J. 1965. Eye movements of the dogfish *Squalus acanthias* L. *J. Exp. Biol.* 43: 107–30.

Herrick, C. J. 1948. *The brain of the tiger salmander*. Chicago: University of Chicago Press.

Hess, W. R. 1943. Das Zwischenhirn als Koordinationsorgan. *Helv. Physiol. Acta* 1:549–65.

Hinde, R. A. 1953. Appetitive behavior, consummatory act and the hierarchical organization of behavior—with special reference to the great tit (Parus major). *Behaviour* 5:189–224.

————. 1966. *Animal behavior: A synthesis of ethology and comparative psychology*. New York: McGraw-Hill.

Holst, E. von. 1935a. Erregungsbildung und Erregungsleitung im Fischrückenmark. *Pflüger. Arch. ges. Physiol.* 235:345–59.

————. 1935b. Über den Prozess der zentralnervösen Koordination. *Pflüger. Arch. ges. Physiol.* 236:149–58.

————. 1939. Über die nervose Funktionsstruktur des rhythmisch tatigen Fischrükenmarks. *Pflüger. Arch. ges. Physiol.* 241:569–611.

————. 1950a. Die Arbeitsweise des Statolithenapparates bei Fischen. *Z. vergl. Physiol.* 32:60–120.

————. 1950b. Quantitative Messung von Stimmungen im Verhalten der Fische. In *Physiological mechanisms in animal behaviour*. Society for Experimental Biology Symposium no. 4, pp. 143–72. Cambridge: Cambridge University Press.

————. 1954. Relations between the central nervous system and the peripheral organs. *Brit. J. Anim. Behav.* 2:89–94.

Holst, E. von, and Saint Paul, U. von. 1963. On the functional organization of drives. *Anim. Behav.* 11:1–20.

Horn, G. 1965. Physiological and Psychological aspects of selective perception. In *Advances in the study of behavior*, ed. D. S. Lehrman, R. A. Hinde, and E. Shaw, 1:155–215. New York: Academic Press.

Ingle, D. J. 1965. The use of the fish in neuropsychology. *Perspectives in biology and medicine*, 8:241–60.

Jacobson, M., and Gaze, R. M. 1964. Types of visual response from single units in the optic tectum and optic nerve of the goldfish. *Quart. J. Exp. Physiol.* 49:199–209.

Lashley, K. S. 1938. Experimental analysis of behavior. *Psychol. Rev.* 45:445–71.

————. 1950. In search of the engram. In *Physiological mechanisms in animal behaviour*. Society for Experimental Biology Symposium no. 4, pp. 454–82. Cambridge: Cambridge University Press.

————. 1951. The problem of serial order in behavior. In *Cerebral mechanisms in behavior: The Hixon symposium*, ed. L. A. Jeffress. New York: John Wiley & Sons, Inc.

Leghissa, S. 1955. La struttura microscopica e la citoarchitettonica del tetto ottico dei pesci teleostei. *Zeit. Anat. Entickl.* 118:427–63.

Lissman, H. W. 1946a. The neurological basis of the locomotory rhythm in the spinal dogfish (*Scyllium canicula, Acanthias vulgaris*). I. Reflex behavior. *J. Exp. Biol.* 23:143–61.

————. 1946*b*. The neurological basis of the locomotory rhythm in the spinal dogfish (*Scyllium canicula, Acanthias vulgaris*). II. The effect of deafferentation. *J. Exp. Biol.* 23: 162–76.

Lorenz, K. Z. 1937. Über die Bildung des Instinktbergriffes. *Naturwissenschaften* 25:289–300.

Lowenstein, O. 1950. Labrynth and equilibrium. In *Physiological mechanisms in animal behaviour*. Society for Experimental Biology Symposium no. 4, pp. 60–82. Cambridge: Cambridge University Press.

Lowenstein, O., and Sand, A. 1940*a*. The mechanism of the semicircular canal: A study of the responses of single-fiber preparations to angular accelerations and to rotation at constant speed. *Proc. Roy. Soc. Ser. B.* 129:256–75.

————. 1940*b*. The individual and integrated activity of the semicircular canals of the elasmobranch labyrinth. *J. Physiol. (Lond.)* 99:89–101.

Mackintosh, J., and Sutherland, N. S. 1963. Visual discrimination by the goldfish: The orientation of rectangles. *Anim. Behav.* 11:135–41.

Mackintosh, N. J., *et al.* 1966. Overtraining, reversal and extinction in the goldfish. *Anim. Behav.* 14:314–18.

Marler, P. 1967. Animal communication signals. *Science* 157:769–74.

Marler, P., and Hamilton, W. J. 1966. *Mechanisms of animal behavior*. New York: John Wiley & Sons, Inc.

Maturana, H. R.; Lettvin, J. Y.; McCulloch, W. S.; and Pitts, W. H. 1960. Anatomy and physiology of vision in the frog (*Rana pipiens*). *J. Gen. Physiol.* 43 Suppl.:129–75.

Mittelstaedt, H. 1964. Basic solutions to a problem of angular orientation. In *Neural theory and modeling*, ed. R. F. Reiss, pp. 259–72. Palo Alto: Stanford University Press.

Myers, R. E.; Sperry, R. W.; and McCurdy, N. M. 1962. Neural mechanisms in visual guidance of limb movement. *Arch. Neurol.* 7:195–202.

Pumphrey, R. J. 1950. Hearing. In *Physiological mechanisms in animal behaviour*. Society for Experimental Biology Symposium no. 4, pp. 3–18. Cambridge: Cambridge University Press.

Schwassmann, H. D., and Kruger, L. 1965. Organization of the visual projection upon the optic tectum of some fresh water fish. *J. Comp. Neurol.* 124:113–26.

Sherrington, C. S. 1906. *The integrative action of the nervous system*. London: Charles Scribner's Sons.

Sokolov, E. N. 1960. Neuronal models and the orienting reflex. In *The central nervous system and behavior*, ed. M. A. B. Brazier. New York: Josiah Macy Jr. Foundation.

Sperry, R. W. 1943. Effect of 180 degree rotation of the retinal field on visuo-motor coordination. *J. Exp. Zool.* 92:263–79.

————. 1944. Optic nerve regeneration with return of vision in anurans. *J. Neurophysiol.* 7:57–70.

————. 1948. Patterning of central synapses in regeneration of the optic nerve in teleosts. *Physiol. Zool.* 21:351–61.

————. 1950. Neural basis of the spontaneous optokinetic response produced by visual inversion. *J. Comp. Physiol. Psychol.* 43:482–89.

————. 1955. On the neural basis of the conditioned response. *Brit. J. Anim. Behav.* 3:41–44.

Sprague, J. M.; Chambers, W. W.; and Stellar, E. 1961. Attentive, affective and adaptive behavior in the cat. *Science* 133:165–73.

Ströer, W. F. H. 1939. Zur vergleichenden Anatomie des primären optischen Systems bei Wirbeltieren. *Z. Anat. Entwicklungsgsch.* 110:301–21.

Sutherland, N. S. 1963. Shape discrimination and receptive fields. *Nature* 197:118–22.

Sutherland, N. S., and Muntz, W. R. 1959. Simultaneous discrimination training and preferred directions of motion in visual discrimination in *Octopus vulgaris* lamark. *Publ. Staz. Zool. Napoli* 31:109–26.

Tinbergen, N. 1951. *The study of instinct*. Oxford: Oxford University Press.

Trevarthen, C. 1965. Functional interactions between the cerebral hemispheres of the split-brain monkey. In *Functions of the corpus callosum*, ed. E. G. Ettlinger. Ciba Foundation Study Group, no. 20, pp. 24–40.

Walls, G. L. 1942. *The vertebrate eye and its adaptive radiation*. Bulletin no. 19, Cranbrook Institute of Science. Michigan: Cranbrook Institute of Science.

Weiss, P. 1941. Autonomous versus reflexogenous activity of the central nervous system. *Proc. Amer. Phil. Soc.* 84:53–64.

Wiersma, C. A. G., and Yamaguchi, T. 1966. The neuronal components of the optic nerve of the crayfish as studied by single unit analysis. *J. Comp. Neurol.* 128:333–58.

Young, J. Z. 1964. *A model of the brain*. Oxford: Oxford University Press.

Part II Anatomy and Function of Fish Forebrain

1

Introductory Remarks on the Telencephalon of Fish

H. N. Schnitzlein

Department of Anatomy
University of Alabama Medical Center
Birmingham, Alabama

A knowledge of the anatomical substrate and an awareness of the comparative neuro-anatomical relationships are always desirable in interpreting functional studies. The following brief general comments are made as an introduction to more specific papers. The great numbers and many variations of fish provide many divergent exaggerations, diminutions, or even additions to certain telencephalic nuclei and tracts.

The use of homologous anatomical terminology can be misleading either if an interpretation of an exact similarity of structure is implied or if a sameness of function (analogy) is suggested. Homologous names are used in the vertebrate brain if they have similar relationships, cell types, and fiber connections. Agreement on such terminology is not currently established.

Such naming can be used in forebrain areas in actinopterygean and dipnoian fish and probably in all fish (Crosby, De Jonge, and Schneider 1966). This is not in agreement with the theory of "eversion" suggested by Dr. Susanna Gage in 1893 (also Nieuwenhuys 1966) on the basis of the connections of a "corpus callosum" in fish. Her reasoning was quite sound, but the anatomical facts were not known in 1893, as she herself stated. Unfortunately, her conclusions have dominated anatomical research for half a century with but a few exceptions (Weston 1937; Fortuyn 1961; Crosby, De Jonge, and Schneider 1966).

Basically, there are six major nuclear regions of the telencephalon of all vertebrates including fish (Crosby, De Jonge, and Schneider 1966)—a dorsomedial, a ventromedial, a ventral, a dorsolateral, a dorsal, and a central or deep area (Fig. 1).

Dorsomedially, the hippocampal formation is characterized by its position between the primordial general pallium and the precommissural septal area. The connections of the hippocampal formation include the medial olfactory tract (at least into its rostral portion), neocortical and septal interrelationships, and a hippocampal commissure characteristically dorsal to the anterior commissure. Fornix fibers pass from the hippocampal formation to

97

the hypothalamus and the medial corticohabenular pathway connects it with the epithalamus.

Ventromedially is the precommissural septum or parolfactory region. It characteristically receives olfactory impulses, in some forms after relay in course, and is interconnected with the hippocampal formation and the olfactory tubercle by association fibers. It is also interconnected with the opposite hemisphere through components of the anterior commissure. The medial forebrain bundle interrelates the septal nuclei with the hypothalamus and perhaps with the more caudal levels and the medial corticohabenular tract contains components from the septum to the habenula.

FISH
TELENCEPHALON

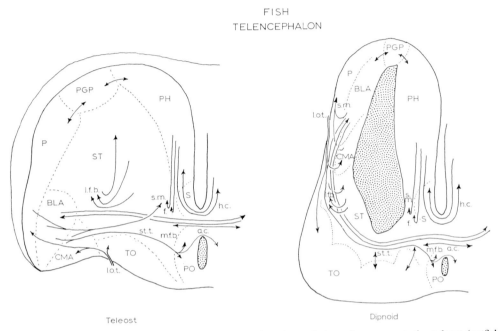

Teleost   Dipnoid

Fig. 1. Diagrammatic transverse sections through the telencephalon of a representative teleost (catfish) and a dipnoid (*Protopterus*) to illustrate the major telencephalic regions and their fiber connections. The arrows indicate the course of fiber bundles; *a.c.*, anterior commissure; *BLA*, basolateral amygdala; *CMA*, corticomedial amygdala; *f.*, fornix; *h.c.*, hippocampal commissure; *l.f.b.*, lateral forebrain bundle; *l.o.t.*, lateral olfactory tract; *m.f.b.*, medial forebrain bundle; *P*, piriform area; *PGP*, primordial general pallium; *PH*, primordial hippocampal formation; *PO*, preoptic area; *S*, septal nuclei; *s.m.*, stria medullaris (or components); *ST*, striatum; *st.t.*, stria terminalis; *TO*, olfactory tubercle.

The olfactory tubercle is situated *ventrally* in the hemisphere, extending ventromedially and, in lungfish, where it is exaggerated, ventrolaterally. It is characterized by the formation of the cells into the so-called islands of Calleja and by the striatal blood vessels which perforate it. The tuberculum has many association connections with adjacent regions, including the striatum, and may receive both the medial (sometimes after relay) and the lateral olfactory tracts. Caudal interrelationships have also been reported (Schnitzlein and Crosby 1967).

The amygdala or amygdaloid complex (archistriatum or epistriatum) and the piriform lobe are located laterally in the hemisphere. The amygdala may be subdivided into two basic parts (Schnitzlein *et al.* 1966), the corticomedial and the basolateral nuclei. The corticomedial amygdala and piriform lobe receive the lateral olfactory tract. The basolateral portion is characteristically connected through the anterior commissure with like regions in the opposite hemisphere, and is intimately related to the striatum and to the neocortex. Projections through the stria terminalis connect the amygdala with the preoptic area and the hypothalamus, and fascicles of the lateral corticohabenular component of the stria medullaris project to the habenula.

The general pallial area which becomes so dominant in higher mammals is located dorsally between the hippocampal formation and the piriform region in fishes. This area is obviously reduced in fish.

The striatal complex situated *deep* within the hemisphere in the lateral wall of the ventricle may be divided into a hyperstriatum, a neostriatum, a paleostriatum primitivum, and a paleostriatum augmentatum in lower vertebrates. Such divisions have not been made in actinopterygean fish. The lateral forebrain bundle interconnects the striatum with caudal regions. The dorsal peduncle of this lateral forebrain bundle includes ascending fibers from the dorsal thalamus. The ventral peduncle largely contains descending fibers from the striatal complex to the hypothalamus, the ventral thalamus, and the midbrain tegmentum. These are in a general way comparable to the ansa lenticularis system of mammals. Association fibers interrelating the striatum with the basolateral amygdala and other areas have been mentioned.

It should be emphasized that there are rarely sharp boundaries between the nuclear areas of the brain. It should also be stressed that the fiber bundles mentioned are not exactly the same in all forms, in that those impulses which are projected over these various fiber bundles are dependent upon the nuclei in which they arise and on the impulses received by those nuclear areas. For example, the connection from the neocortex to the hippocampus in most lower vertebrates, including fish, is minor. In primates, these connections from the neocortex are some of the most obvious, and quantitatively the largest, to the hippocampus. The impulses projected out of the hippocampus over the fornix are certainly influenced much more strongly by the neocortical relationships in man than they are in the fish. Consequently, the function of the hippocampus (or fornix) is not the same in these two forms. Similar examples could be made for many regions.

Function in terms of behavior is difficult to describe in lower forms. Sensation is not the same in fish as in man. Motor responses are most frequently total body responses involving wide areas of the nervous system—which are not exactly the same even in any two individuals. The relationships of structure and function have always provided fertile grounds for speculation. Unfortunately, in nature the various nuclei and fiber tracts are neither labeled with a name nor colored red or blue. Anatomy and function may eventually be described in an understandable and harmonious terminology—but the facts must first be found and utilized.

Acknowledgment

This investigation was supported in part by Grant NB-04295 from the National Institute of Neurological Diseases and Blindness, The National Institutes of Health, United States Public Health Service.

References

Crosby, E. C.; DeJonge, B. R.; and Schneider, R. C. 1966. Evidence for some of the trends in the phylogenetic development of the vertebrate telencephalon. In *Evolution of the forebrain*, pp. 117–35. Stuttgart: Georg Thieme Verlag.

Droogleever Fortuyn, J. 1961. Topographical relations in the telencephalon of the sunfish, *Eupomotis gibbosus. J. Comp. Neurol.* 116:249–63.

Gage, Susanna P. 1893. The brain of *Diemyctylus viridescens* from larval to adult life. In *Wilder quarter century book*, pp. 259–314. Ithaca, N.Y.

Nieuwenhuys, R. 1966. The interpretation of the cell masses in the teleostean forebrain. In *Evolution of the forebrain*, pp. 32–39. Stuttgart: Georg Thieme Verlag.

Schnitzlein, H. N., and Crosby, E. C. 1967. The telencephalon of the lungfish, *Protopterus. J. Hirnforsch.* 9:106–49.

Schnitzlein, H. N.; Hoffman, H. H.; Hamel, E. G., Jr.; and Ferrer, N. G. 1966. Parallelism in fiber relations and variations in nuclear patterns in the phylogeny of the amygdala. *Archivos Mexicanos de Anatomia.* 26:25–63.

Weston, J. K. 1937. Notes on the telencephalon of *Mormyrus* and *Gnathonemus. Proc. Kon. Ned. Akad. Wet.* 40:894–904.

2

Regeneration in Teleost Olfactory System

R. J. von Baumgarten / H. J. Miessner

Mental Health Research Institute
University of Michigan
Department of Physiology
University of Göttingen

The following is a combined behavioral, electrophysiological, and histological study of the problem of (1) whether dissected olfactory tracts in fish can regenerate; (2) how well fish can use their sense of smell after the regeneration; and (3) whether or not this regeneration is specific.

Fish are well suited for olfactory experiments for the following reasons: The olfactory system of fish resembles to a high degree that of higher vertebrates, including man (Allison 1953; Burne 1909). Many fish have an excellent sense of smell which outperforms that of most mammals (Frisch 1941; Teichmann 1962). Olfactory stimulations with pure odorants require a constancy of concentration which can be achieved and measured more easily in water than is possible with the vaporized odors used in studies with land animals. The olfactory nerve fibers and the olfactory tract in cyprinide fish are relatively long and can be exposed easily for recording and dissection. Fish have a remarkable capacity for regeneration, as is known from other studies (Attardi and Sperry 1963; Sperry 1963).

In experiments with R. Westerman we studied the ability of young carp to regain their ability to smell after both medial and lateral olfactory tracts had been dissected bilaterally (Westerman and von Baumgarten 1964). As a test we used two identical gauze sacks, one containing concealed minced earthworms or tubifex worms (positive sacks) and the other, stones. The sacks were suspended in an aquarium and strikes of the fish against the sacks were recorded and counted electrically by an electromechanical transducer system. Normal fish struck the worm-filled bag significantly more often than fish with recently dissected olfactory tracts. This response was also observed in complete darkness, which excluded any visual clues. After 40 days of regeneration the operated fish started locating the positive sacks again and subsequently regained almost full olfactory capacity in another 20 days.

In further experiments, carp and large goldfish were preoperatively trained to discriminate two odors which were displayed at the opposing sides of the fish tank through jets,

101

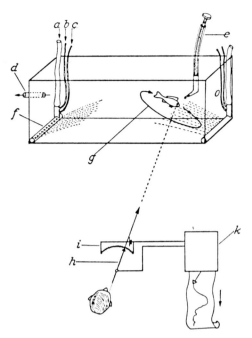

FIG. 1. Olfactory stimulation and graphical recording of fish movements; *a*, water inlet; *b* and *c*, inlets for odorants; *d*, water outlet; *e*, feeding pipette; *f*, jets for water-odorant mixture; *g*, circular movement of fish; *h*, optical sight with pointer; *i*, electrical potentiometer; *k*, chart recorder (Miessner and von Baumgarten 1966).

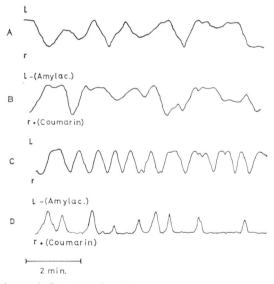

FIG. 2. Control experiments before operation. The curves represent the movements of the fish in respect to the left (up in the curve) and right (down in the curve) side of the fish tank. *a*, control without odorant; *b*, untrained fish, stimulation with two odorants—no definite preference for one side; *c* and *d*, the same fish after the discrimination training. Coumarin was rewarded, amyl acetate was not. *c*, control without odorants; *d*, coumarin was displayed at the right and amyl acetate at the left side of the tank. The fish preferred the right (positive) side.

similar to Hasler's method. One odor was rewarded by food and the other was not. As odorants, coumarin and amyl acetate at concentrations of 10^{-5} w/v were used. Control experiments proved that these substances did not attract the fish without previous training. The movements of the fish in the tank before, during, and after the olfactory stimulation were recorded by a newly developed method (Miessner and von Baumgarten 1966) (Fig. 1). The pointer of an optical sight was continuously directed by an observer toward the eye of the fish during the experiment. The pointer was attached to a potentiometer which divided the battery voltage. The movements of the fish were thereby transferred into voltage differences

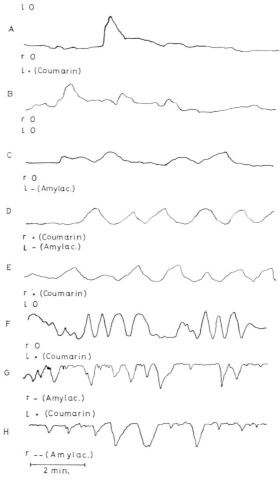

Fig. 3. The same fish as in Fig. 2 after bilateral dissection of the olfactory tracts. *a* and *b*, three days after the operation; *a*, control; *b*, after application of coumarin—no definite response to the olfactory stimulation. *c*, *d*, and *e*, the same fish after 21 days of regeneration. *c*, control without odorants; *d*, stimulation with two odorants. The fish shows signs of arousal but no discriminative behavior. *e*, change of the side of odors does not alter the behavior of the fish. *f*, *g*, and *h*, the same fish 135 days after the operation; *f*, control without odors; *g*, the two odorants are displayed on different sides in equal concentration. The fish prefers again the side of the "positive" odor (coumarin). *h*, the same stimulation, but the concentration of the negative odorant (amyl acetate) was doubled. The fish still prefers the positive (coumarin) odorant.

which were plotted on a chart recorder. The recorded swimming patterns revealed preferences of the fish for one or the other side of the fish tank (Fig. 2). After the fish had reached a high degree of discriminative performance, the medial and lateral olfactory tracts were completely dissected. During the first week after the operation the fish did not respond to any odor stimulation (Fig. 3*a* and *b*). After 60 to 90 days without any reinforcement most of the operated fish showed a significant preference for that odor which was coupled with reward before the operation (Fig. 3*f*, *g*, and *h*). This effect was not due to any concentration differences of the odors. Control experiments with the same trained fish before the operation had shown that a "forgetting period" of 60 to 90 days without reinforcement was not sufficiently long to completely extinguish the odor discrimination. On the other hand it was found that the fish remembered the olfactory discrimination tasks better when the olfactory tracts were cut during the forgetting period than if they had an intact olfactory system and were perhaps unintentionally distracted by spurious new olfactory experiences.

All the fish which showed olfactory regeneration behaviorally were subsequently killed and examined histologically. Serial paraffin sections of the whole fish heads were taken and

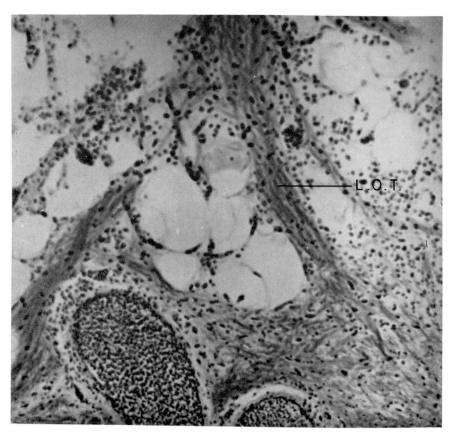

FIG. 4. Histological section of the fish head 5 months after dissection of the olfactory tract. The Bodian staining shows regenerated nerve fibers of the olfactory tract (L.O.T.).

stained with Bodian's method. Outgrowth of new nerve fibers invariably bridged the gap of the former dissection (Fig. 4).

The finding that olfactory fibers regenerate specifically is in accord with reports in the literature concerning histological and functional regeneration of the optic tract.

It can be concluded from these experiments that regeneration of the olfactory tract restored the connection between olfactory bulbs and the brain. Moreover, this regeneration allowed the fish to distinguish odors again. Finally, the two different odorants triggered the same behavioral pattern as before the operation. A simple explanation for these results would be that the regeneration reconnected the former pathways in a point-to-point fashion. An alternative explanation is that the information about different odors was transformed by the olfactory bulb into a "language" of temporary coded action potentials. In this case, all the fibers would carry the same pattern of information uniformly, and a specific point-to-point regeneration would not need to be invoked. To study this question, Nanba, Jahan-Parvar, and von Baumgarten (1966), recorded the action potentials of single fibers of the olfactory tracts of goldfish and cyprinides (*Abramis abrama*) during olfactory stimulation, again using coumarin and amyl acetate as we did in the behavioral studies. These results showed clearly that almost every fiber we recorded responded with a different pattern of action potentials to the same odorant. Such a high degree of functional organization within the olfactory tract does not seem to be compatible with random regeneration, since the fish were finally able to discriminate previously learned odors. On the contrary, an extremely high degree of point-to-point specific regeneration would have to be postulated, since our results seem to indicate that many functionally different olfactory tract fibers transmit their own specific information within a spatially coded system.

References

Allison, A. C. 1953. The morphology of the olfactory system in the vertebrates. *Biol. Rev.* 28:195–244.

Attardi, D. C., and Sperry, R. W. 1963. Specificity in regeneration of optic and olfactory pathways in teleost fish. *Exp. Neurol.* 7:46.

Burne, R. H. 1909. The anatomy of the olfactory organ of teleostean fishes. *Proc. Zool. Soc. Lond.* 2:610–63.

Frisch, K. von. 1941. Die Bedeutung des Geruchssinnes im Leben der Fische. *Naturwissenschaften* 291:321–33.

Miessner, H. J., and Baumgarten, R. von. 1966. Untersuchungen über die Geruchswahrnehmung und das Geruchsgedächtnis des Goldfisches. *Pflüger. Archiv. ges. Physiol.* 288:118–33.

Nanba, R.; Jahan-Parvar, B.; and Baumgarten, R. von. 1966. Erregungsmuster einzelner Fasern des Tractus olfactorius laterales des Fisches bein Reizung mit verschiedenen Geruchsstoffen. *Pflüger. Archiv. ges. Physiol.* 288:134–50.

Sperry, R. W. 1963. Specificity in regeneration of optic and olfactory pathways in teleost fish. *Proc. Natl. Acad. Sci. U.S.A.* 50:703.

Teichmann, H. 1962. Die Chemoreception der Fische. *Ergebn. der Biol.* 25:177–205.

Westerman, R. A., and Baumgarten, R. von. 1964. Regeneration of olfactory paths in carp. *Experientia* 20:519–23.

3

Function of the Teleostean Forebrain

Lester R. Aronson/Harriett Kaplan

Department of Animal Behavior
American Museum of Natural History, New York

Department of Biology
New York University, New York

Although our knowledge and comprehension of the functioning of the cerebrum of mammals is advancing at a rapid pace, equivalent research on forebrain function in lower vertebrates barely exists. Only among teleost fishes has some interest in the forebrain been shown over the past few decades, but even here our knowledge is, as yet, in a rather primitive state. We are still asking, for example, simple questions about the function of the fish forebrain as a whole, although we know that anatomically it is divided into a number of distinct regions, and we recognize that these regions may have specific, and possibly even antagonistic, actions.

This article surveys briefly our present understanding of the role of the teleost forebrain in the mediation of behavior. It is organized as a series of seven problems with our tentative answers to them, based both upon the existing literature and upon our own research: (1) forebrain variability among teleosts; (2) forebrain homologies with higher vertebrates; (3) the relation of the teleost forebrain to olfaction; (4) nonolfactory functions of the forebrain; (5) regulation of lower brain mechanisms by the forebrain: a hypothesis; (6) the nature of arousal in fishes; and (7) relationship of the forebrain to the visual system.

Forebrain Variability among Teleosts

The forebrains of all fishes have certain basic features in common which distinguish them from those of all other vertebrates. Even by gross visual inspection one can confidently designate an unknown forebrain as belonging or not belonging to a teleost. If microscopic examination is included, specific features can be found which would make identification al-

Dr. Kaplan is now at the New York State Institute for Basic Research in Mental Retardation, Staten Island, New York.

most certain. In a cross section through any teleostean forebrain one would find a solid mass of nerve cells divided into pallial and subpallial portions and covered over by a very broad nonnervous membranous tela which encloses a single median ventricle (Ariëns Kappers, Huber, and Crosby 1936). To this extent one can speak about any teleost forebrain.

The subdivision, on the other hand, of both the pallial and subpallial areas into a variable number of discrete nuclei and the dramatic enlargement of certain pallial areas in some teleost families (Meader 1939) warn against broad generalizations. It may be assumed that these specialized nuclei and related fiber tracts reflect specialization of function, although we actually do not have experimental evidence for this at the present time. The majority of experimental studies of brain function in teleosts have been performed on ostariophysine species, especially European minnows, carp, and goldfish. Although the basic pallial divisions can be recognized in this group, the nuclei and related tracts are not highly differentiated and are not extensively subdivided. In other words, the majority of experimental studies have been performed on species with a rather poorly differentiated forebrain. At the present state of our knowledge, therefore, extrapolations from one group of fishes to another should be made with caution and with consideration of the anatomical similarities of the brains.

Forebrain Homologies with Higher Vertebrates

The forebrain of teleosts (and of related actinopterigian fishes) is unique among vertebrates in that it develops by *eversion* of the thickened side walls of the embryonic neural tube. In all other vertebrates the forebrain develops by lateral *evagination* of the median ventricle (forming the paired lateral ventricles) and by *inversion* of the dorsal portion of the side walls (see Holmgren 1922; Herrick 1922; Nieuwenhuys 1960, 1966, 1967). The process of eversion, coupled with massive thickening of the side walls, produces a rather different-looking structure in fishes compared with that of all other vertebrates. Many biologists would say that this highly specialized structure must have unique functions whose study is unlikely to shed much light on the functional evolution of the vertebrate cerebrum. This argument is countered by the fact that the teleost forebrain is composed of the same primary divisions and has essentially the same connections as in other lower vertebrates.

While some neuroanatomists do not accept the concept of eversion as basic to the formation of the teleost forebrain (Droogleever Fortuyn 1961; Schnitzlein 1964; Story 1964), all seem to agree that the teleost forebrain, like that of other vertebrates, can be divided into a pallial portion and a subpallial portion. Since the process of eversion appears to change the fundamental organization of the pallium, some investigators (e.g., Herrick 1922; Källén 1951; Segaar 1965; Nieuwenhuys 1967) are reluctant to homologize the several specialized areas of the teleost pallium with those of other animals. Other investigators, however, including those not favoring the eversion hypothesis, recognize primary subdivisions of the pallium similar to pallial areas of other vertebrates. These are a medial hippocampal area, a lateral pyriform area, and between these a dorsally situated general pallium (Droogleever Fortuyn 1961); but depending on how one views the process of eversion, the location of the hippocampal and pyriform areas may be reversed (Holmgren 1922). In the subpallium, structures homologous to the typical septal and striatal areas are accepted by most investigators.

As in other vertebrates, the forebrain receives fibers from the olfactory bulbs and to a lesser extent from the diencephalon, and projects fibers back to the olfactory bulbs and to the preoptic area, hypothalamus, epithalamus, dorsal thalamus, and mesencephalon. Also, as in other forms, the several components of the anterior commissure form the basic inter-hemispheric connections (Ariëns Kappers, Huber, and Crosby 1936; Nieuwenhuys 1959). These fundamental structural similarities of the fish and mammalian cerebrum, along with the functional comparisons to be discussed later, have led several investigators (Aronson 1963; Segaar 1965; Hainsworth, Overmier, and Snowdon 1967) to compare the teleost fore-brain with the limbic system of mammals.

The suggestion has been made elsewhere (Aronson 1967) that eversion is not necessari-ly an adaptation resulting in unusual functions. Rather, it may be an adaptation to fit the forebrain into the smallest possible space. In many teleost species this requirement for streamlining is important in fry and juvenile stages, where cranial space is at a premium. In the West African mouthbreeder, *Tilapia heudeloti macrocephala*, for example, the forebrain is packed very tightly into the cranium of young fry. As the fry develop into juveniles, the cranium enlarges at a rapid rate while the brain grows much more slowly, so that the need for a tightly compacted brain is no longer evident. In the adult fish the continuing differential between cranial growth and brain growth results in the formation of a large intracranial space above the forebrain which is filled with loose fatty connective tissue. Nevertheless, the space requirements of the brain of the actively swimming fry may be the critical determinants of eversion.

Despite possible transpositions of structures in the teleost forebrain, the development of interconnecting fiber tracts and of functional relationships may be the same as in other verte-brates. We believe, therefore, that the study of forebrain function in teleosts is more than an isolated area of research. Rather, it will be understood best in relation to forebrain func-tion of other vertebrates, and it will provide insight into the evolution of the vertebrate cerebrum.

The Relation of the Teleost Forebrain to Olfaction

As in all vertebrates, the olfactory nerves terminate in the olfactory bulbs which, in turn, send fibers via the olfactory tracts to the cerebrum, to the hypothalamus, and possibly, in some species, to the contralateral bulb. Formerly it was believed that olfactory fibers per-meated all portions of the cerebral hemispheres, but recent evidence (Aronson 1963; Nieuwenhuys 1967) indicates that, particularly in the more specialized teleosts with moder-ate to large forebrains, olfactory fibers do not reach the major pallial areas, which presum-ably have functions other than olfaction. (See the following section.)

Papez (1929) suggested on the basis of anatomical evidence that the forebrain serves to correlate olfaction and taste. A series of experiments by Wrede (1932—described in detail by Segaar 1965) supports this view. Blind minnows conditioned by food reinforcement to bite at a wad of cotton soaked in fish mucus would not respond to cotton soaked in sugar, quinine, salt, or acid. Forebrainless fish that responded positively to mucus wads (via taste sense) also responded positively to wads soaked in salt and acid. Mucus is apparently tasted and smelled by intact fish, which makes it possible for them to discriminate between mucus and the major taste substances. Without the forebrain this discrimination could not be made for all substances.

When the experiments involve olfaction, the role of the olfactory bulbs is revealed. In the study by Grimm (1960), stimulation from bipolar electrodes implanted in the olfactory bulbs of goldfish induced stereotyped feeding reactions which were indistinguishable from normal feeding. Døving and Gemne (1966) cut portions of the olfactory tracts of the burbot (cod family) and recorded spontaneous electrical activity from the central stumps, thus supporting the conclusions of the neuroanatomists that there are efferent fibers from the hemispheres to the bulbs. Evoked potentials could also be obtained by electrical stimulation of the ipsi- and contralateral olfactory tracts. Additional electrophysiological evidence indicates that one olfactory bulb influences the other, but only through synapses in the forebrain. The direct connections between one bulb and the other postulated by some neuroanatomists (Holmgren 1920) could not be demonstrated in this species. Also of interest is their finding that tactile stimuli to the body of the fish inhibited this spontaneous activity of the central stumps. Kandel (1964) obtained graded excitatory postsynaptic potentials in the large cells of the preoptic nucleus upon electrical stimulation of the olfactory tracts in goldfish. This indicates a direct connection between olfactory bulbs and preoptic nucleus.

In another study, Hara, Ueda, and Gorbman (1965) and Ueda, Hara, and Gorbman (1967) demonstrated by similar electrophysiological methods that high-amplitude EEG responses can be obtained from the olfactory bulbs of adult salmon when the nasal sacs were infused with water from the spawning site at which the fish were obtained. When the sacs were infused with water from strange spawning sites few or no responses occurred. Although these results could be interpreted as chemical conditioning of the bulbs to the water in which they were captured, these investigators present evidence that the bulbs are reflecting the memory of the chemical composition of the home stream which the fish acquired several years before when they descended these streams as fingerlings in a seaward migration.

In teleost embryos the olfactory bulbs are adjacent to the nasal sacs, so that the olfactory nerves from the nasal mucosa to the bulbs are very short. Similarly, the olfactory bulbs form the anterior end of the forebrain and the olfactory tracts running caudally from the bulbs are also short. As the fry and juveniles grow, the cranium enlarges and a space of varying size develops between the nasal pits and the anterior end of the forebrain. In most teleost species the olfactory nerves elongate in order to negotiate this increasing space, but in three groups of fishes, namely the Ostariophysi (carp families), the Anacanthini (cod families), and Mormyrids (elephant fishes), the olfactory bulbs remain adjacent to the nasal sacs while the olfactory tracts elongate. It is interesting to speculate on the possible adaptive advantage of the elongated olfactory tracts. The olfactory nerves are unmyelinated, while the olfactory tracts are largely myelinated and hence conduct nerve impulses more rapidly (Prosser 1961). Ordinarily it would be hard to see how this slight difference in conduction time (considering the relatively short distances involved) would provide any real functional advantage, except if the correlation of smell and taste were involved and precise electrophysiological synchronization were required for this. It may be significant, therefore, that the three groups of teleosts having elongated olfactory tracts also have elaborate central and peripheral taste systems, with numerous taste buds located on the fins, barbels, head, and body. Recently Døving (1967) has confirmed the presence of fast-conducting myelinated fibers in the olfactory tracts of seven anacanthinine and ostariophysine species.

Nonolfactory Functions of the Forebrain

The neuroanatomists of the last century and the early part of the present century were emphatic in stating that the forebrain of fish was essentially an olfactory mechanism. In fact, the cerebral hemispheres were frequently referred to in the literature as olfactory lobes. Although it has been known for several decades now that the forebrain has other functions, the powerful influence of the neuroanatomists persists, and statements as to the olfactory nature of this portion of the fish brain still appear regularly, especially in textbooks and review papers. However, a considerable number of nonolfactory functions have been attributed to the forebrain by various investigators. These have been reviewed by Ten Cate (1935), Healey (1957), Aronson (1963, 1967), and recently by Segaar (1965) in an excellent and detailed study. We have divided these functions into two categories: species-typical behavior and conditioning.

Coordination and Integration of Species-Typical Behavior Patterns

After lesions or complete extirpation of the forebrain, deficits have been found in the following behaviors.

Schooling Behavior. Kumakura (1928) studying goldfish and Hosch (1936) and Berwein (1941) using the European minnow (*Phoxinus*) observed only a transient reduction in schooling behavior after forebrain extirpation. When Hosch's minnows eventually schooled, they tended to remain together longer. He interpreted these results as lowered responsiveness of the operated subjects to new stimuli. Similarly, Berwein (1941) showed that a school of forebrainless minnows was faster to accept a strange minnow than was a comparable school of intact individuals, indicating a reduced ability of the operated animals to discriminate. In the jewel fish, *Hemichromis* (Noble 1936), and in the percoid fishes, *Box* and *Smaris* (Wiebalck 1937), the reduction in schooling was much more permanent. It is possible that these more lasting deficits are related to the more complexly organized forebrains in these species.

A number of investigators (e.g., Shlaifer 1939) have shown that the oxygen consumption of a school is likely to be less than the total consumption when each fish in a school is measured in isolation. This is known as the "group effect." Koshtoiants, Maliukina, and Aleksandriuk (1960) showed in the percoid fishes, *Smaris* and *Mullus*, in the minnow, *Phoxinus*, and in the carp, *Carassius carassius*, that after forebrain extirpation, the group effect disappears. This finding correlates with their observations that isolated forebrainless individuals become less active while those in the school become more active. It is important, in conclusion, to note that in all of the species referred to in this section, schooling behavior was changed by the removal of the forebrain, but was not eliminated.

Aggressive Behavior. Following partial or complete destruction of the forebrain in the jewel fish, *Hemichromis*, the fighting fish, *Betta*, the swordtail, *Xiphophorus*, and in *Danio* (Noble 1939; Noble and Borne 1941) the specific social situations which normally induce fighting were markedly altered, providing fewer opportunities for aggressive behavior, although when fighting did occur, it was as vigorous as in intact fish. Hale (1956b) noted marked quantitative deficiencies in aggressive behavior in sunfish (*Lepomis*) after extensive to complete destruction of the forebrain. In order to elicit fighting in the operated animals, higher intensity stimuli were required; but once fighting started, it did not differ from that of intact fish. Hale, therefore, concluded that fighting behavior must be organized in lower brain levels while the forebrain facilitates initiation of the behavior. Similar results were obtained by Schönherr (1955), who studied aggressive behavior in the three-spined stickleback, *Gasterosteus*. Extensive decrements in aggressive behavior in this species were also reported by Segaar (1961, 1965) and Segaar and Nieuwenhuys (1963). These will be described in the next section. In summary, these varied studies seem to show that aggressive behavior is organized in lower centers while the forebrain facilitates responses to the stimuli and integrates the information required to elicit the behavior. Once fighting is elicited in these deprived animals it does not differ from the fighting of intact individuals.

Reproductive and Parental Behavior. Most of the investigators who studied the effects of forebrain ablation on aggression also described the effect of the operation on reproductive behavior. There is good agreement among them that extensive destruction of the forebrain causes major deficiencies in spawning and parental behavior, but there are major differences of interpretation as to the mechanism underlying the disturbance.

Aronson (1948), working with the West African mouthbreeder, *Tilapia h. macrocephala*, and Kamrin and Aronson (1954), studying forebrain function in the live-bearing platyfish, *Xiphophorus*, were impressed by the fact that forebrain extirpation caused a marked decline in the frequency of occurrence of many of the behavioral items associated with reproduction and that none were completely eliminated. These data led to the conclusion that these patterns of behavior must be organized in lower centers, while the forebrain acts as a regulatory or arousal mechanism which facilitates the lower centers by neural processes of excitation or inhibition. The arousal hypothesis will be discussed further in the next section.

Noble (1936, 1937, 1939) and Noble and Borne (1941) made lesions of varying sizes in the forebrains of several cichlid, cyprinodont, and anabantid species. Their evidence, based particularly on small lesions, suggested to them that the organization of the various reproductive patterns is localized in different areas of the forebrain, which serves to integrate and synchronize these into effective sequences of behavior. They did note, however, that in the jewel fish and African mouthbreeder, different lesions sometimes produced the same behavioral changes.

Similar conclusions were reached by Schönherr (1955), Segaar (1961, 1965) and Segaar and Nieuwenhuys (1963), who studied spawning and parental behavior in the three-spined stickleback, *Gasterosteus aculeatus*. Segaar and his collaborators have done the most extensive work in this area. Essentially, they analyzed the behavior of males during a two-week breeding cycle on the basis of three major component systems, namely aggressive (*A*), sexual (*S*), and parental (*P*). By the use of standard stimuli which evoke one or another of these behavioral component systems, quantitative measurements were made during each day of the cycle. Aggression was measured as the number of bites against an opponent; sexual drive as the number of zigzags in front of a female; parental behavior as duration of nest fanning. These data showed that the motivational level of each system changed in a regular way at different stages in the reproductive cycle (Fig. 1, left). After removal of the lateral parts of both hemispheres, or the dorsorostral area, *A* and *S* were depressed, while *P* remained high (Fig. 1, right). After removal of the medial or caudal areas, *A* and *S* remained high, while *P* was low (Fig. 1, middle). Variations of these basic changes occurred with more restricted lesions. Segaar concludes that the forebrain maintains an adaptive balance among the three components, *A*, *S*, and *P*, with each localized in a separate part of the brain. Moreover, with respect to parental fanning, special centers are claimed in the dorsomedial nucleus of the pallium for excitation and inhibition. Although Segaar emphasizes localized integrative functions of the forebrain, he does recognize (Segaar 1965, p. 224) that this part of the teleost brain may also have more general facilitative and inhibitory functions.

Mediation of Learning Processes

A number of investigators found no changes in conditioning after total forebrain extirpation. Various instrumental techniques were used by Scharrer (1928), Nolte (1932), Janzen (1933), and Hosch (1936), using light as the conditioned stimulus, and by Berwein (1941), using temperature as the CS. Kholodov (1962), using an operant technique (bead pulling), found no changes after total forebrain extirpation in goldfish and carp even when

the experiments involved complex discriminations. Karamian (1956) found neither qualitative nor quantitative changes in speed of formation and stability of the classically conditioned defense reflex after forebrain removal in a variety of teleosts, with light or sound
as the conditioned stimulus. Similarly Bernstein (1962), using autonomic conditioning
(heart rate), found no essential loss in the ability of forebrainless goldfish to discriminate
colors. Furthermore, Bernstein (1961) claimed that forebrainless fish learned a brightness
discrimination, via cardiac conditioning, that normal fish had failed to master.

When Ingle (1965a, b) trained naïve goldfish in a Y-maze, he obtained performance
from forebrain-lesioned subjects equal to that of controls in an alternation problem, and
better performance in a positional habit. He interpreted the latter result as "superior learning," but the performance of the lesioned subjects suggested to him that this "superiority"
resulted from "the reduction of a normal error-making tendency." From our point of view,
this apparent inflexibility of the forebrainless fish constitutes a behavioral deficit. This

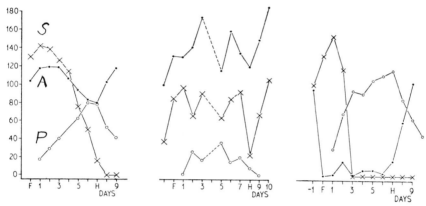

FIG. 1. Changes in aggressive (.———.), sexual (X———X), and parental (O———O) tendencies on varying
days after spawning of the three-spined stickleback. *Left*, averages of 13 control males. *Middle*, behavior of
a male 16 days after causing a large mediocaudal lesion in both hemispheres. *Right*, typical modification of
behavior after either frontal or bilateral lesions of the forebrain. *F*, day eggs are spawned and fertilized. *H*,
day eggs hatch. Modified from Segaar (1963).

perseverative tendency did result in poorer maze performance for lesioned fish when the
alternation task *followed* training on a "go left" problem.

Several investigators, on the other hand, have found important decrements in learning
following removal of the forebrain. Hale (1956a) reported that grouped and isolated forebrainless sunfish *Lepomis* responded much more slowly in a Welty-type maze than the corresponding intact fish. About 50 per cent of the isolated operates showed no evidence of
learning. Warren (1961) tested forebrain-lesioned paradise fish in a series of detour and maze
problems, including reversal learning. He found that the operated fish were significantly inferior to the intact control animals in the reversal learning and in six of twelve detour problems and interpreted his results in terms of Aronson's (1957) nonspecific arousal hypothesis.
Aronson and Herberman (1960) trained West African mouthbreeders to push a small plastic
paddle, with food as a reward. They measured the time from introduction of the paddle to
the response. With training, intact fish reduced this latency to a few seconds and they were
very consistent between trials and sessions. When tested after total ablation of the forebrain,
the subjects still responded to the introduction of the paddle, but the median latency of re-

sponse went up considerably and variability between trials and sessions became very high. In other words, the response was slow and erratic. Interestingly, in all of the five subjects, the median latencies in the first few tests after operation were still relatively low. Latencies increased rapidly in subsequent tests until they reached an asymptote, which was followed over several months by gradual improvement.

In an unpublished study Kaplan and Aronson trained *Tilapia* to discriminate between vertically striped and horizontally striped paddles placed side-by-side, in order to obtain food. After the initial training, correct responses varied between 80 per cent and 100 per cent. Ablating the forebrain resulted in a drastic decrease in the number of strikes and a tremendous increase in latency, with subjects often taking up to 20 minutes to make a response. The discrimination was not obliterated, but the subjects were extremely variable from day to day, the percentage of correct responses now varying from 50 per cent to 100 per cent. The performance of some subjects deteriorated with continued testing while that of others showed considerable improvement, but the latter never were as stable as they had been preoperatively.

Aronson and Kaplan (1963, 1965) and Kaplan and Aronson (1967), using an avoidance conditioning paradigm, trained *Tilapia* to swim through a hole in a partition to avoid electric shock. Light was used as the conditioned stimulus. With training, the intact fish learned to respond with considerable regularity and achieved at least 80 per cent avoidances in almost all sessions. After ablation of the forebrain, the number of avoidances was markedly reduced, and the latencies of response became erratic (Fig. 2). Qualitative observations showed that the operated fish no longer maintained efficient intertrial habits, such as waiting near the hole for the onset of the light. Responses to the CS were not as immediate or as well oriented as before, and swimming speed of some subjects seemed considerably slower. As in the previous experiments, three of the seven subjects showed a progressive decline in performance after operation (Fig. 2, top). When the forebrain was ablated at the beginning of the experiment, the training period was long and the performance inconsistent, but eventually the fish learned to avoid the shock with some regularity (Fig. 2, bottom).

Similar experiments were performed by Kaplan and Aronson, using a 500-Hz sound as the conditioned stimulus. Postoperative observations were continued in some animals for nine months. The results were very similar to the light experiments with additional information available on the recovery phase. In most cases recovery was pronounced but this phase was interspersed with sudden periods of very poor performance followed by rapid improvement. Again, the behavior of the fish was erratic and unpredictable as compared with the consistent behavior of the control animals. The results of our experiments have been interpreted in terms of nonspecific arousal, which will be considered in the next section.

Similar avoidance conditioning experiments were performed by Hainsworth, Overmier, and Snowdon (1967) on goldfish. They, too, found major deficits in avoidance learning and retention which they attribute to deficiencies in the arousal mechanism. (See also the chapter by Savage in this volume.)

In view of the striking changes reported in the above studies, it is difficult to understand why some experimenters report no changes in learned responses after forebrain extirpation. Some possible explanations for the failure of several authors to find differences are suggested:

a) Variations in apparatus and techniques. It is possible that certain procedures reduce or mask actual deficiencies. We cannot be sure, for example, whether Bernstein (1962) would have obtained the same results in hue and brightness discriminations if he had used operant rather than autonomic conditioning. Several of the negative studies were based on classical conditioning, while all of the positive studies used instrumental conditioning or more complex learning problems. It is possible that the forebrain is not necessary for classical conditioning, but that it is important for more complex learning processes where extensive sensory and motor integration is involved.

b) Incomplete extirpation of forebrain. Few of the negative studies included histological examination of the brains or even descriptions of the lesions based on gross examination. In addition to the difficulties of surgery, the possibilities of regeneration must be considered (Segaar 1965).

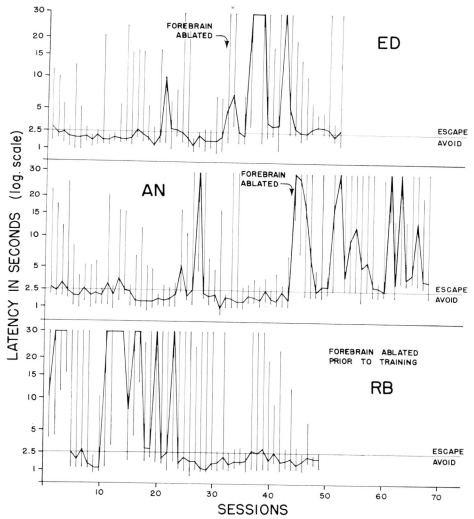

Fig. 2. Comparison in an avoidance conditioning situation of median latencies of three African mouthbreeders before and after complete ablation of the forebrain. Vertical lines represent the range of response for each session of 15 trials. A latency of 30 sec indicates that the subject neither avoided nor escaped. In the bottom graph the forebrain was ablated prior to training. Note in *ED* that the latencies did not rise precipitously until the fifth postoperative session. From Kaplan and Aronson (1967).

c) *Length of tests.* Since the deficits may not be pronounced in the first few tests after operation, and the behavior tends to be erratic, a considerable period of postoperative testing may be needed to reveal the full effects of forebrain ablation.

d) *Differences in experimental design and interpretation.* Many of the experiments were not designed to uncover the kind of deficiencies that we have found, and in some cases examination of the data reveals changes in behavior which the authors do not evaluate. For example, Figure 14 in Nolte (1932) shows a marked decline and variation in pattern discrimination after forebrain removal which the author notes in passing but does not use in his interpretation.

e) *Species differences.* All of the negative studies were based in part or entirely on ostariophysine species, while the positive studies, with one notable exception, used species with more complex forebrains.

Regulation of Lower Brain Mechanisms by the Forebrain: A Hypothesis

From many of the above studies it is evident that invasions of the forebrain often result in the decline or change but not the elimination of certain behavioral patterns. Even in those studies where this fact is not explicitly stated, it can sometimes be deduced from the authors' graphs and tables. In the reproductive studies of the stickleback, for example, lesions in the forebrain changed the motivational levels of aggressive, sexual, and parental behavior and the time during the reproductive cycle in which they appeared (Segaar 1961; Segaar and Nieuwenhuys 1963) but there is no indication that any behavior patterns associated with these components were eliminated by the operation.

Particularly, in our various conditioning experiments, in the first test after complete removal of the forebrain (as verified by histological examination) the fish still made some conditioned approach responses, avoidances, escapes, and correct discriminations. Clearly, the connections between CS and US and the organization of the response must be made in other parts of the brain. In the case of visual stimuli, the organization probably occurs in the tectum, since tectal invasion eliminates conditioned responses (Sears 1934; Botsch 1960). In the case of auditory stimuli, the locus of organization may be the torus semicircularis of the midbrain or the auditory centers of the medulla oblongata, but experimental evidence is lacking. In the case of olfactory stimuli, the organization may be in the olfactory bulbs. Since the forebrain does not organize behavior, but nevertheless exerts a strong influence over almost every complex pattern that has been studied, two conclusions are reached, namely, the function of the forebrain is (1) nonspecific and (2) facilitative. Since deprivation of forebrain tissue most often results in the depression but not the elimination of particular activities, facilitation is readily related to the popular mammalian concept of an arousal mechanism. As pointed out by Herrick (1948) and by Aronson (1957), facilitation may be achieved through inhibitory or excitatory processes. An actual increase in the amplitude and duration of photically evoked responses from the tectum following forebrain removal was reported by Zagorul'ko (1965).

Anatomically, the major portion of the forebrain of fishes seems to represent most closely the precursors of those rhinencephalic structures in mammals—hippocampus, pyriform cortex, amygdala, and septum—which form the core of the limbic system. As is well known, this system is also thought of, in more general terms, as a nonspecific modulator of behavior patterns organized in other parts of the brain (Gloor 1960) and as a regulator of the awareness of experience (Douglas and Pribram 1966). As it is phrased by Gloor, these rhinencephalic structures provide the "motivational mechanisms which normally allow selection of behavior appropriate to a given situation."

The deterioration in behavior after forebrain ablations which we observed in our conditioning experiments can be explained by hypothesizing reverberating circuits in the lower centers which run down when no longer primed by the forebrain. In this connection one should recall that the major fiber tracts of the forebrain form a descending system running caudally to the diencephalon and midbrain, which suggests a dynamic influence of the forebrain on lower centers. Only a few relatively small tracts run in the opposite direction.

The deterioration in behavior can also be thought of as resulting from the depletion of a biogenic substance which is normally secreted by the forebrain and which impinges on lower centers. Schildkraut and Kety (1967), for example, recently suggested that norepinephrine may produce a nonspecific state of arousal. In addition, Kusunoki and Masai (1966) and Masai, Kusunoki, and Ishibashi (1966) found substantial quantities of monoamine oxidase (a catecholamine inactivator) in the olfactory bulbs, and in certain pallial and subpallial areas of the goldfish forebrain. The monoamine oxidase in the forebrain may indicate the presence of norepinephrine or other catecholamines, and in ablating the forebrain we may be removing part of a feedback system involved in a neurohumoral arousal process.

In our conditioning experiments we also noted gradual improvement which became apparent in most subjects several months after operation. This can be explained as a compensatory process in which other areas of the brain gradually take over the missing functional contribution of the forebrain. The behavior at any given time after forebrain removal must be considered a result of these two opposing processes, deterioration and compensation.

Janzen (1933) was the first to recognize this nonspecific facilitory function of the forebrain. He noted that: (1) in forebrainless goldfish opercular and eye movements were much more steady than in intact fish; (2) in an optokinetic apparatus forebrain-deprived fish would follow the stripes more consistently; (3) in a tank divided by closely spaced bars, intact fish would readily swim between the bars to the other side, but forebrainless fish would not; (4) when given a choice of swimming from a main tank to a light or dark chamber, intact fish showed definite preferences while forebrainless fish did not; (5) using instrumental conditioning, forebrainless fish took longer to learn a color discrimination than intact individuals; (6) the normal tendency to be hesitant in strange situations was lost after decerebration. All of these symptoms suggest an interference with the forebrain arousal system. Janzen recognized two processes which he called "spontaneity" and "initiative" and interpreted the major changes after ablation of the forebrain as loss of initiative.

Hale (1956a) studied group behavior in the sunfish (*Lepomis*) by measuring the time for isolated and grouped individuals, intact and forebrainless, to pass through a door into a small compartment, using food as a reward. In this situation the operated fish were inferior to the intact controls. Hale discusses these findings in terms of social facilitation. As noted in previous pages, other investigators have also found the arousal concept useful in explaining decrements in behavior caused by destruction of the forebrain.

The Nature of Arousal in Fishes

The concept of arousal is very general, and has been used to explain a multitude of situations where specific either-or, cause and effect relationships do not seem to apply. Herrick (1948) viewed arousal as a diffuse, nonspecific function, but to maintain its usefulness, we must now begin to think of the concept in more definitive terms.

Electrophysiologically, an aroused brain is characterized by fast activity, low voltage, and desynchronization in fish (Enger 1957; Schadé and Weiler 1959) as well as in mammals (Moruzzi and Magoun 1949). This EEG activation has been correlated with reduced reaction time (Lansing, Schwartz, and Lindsley 1959) and thus from the point of view of behavior, arousal may be defined operationally as reduced reaction time.

In our conditioning experiments, low latency of response (reduced reaction time) has been used as one of the signs of arousal, but we have also attempted to define the characteristics of the aroused animal which resulted in the low latencies. In the avoidance-conditioning experiments, for example, the controls generally responded immediately to the conditioned stimulus by swimming directly through the hole to the opposite compartment. The responses of the forebrain-ablated subjects were often delayed and slow. Frequently, the operated fish did not respond immediately to the onset of the CS, but began to move only after 2 or 3 sec. In addition, some of the experimental subjects swam so slowly that even if a correct response was initiated, it was impossible at that speed to avoid the shock. The same fish, however, were observed to swim at normal speeds in other situations, even in the same test tank.

There were additional factors responsible for the higher latencies of the experimental animals. Whereas the response of the controls was directly to and through the hole, the behavior of the forebrainless subjects was often circuitous and poorly oriented. Many times the first response to the CS was to turn, even when they had been facing in the correct position before the light or sound was turned on. The operates also wasted valuable moments nosing the walls of the tank or the partition before going through the hole.

The low latencies of the controls were facilitated by their intertrial behavior, their so-called preparatory responses. Often these animals waited beside or right in front of the hole, which was, of course, the most efficient place to wait. In addition, they would duck their heads in and out of the hole and they often crossed over to the opposite compartment, turned and waited at the hole again. After operation, when the forebrainless fish were responding poorly, they showed very little of this behavior, but as their responses began to improve, they, too, acquired some of these more efficient ways of responding.

In short, the intact animal can adjust rapidly and efficiently to exigencies of new situations; the forebrainless fish cannot. It is, we think, only when the compensatory brain mechanisms begin to function that some of the former efficiency begins to return, but even after nine months, in our own experiments, very few of the brain-operated fish reached the stability of their intact counterparts.

In the analysis of these qualitative changes in behavior following removal of the forebrain, we begin to see some similarities with the kinds of changes produced by destruction of the amygdala and hippocampus in mammals. Douglas and Pribram (1966) and Douglas (1967) suggest a model whereby the hippocampus is essentially an inhibitory gating mechanism which reduces or eliminates irrelevant stimuli as well as specific stimuli associated with nonreinforcement. By contrast, the amygdala is a register which increases attention to stimuli as a function of reinforcement, by facilitation of appropriate sensory input. It is very possible that primitive counterparts of these two processes can be found in the forebrain of fishes and that these may be related to the observed morphological differentiations of the forebrain.

According to our arousal hypothesis, very simple learning processes should be affected minimally by forebrain deprivation, while the more complex the problem, the greater the deficit. The limited evidence available supports this position. Thus far, no one has found any deficits in simple classical conditioning experiments.

Ingle (1965*a*, *b*), who maintains that the forebrain does not contribute directly to learning processes, uses a very simple avoidance-conditioning design. The fish is placed in a compartment only slightly larger than its body. When the CS is given, these subjects have little choice of response; they can either remain still, back up, or swim forward a few inches through the swinging door which they face. In fact, Ingle describes his task as "go" or "no go." The results of Ingle (1965*a*, *b*), using a simple Y-maze, also seem compatible with our hypothesis. Forebrainless fish were not inferior in either "go left" or "alternate left-right" tasks when trained without previous experience, but lesioned subjects were definitely deficient in learning an alternation problem following training on the unidirectional habit (a more difficult problem for controls as well).

The "detour" problems and reversal learning tasks in the T-maze used by Warren (1961) are more complex, and here lesions in the forebrain produced obvious deficits in learning in many of the tests. Our own avoidance situation (Kaplan and Aronson 1967) is even more complex. A fish about 2 in long was placed in a relatively large compartment, 7 in square, with water about 6 in deep, and was required to find and swim through a 1.5 in escape hole within 2.5 sec after the onset of the conditioned stimulus. To perform efficiently the fish has to "anticipate" the CS by taking an appropriate position in the compartment. It must then react immediately to the onset of the CS, ignore irrelevant stimuli, orient correctly in three dimensions to the hole, and swim at an appropriate speed. After escaping from the dangerous side the fish has to reverse orientation in the next trial. We have previously proposed (Aronson 1963) that the forebrain facilitates the initiation, ordering, and timing of neural processes in lower centers that organize these complex patterns. At the same time the forebrain helps to filter out irrelevant information and to suppress maladaptive behavior.

It seems most probable that the forebrain arose in prehistoric ancestral vertebrates in relation to the olfactory nerve, and that its earliest function was the mediation and integration of olfactory information. The nonolfactory arousal functions described in this report are apparently a much later development. Olfaction is primarily a diffuse arousal process whereby attractive or repulsive odors are perceived by the olfactory system, which in turn activates other sensory and motor systems to take appropriate action. It is not too difficult to see how, out of nonspecific olfactory arousal, the general, nonolfactory arousal mechanisms evolved. However, olfaction in fishes may also be discrete, as in olfactory discriminations. According to the work of Hasler (1957, 1966) and others, an extreme degree of acuity has been demonstrated in the chemical discriminations of fishes, including those concerned with localization in space. From this it would seem that the olfactory mechanism incorporates two physiological processes, namely, a diffuse arousal and a discrete system for orientation to low-order chemical gradients.

Recently, however, Kleerekoper (1967) has found that olfactory orientation can be explained best in terms of arousal. According to this investigator, when a biologically significant odor is introduced unidirectionally, but in such a manner that it is not associated with increased rate of flow of water, the fish cannot localize the source of the odor. Therefore, odor alone does not provide a cue to orientation. When, however, the odor is combined with a slightly higher rate of flow, localization is readily achieved. The perception of a specific odor, therefore, may activate, through the arousal mechanism, a positive response to flow (positive rheotaxis). The odor itself is not an orienting cue in the weak gradients normally prevailing in nature. If Kleerekoper's ideas are sustained, it is unnecessary to postulate dual olfactory processes. Olfactory arousal may be sufficient to explain all behavior arising from olfactory stimulation, and the evolution of this unitary process to nonolfactory arousal then provides the basis for forebrain function in teleosts, and the substrate for the evolution of the mammalian cerebrum.

Relationship of the Forebrain to the Visual System

Evidence derived from the experiments described in previous pages indicates clearly that the forebrain influences processes related to olfaction, taste, vision, audition, and touch. Data relative to the lateral line system are conspicuously absent, but this is probably because of the difficulties of working with this system.

A few years ago we felt certain that aside from the obvious connections with the olfactory and gustatory systems, the forebrain might have a special relationship with the visual system. Although more recent experiments weaken some of the original arguments, this hypothesis may still be valid and a brief review of the evidence seems worthwhile.

1. A majority of the experiments described in previous sections of this article involved partly or exclusively visual stimuli.

2. Tonic changes in the electrical activity of the forebrain following photic stimulation have been reported by Enger (1957) in codfish and by Schadé and Weiler (1959), Voronin and Gusel'nikov (1959) and Maliukina and Flerova (1960) in goldfish and other ostariophysine species. Gusel'nikov, Onufrieva, and Supin (1964), however, provide evidence that the brief, flash-evoked forebrain potentials reported by certain investigators are artifacts, derived from tectal potentials.

In a later study, Timkina (1965) reported that EEG responses from the surface of the tectum to single flashes were modified when the forebrain was strychninized or the ipsilateral olfactory tract was stimulated electrically. Similarly, responses in the forebrain to electrical stimulation of the ipsilateral olfactory tract were reduced in amplitude by application of strychnine to the tectum. This forebrain response could be altered in a similar way by exposing the fishes' eyes to light. In a related study, Zagorul'ko (1965) found that strychnine spikes evoked from the forebrain of carp were suppressed by rhythmical photic stimulation. Also, removal of the forebrain in fish resulted in increased amplitude and duration of photically evoked responses from the tectum, and both chemical (strychnine) and electrical (square wave) stimulation of the forebrain inhibited evoked responses to photic stimulation. Thus, despite the negative findings of Gusel'nikov and his co-workers, there is still substantial evidence of physiological connections between the forebrain and the major midbrain optic centers.

3. Kholodov (1959—cited in Kholodov 1962) showed that the elaboration of defense conditioned reflexes to a bell and to a magnetic field were not affected by forebrain removal, but when light was used as the conditioned stimulus, the operation affected the stability of the conditioned reflex.

4. The reef-inhabiting squirrel fish, *Holocentrus*, has very large eyes and is obviously a visually dominated species. Meader (1934) showed that the midbrain and diencephalic visual apparatus are large and intricate. This is particularly true of the geniculate complex. Also, in *Holocentrus*, the forebrain is very large with particular proliferation of the pars dorsolateralis of the pallium (Aronson 1963). In an unpublished study Aronson has observed a correlation between large eyes, visually dominated behavior, elaborate visual apparatus of midbrain and diencephalon, and elaboration of the pars dorsolateralis of the dorsal (pallial) area of the forebrain.

It is suggested, in summary, that the forebrain, mainly through its descending fiber systems, impinges on all other sensory systems. In some groups of fishes where vision dominates, the forebrain develops elaborate structures and interconnections with the geniculate complex and tectum. These connections are probably indirect, via the hypothalamus. It is possible that in fishes where other sensory mechanisms dominate, the forebrain develops special structures and interconnections with these systems, but this is speculative since so far no such arrangement has been described.

Summary

The forebrains of all teleosts have a number of basic features in common, but there is considerable variation in size, in complexity, and in the development of specialized areas in different species. Therefore, extrapolations of functions from one group of fishes to another should be made with circumspection. Despite the superficial morphological uniqueness of the teleostean forebrain, it has many basic features in common with other vertebrates. Studies of teleostean forebrain mechanisms should therefore contribute to our understanding of the evolution of forebrain function in vertebrates. We have suggested that the unique eversion of the teleost brain is an adaptation to fit the brain into the smallest possible space in fry and juveniles and is not related to unusual functions.

Concerning olfactory function in fishes, a number of recent advances, particularly by those using the techniques of the electrophysiologist, were reviewed. We also discussed the possibility that speed of conduction may be the adaptive advantage in those fishes where the olfactory bulbs are adjacent to the nasal sacs and are connected to the cerebral hemispheres by long olfactory tracts.

Evidence shows that the forebrain has major functions other than olfaction. These are discussed under two main categories: integration of species-typical behavior patterns and mediation of conditioning and other learning processes. We note that in the majority of experiments, removal of the forebrain does not eliminate behavior patterns or learned responses. Rather, it reduces the frequency of occurrence or the efficiency of the responses. On the basis of this evidence we interpret a major function of the forebrain as a nonspecific arousal mechanism which impinges on lower centers and keeps them operating at high levels of efficiency. Qualitative changes in behavior after forebrain removal are related to changes in arousal, and the similarity of these changes to those following lesions of the limbic system in mammals is noted. On the basis of the arousal hypothesis, we predict that the more complex the learning paradigm, the greater will be the effect of forebrain ablation.

The evidence that the forebrain has a special relation to the visual system was evaluated, and it was suggested that in some groups of fishes where vision is the dominant sensory modality, the forebrain may develop elaborate structures and interconnections particularly related to the visual process.

Acknowledgment

The authors wish to thank Dr. Ethel Tobach for reading the manuscript and for many helpful discussions. Several students of the American Museum's Undergraduate Research Training Program, supported by Special Projects in Science Education, National Science Foundation Grant GY-350, participated in the recent experiments of the authors which are referred to in this article. This paper was prepared while the second author held United States Public Health Service Predoctoral Research Fellowship 5-F1-MH-14, 999.

References

Ariëns Kappers, C. U.; Huber, G. C.; and Crosby, E. 1936. *The comparative anatomy of the nervous system of vertebrates, including man.* 3 vols. Reprinted 1960 by Hafner, New York.

Aronson, L. R. 1948. Problems in the behavior and physiology of a species of African mouth-breeding fish. *Trans. New York Acad. Sci., Ser. 2* 2:33–42.

———. 1957. Reproductive and parental behavior. In *The physiology of fishes*, ed. M. E. Brown, 2:271–304. New York: Academic Press.

———. 1963. The central nervous system of sharks and bony fishes with special reference to sensory and integrative mechanisms. In *Sharks and survival*, ed. P. W. Gilbert, pp. 165–241. Boston: D. C. Heath & Co.

———. 1967. Forebrain function in teleost fishes. *Trans. New York Acad. Sci., Ser. 2* 4: 390–96.

Aronson, L. R., and Herberman, R. 1960. Persistence of a conditioned response in the cichlid fish, *Tilapia macrocephala* after forebrain and cerebellar ablations. *Anat. Rec.* 138:332.

Aronson, L. R., and Kaplan, H. 1963. Forebrain function in avoidance conditioning. *Amer. Zool.* 3:483–84.

———. 1965. Effect of forebrain ablation on the acquisition of a conditioned avoidance response in the teleost fish, *Tilapia h. macrocephala. Amer. Zool.* 5:654.

Bernstein, J. J. 1961. Brightness discrimination following forebrain ablation in fish. *Exp. Neurol.* 3:297–306.

———. 1962. Role of the telencephalon in color vision of fish. *Exp. Neurol.*, 6:173–85.

Berwein, M. 1941. Beobachtungen und Versuche über das gesellige Leben von Elritzen. *Z. Vergl. Physiol.* 28:402–20.

Botsch, D. 1960. Dressur- und Transpositionversuche bei Karauschen (*Carassius, teleostei*) nach partieller Exstirpation des tectum opticum. *Z. Vergl. Physiol.* 43:173–230.

Døving, K. B. 1966. Comparative electrophysiological studies on the olfactory tract of some teleosts. *J. Comp. Neurol.* 131:365–69.

Døving, K. B., and Gemne, G. 1966. An electrophysiological study of the efferent olfactory system in the burbot. *J. Neurophysiol.* 29:665–74.

Douglas, R. J. 1967. The hippocampus and behavior. *Psychol. Bull.* 67:416–42.

Douglas, R. J., and Pribram, K. H. 1966. Learning and limbic lesions. *Neuropsychologia* 4:197–220.

Droogleever Fortuyn, J. 1961. Topographical relations in the telencephalon of the sunfish, *Eupomotis gibbosus. J. Comp. Neurol.* 116:249–64.

Enger, P. S. 1957. The electroencephalogram of the codfish (*Gadus callarias*). *Acta Physiol. Scand.* 39:55–71.

Gloor, P. 1960. Amygdala. In *Handbook of physiology*, ed. J. Field, H. Magoun, and V. Hall, Section 1, Neurophysiology 2:1395–1420, Washington, D.C.: Amer. Physiol. Soc.

Grimm, R. J. 1960. Feeding behavior and electrical stimulation of the brain of *Carassius auratus. Science* 131:162.

Gusel'nikov, V. I.; Onufrieva, M. I.; and Supin, A. Ya. 1964. Projection of visual, olfactory and lateral line receptors in the fish brain. *Fiziologecheskii Zhurnal SSSR imeni L. M. Sechenova*, 50:1104. Translated in *Fed. Proc., Trans. Suppl.* 24 (5–2): T768, 1965.

Hainsworth, F. R.; Overmier, J. B.; and Snowdon, C. T. 1967. Specific and permanent deficits in instrumental avoidance responding following forebrain ablation in the goldfish. *J. Comp. Physiol. Psych.* 63:111–16.

Hale, E. B. 1956*a*. Social facilitation and forebrain function in maze performance of green sunfish, *Lepomis cyanellus. Physiol. Zool.* 29:93–107.

———. 1956*b*. Effects of forebrain lesions on the aggressive behavior of green sunfish, *Lepomis cyanellus. Physiol. Zool.* 29:107–27.

Hara, T., and Gorbman, A. 1967. Electrophysiological studies of the olfactory system of the goldfish, *Carassius auratus* L. I. Modification of the electrical activity of the olfactory bulbs by other central nervous structures. *Comp. Biochem. Physiol.* 21:185–200.

Hara, T.; Ueda, K.; and Gorbman, A. 1965. Electroencephalographic studies of homing salmon. *Science* 149:884–85.

Hasler, A. D. 1957. Olfactory and gustatory senses of fishes. In *The physiology of fishes*, ed. M. E. Brown, 2:187–209. New York: Academic Press.

———. 1966. *Underwater guideposts*. Madison, Wis.: Univ. of Wisconsin Press.

Healey, E. G. 1957. The nervous system. In *The physiology of fishes*, ed. M. E. Brown, 2:1–119. New York: Academic Press.

Herrick, C. J. 1922. Functional factors in the morphology of the forebrain of fishes. In *Libro en honor de D. S. Ramón y Cajal*, vol. 1, pp. 143–204. Madrid: Jiménez y Molina.

———. 1948. *The brain of the tiger salamander*. Chicago: University of Chicago Press.

Holmgren, N. 1920. Zur Anatomie und Histologie des Vorder- und Zwischenhirns der Knockenfische. *Acta Zool.* 1:137–315.

———. 1922. Points of view concerning forebrain morphology in lower vertebrates. *J. Comp. Neurol.* 34:391–459.

Hosch, L. 1936. Untersuchungen über Grosshirnfunktionen der Elritze (*Phoxinus laevis*) und des Gruendlings (*Gobio fluviatilis*). *Zool. Jahrb. Abt. Allgem. Zool. Physiol. Tiere* 57:57–98.

Ingle, D. J. 1965*a*. The use of fish in neuropsychology. *Perspect. Biol. Med.* 8:241–60.

———. 1965*b*. Behavioral effects of forebrain lesions in goldfish. *Proc. Amer. Psychol. Assoc.* 1:143–44.

Janzen, W. 1933. Untersuchungen über Grosshirnfunktionen des Goldfisches. *Zool. Jahrb. Abt. Allgem. Zool. Physiol. Tiere* 52:591–628.

Källén, B. 1951. Some remarks on the ontogeny of the telencephalon in some lower vertebrates. *Acta Anat.* 11:537–48.

Kamrin, R. P., and Aronson, L. R. 1954. The effects of forebrain lesions on mating behavior in the male platyfish, *Xiphophorus maculatus. Zoologica* 39:133–40.

Kandel, E. R. 1964. Electrical properties of hypothalamic neuroendocrine cells. *J. Gen. Physiol.* 47:691–717.

Kaplan, H., and Aronson, L. R. 1967. Effect of forebrain ablation on the performance of a conditioned avoidance response in the teleost fish, *Tilapia h. macrocephala. Anim. Behav.* 15:436–46.

Karamian, A. I. 1956. *Evolution of the function of the cerebellum and cerebral hemispheres.* Leningrad: Medgiz. Translated by National Science Foundation, Washington, D.C.

Kholodov, Yu. A. 1962. Simple and complex food-obtaining conditioned reflexes in normal fish and in fish after removal of the forebrain. *Proc. Inst. Higher Nerv. Activ. Physiol.* 5:194–201.

Kleerekoper, H. 1967. Some aspects of olfaction in fishes, with special reference to orientation. *Amer. Zool.* 7:385–95.

Koshtoiants, Kh. S.; Maliukina, G. A.; and Aleksandriuk, S. P. 1960. Role of the forebrain in the manifestation of the "group effect" in fishes. *Fiziol. Zh. SSSR Sechenov (Eng.)* 46:1209–16.

Kumakura, S. 1928. Versuche an Goldfischen, denen beide Hemisphären des Grosshirns exstirpiert worden waren. *Nagoya J. Med. Sci.* 3:19–24.

Kusunoki, T., and Masai, H. 1966. Chemoarchitectonics in the central nervous system of goldfish. *Arch. Histol.* 27:363–71.

Lansing, R. W.; Schwartz, E.; and Lindsley, D. B. 1959. Reaction time and EEG activation under alerted and nonalerted conditions. *J. Exp. Psychol.* 58:1–7.

Maliukina, G. A., and Flerova, G. N. 1960. New data on the functions of the forebrain in teleosts. *Zh. Obshch. Biol.* 21:381–82.

Masai, H.; Kusunoki, T.; and Ishibashi, H. 1966. The chemoarchitectonics in the forebrain of bony fishes. *Yokohama Med. Bull.* 17:197–99.

Meader, R. G. 1934. The optic system of the teleost, *Holocentrus*. I. The primary optic pathways and the corpus geniculatum complex. *J. Comp. Neurol.* 60:361–407.

———. 1939. The forebrain of bony fishes. *Proc. Konin. Nederl. Akad. Wet.* 42:3–16.

Moruzzi, G., and Magoun, H. W. 1949. Brain stem reticular formation and activation of the EEG. *Electroencephalog. Clin. Neurophysiol.* 1:455–73.

Nieuwenhuys, R. 1959. The structure of the telencephalon of the teleost *Gasterosteus aculeatus. Proc. Konin. Ned. Akad. Wet.* C, 62:341–62.

———. 1960. Some observations on the structure of the forebrain of bony fishes. In *Structure and function of the cerebral cortex*, ed. D. B. Tower and J. P. Schadé, Amsterdam: Elsevier.

———. 1966. The interpretation of the cell masses in the teleostean forebrain. In *Evolution of the forebrain*, ed. R. Hassler and H. Stephan, pp. 32–39, Stuttgart: Georg Thieme Verlag.

———. 1967. Comparative anatomy of olfactory centers and tracts. In *Progress in brain research*, ed. Y. Zotterman, 23:1–64. New York: Elsevier Pub. Co.

Noble, G. K. 1936. Function of the corpus striatum in the social behavior of fishes. *Anat. Rec.* 64 Suppl.: 34.

———. 1937. Effect of lesions of the corpus striatum on the brooding behavior of cichlid fishes. *Anat. Rec.* 70:58.

———. 1939. Neural basis of social behavior in vertebrates. *Collecting Net* 14:121–24.

Noble, G. K., and Borne, R. 1941. The effect of forebrain lesions on the sexual and fighting behavior of *Betta splendens* and other fishes. *Anat. Rec.* 79, Suppl. 49.

Nolte, W. 1932. Experimentelle Untersuchungen zum Problem der Lokalisation des Assoziations-Vermögens im Fischgehirn. *Z. Vergl. Physiol.* 18:255–79.

Papez, J. W. 1929. *Comparative neurology.* New York: Crowell.

Prosser, C. L. 1961. Nervous system. In *Comparative animal physiology*, ed. C. L. Prosser and F. A. Brown, pp. 587–661. Philadelphia: W. B. Saunders.

Schadé, J. P., and Weiler I. J. 1959. Electroencephalographic patterns of the goldfish (*Carassius auratus* L.). *J. Exp. Biol.* 36:435–52.

Scharrer, E. 1928. Die Lichtempfindlichkeit blinder Elritzen. *Z. Vergl. Physiol.* 7:1–38.

Schildkraut, J. J., and Kety, S. 1967. Biogenic amines and emotion. *Science* 156:21–30.

Schnitzlein, H. N. 1964. Correlation of habit and structure in the fish brain. *Amer. Zool.* 4:21–32.

Schönherr, J. 1955. Über die Abhängigkeit der Instinkthandlungen vom Vorderhirn und Zwischenhirn (*epiphyse*) bei *Gasterosteus aculeatus* L. *Zool. Jahrb. Abt. Allgem. Zool. Physiol. Tiere* 65:357–86.

Sears, R. R. 1934. Effect of optic lobe ablation on the visuomotor behavior of goldfish. *J. Comp. Psychol.* 17:233–65.

Segaar, J. 1961. Telencephalon and behavior in *Gasterosteus aculeatus*. *Behaviour* 28:256–87.

———. 1965. Behavioral aspects of degeneration and regeneration in fish brain: a comparison with higher vertebrates. In *Progress in brain research*, ed. M. Singer and J. P. Schadé, 14:143–231. New York: Elsevier Pub. Co.

Segaar, J., and Nieuwenhuys, R. 1963. New ethophysiological experiments with male *Gasterosteus aculeatus*. *Anim. Behav.* 11:331–44.

Shlaifer, A. 1939. An analysis of the effect of numbers upon the oxygen consumption of *Carassius auratus*. *Physiol. Zool.* 12:381–92.

Story, R. H. 1964. The olfactory bulbar formation and related nuclei of the paddlefish (*Polyodon spathula*). *J. Comp. Neur.* 123:285–97.

Ten Cate, J. 1935. Physiologie des Zentralnervensystem der Fische. *Ergebn. Biol.* 11:335–409.

Timkina, M. I. 1965. Relationship between different sensory systems in bony fish. *Zh. Vyssh. Nerv. Delat. Pavlov.* 15:927. Trans. in *Fed. Proc., Trans. Suppl.* 25 (5–2): T750–52.

Ueda, K.; Hara, T.; and Gorbman, A. 1967. Electroencephalographic studies on olfactory discrimination in adult spawning salmon. *Comp. Biochem. Physiol.* 21:133–43.

Voronin, L. G., and Gusel'nikov, V. I. 1959. Some comparative physiological data on the biological reactions of the brain. *Zh. Vyssh. Nerv. Delat. Pavlov.* 9:398–408. Office of Technical Services, U.S. Dept. of Commerce, Washington, D.C.

Warren, J. M. 1961. The effect of telencephalic injuries on learning by paradise fish, *Macropodus opercularis*. *J. Comp. Physiol. Psychol.* 54:130–32.

Wiebalck, U. 1937. Untersuchungen zur Funktion des Vorderhirns bei Knochenfischen. *Zool. Anz.* 117:325–29.

Wrede, W. L. 1932. Versuche über den Artduft der Elritzen. *Z. Vergl. Physiol.* 17:510–19.

Zagorul'ko, T. M. 1965. Interaction between the forebrain and visual centers of the midbrain in teleosts and amphibians. *Zh. Evolyuts Biokhim. Fiziol.* 1:449–58.

4

Function of the Forebrain in the Memory System of the Fish

G. E. Savage

Department of Anatomy
University College, London

Although the study of memory is one of the major problems of biology today, diverse kinds of research in this field have not yet brought hopeful signs of resolution. Compared with the more successful studies in molecular biology or in neurophysiology, there have been no adequate methods developed for attacking the neural basis of memory. Of course, the complexity of the brain is several orders beyond that of the gene or the neuron. For this reason it may be useful to study the functions of simpler types of brains. Indeed, Young (1964) has remarked that our obsession with probing the mammalian brain leads us to forget the fact that studies of lower organisms have often provided definitive knowledge of mechanisms of neural integration. This line of reasoning has led me to the teleost fish, which combines a relatively simple and accessible brain with the capacity to learn rapidly and to discriminate within several sensory modalities. By choosing a vertebrate, it was possible to draw on a wealth of literature for comparative studies, and to study our own type of nervous system at its simplest. As a beginning in relating the parts of the fish brain to memory processes, I have conducted experiments on the role of the forebrain. It is generally accepted that the forebrain in higher vertebrates is closely related to the processes of learning and retention, and it was of interest to see whether such function was foreshadowed in the lower vertebrates, or whether, as is often stated, the forebrain was purely olfactory in function.

Review of the Literature

The functions of the teleost forebrain have long been elusive, and our present uncertainty constitutes a serious gap in our knowledge of the fish brain. Early workers, such as Vulpian (1866), found that removal of the forebrain had little effect upon orientation or locomotion of fish, provided that lesions did not invade the diencephalon. Later workers have agreed on this point; thus our considerations about possible deficits in learning capacities

127

will assume that motor functions are normal. Sharrer (1928) trained blinded minnows to feed in response to light (using the light-sensitive cells in the diencephalic roof) and found that this conditioned response persisted after forebrain removal. Similarly, Nolte (1933) trained sticklebacks to discriminate between colors and between simple shapes, and concluded that removal of large areas of the forebrain had little effect on visual memory. Although his data for color discriminations support this claim, it is notable that the one shape-discriminating fish with good postoperative survival behaved quite inconsistently following forebrain removal. Janzen (1933) also found retention of visual discriminations by goldfish after removal of forebrain. However, he observed that lesioned fish trained to discriminate red from blue made at least 20 per cent errors for the first 60 postoperative trials, while each normal fish made fewer errors at this time. Although the studies of Nolte and of Janzen are cited in the literature as providing evidence of lack of effect of forebrain lesions, we question the basis for this conclusion.

More recently, Karamyan (1955) concluded that forebrain lesions had little effect on either acquisition or retention of auditory or visual conditioned responses when a classical conditioning paradigm was employed. Bernstein used a classical cardiac conditioning procedure, and showed that forebrainless goldfish show excellent acquisition and retention of a brightness discrimination (Bernstein 1961b) or of a color discrimination (Bernstein 1961a, 1962). In fact, when the brightness discrimination was used, some lesioned subjects actually learned *more* rapidly than did intact control subjects. These clear-cut results indicate that simple discrimination learning does not depend upon participation of the forebrain. However, it is nevertheless possible that the forebrain plays an important role in the acquisition of active responses by the organism.

The first clear indication that the forebrain might be involved in the memory system came from the work of Zunini (1954), who noted a deficit in maze-learning abilities following forebrain lesions. Hale (1956a) also found that lesioned sunfish took significantly longer to learn a maze. It is notable that Hale's subjects never regained their prelesion capacities, when time scores are considered. Using the paradise fish, Warren (1961) found clear deficits in acquisition and discrimination reversal performance, using a simple T-maze response reinforced by food. However, Ingle (1965a, b) used aversive reinforcement in a Y-maze situation, and found forebrainless goldfish surprisingly *superior* to operated controls in learning and reversing directional habits. The lesioned fish performed as well as controls even when confronted with a more difficult "left-right alternation" problem. Only when subjects were pretrained on a "go left" task did the lesioned fish fail to learn the alternation habit as well as did the controls. Aronson and Kaplan (1963, 1965), working with *Tilapia*, used an avoidance situation and found that there was considerable postoperative deficit in learning. The times taken to escape shock increased, and the animals took a long time to relearn the problem to their preoperative level.

In spite of this work, the most dramatic indications of forebrain function and of localization of function have come from ethology. Aronson (Aronson and Kamrin, 1954), Hale 1956b), and Segaar (Segaar and Nieuwenhuys, 1963) have shown that reproductive and social behavior is impaired by forebrain lesions, and the tiny lesions of Segaar show that the system is a very delicate one, with more localization of function than was hitherto suspected. It seems unlikely that a structure so intimately concerned with the regulation of instinctive behavior should be unconcerned with learning.

Considering the evidence for and against forebrain implication in learning, it seems that there has often been a failure to examine the problem from the appropriate angle. In spite of differences on interpretation, the anatomists have always agreed that the structures represented by the forebrain are subcortical. It is rather surprising, therefore, to find that many of the workers seeking the function of this area should examine it with the properties of the cerebral cortex in mind. The functions of the forebrain might have been more easily elucidated if an attempt had been made to examine the behavioral effects of limbic lesions in higher forms, and to apply these to fish. For example, limbic lesions in mammals affect avoidance and "go–no go" learning.

Sherrington (1906) suggested that the evolution of the cerebral cortex from the basal forebrain areas came about as a result of the macrosmatic nature of early vertebrates, especially early mammals. Thus odors signifying prey would be analyzed by the forebrain, and the rest of the system alerted by that area, which might also maintain excitation in the interval between detection and eating of the prey. It might be expected, therefore, that paradigms placing emphasis on the alerting of the animal should show up the function of the forebrain.

Procedure

The apparatus used for avoidance training is illustrated in Figure 1. Subjects (*Carassius auratus* L.) learned to swim from the start box through the oval door and into the goal box on presentation of the conditioned stimulus. During intertrial intervals these compartments

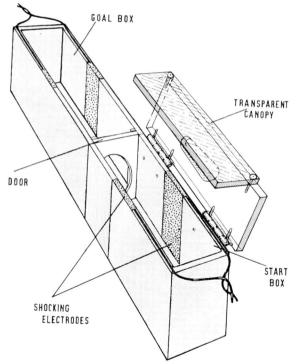

FIG. 1. The simple shuttle box used in Experiment 1. The start and goal boxes were separated by a vertically sliding door, not shown in this figure. Note the paired electrodes in each box. The transparent canopy was used to confine fish for long periods for activity measurement.

were separated by a sliding door (not shown in Fig. 1) in order to prevent spontaneous avoidance responses. Fish that failed to avoid within the time allowed (either 5 or 15 sec) were punished by an a.c. shock of 4 volts, lasting 0.25 to 0.5 sec. The shock was repeated at 5-sec intervals until the subject escaped into the goal box. Conditioned stimuli consisted of (*a*) the onset of an overhead light or (*b*) a sound of 400 Hz emitted from a buzzer fixed to the wall of the tank. Fish were given 10 trials daily. The acquisition curves for normal fish were similar to those obtained by Bitterman (Behrend and Bitterman 1962) with a sharp rise for the first 50 to 70 trials, until a stable plateau was attained.

When subjects had attained a criterion performance of at least 70 per cent avoidances for each of five days, a control operation was performed. A circle of bone was trephined from the dorsal skull, and the brain was gently swabbed. Finally, the bone was replaced and fastened with cement. This control operation produced no significant performance decrement for any group when training recommenced after a 5-day recovery period. The forebrain was removed by fine dissection instruments, under a stereomicroscope. The preoptic nucleus was left intact, as far as possible. Histological examinations of the first experimental group indicated that lesions removed 85 per cent of the forebrain, on the average. This operation was standardized and results were quite repeatable. For the following experiments, "forebrainless" may be taken to mean "at least 80 per cent removed."

Experiment 1—Bilateral Lesions

Group 1 was trained to avoid light, using a 15-sec CS–US interval, and was lesioned after meeting the 5-day performance criterion. None of these forebrainless fish continued to make effective avoidance responses when training was initiated 5 days postoperatively. Furthermore, retraining did not produce a normal acquisition curve, as had been obtained preoperatively. Therefore, it appears that both *retention* and *relearning* performances were drastically impaired by forebrain removal. The results for Group 2, lesioned before avoidance training, also showed that learning *de novo* was impaired. During the first 20 trials these fish made no avoidance responses at all, which was inferior to the performance of Group 1 during postoperative retraining. Only after 50 trials did the performance of Group 2 approach that of Group 1 postoperatively. These differences indicate that forebrainless fish did retain something from their preoperative training experience. The results obtained for Groups 1 and 2 were duplicated by Groups 3 and 4, trained with a 5-sec light CS, and by Groups 5 and 6, trained with a 5-sec sound CS. Again some savings in retraining were observed in the preoperatively trained fish. As a control procedure, two fish were subjected to bilateral transection of the olfactory tracts. Since their learning performance was normal, we can assume that olfactory loss does not account for the striking avoidance impairment that follows forebrain removal.

In contrast to Aronson's observations on *Tilapia*, none of the fish of Groups 1–4 showed increased escape times when shocked in the start box. In fact, some fish escaped more rapidly after the operation, even though they failed to initiate such a response prior to the punishment. It is clear that insensitivity to pain or inability to carry through the appropriate movements cannot be the basis for the deficit in conditioned avoidance behavior. However, the spontaneous behavior of subjects within the apparatus was by no means normal following forebrain removal. The lesioned subjects were conspicuous for their lack of activity. This was measured by a photocell fitted into the base of the start box. These spontaneous movements, monitored by an event recorder, measured only 1–2 per cent of normal activity.

This condition was evident during extinction trials, in which lesioned subjects avoided on only 20–30 per cent of trials on the first day, as compared with 60 per cent responding by normal fish.

From these initial experiments, we may conclude that forebrain removal can strikingly diminish avoidance behavior without blunting reactions to the aversive shock. The deficit is not one of pain-elicited arousal, but of conditioned arousal to the CS. Perhaps the entire training situation serves as a CS to general activity. If this were so, then the striking inactivity of lesioned subjects during intertrial intervals could also be viewed as a decrement in conditioned behavior. The deficit does not seem to be related to the stimulus modality, since it was observed when using either visual or auditory signals; nor does it consist simply in a "slowing down" of the fish, since groups with 5–15 sec intervals showed comparable avoidance deficits. Although the deficit is quite apparent, we must conclude that the forebrain is not essential for this task, since relearning did occur to some extent. That relearning was facilitated by preoperative training indicates that a store of memory persisted in some lower structure.

Experiment 2—Interocular Transfer

Earlier work by Sperry and Clark (1949), Schulte (1957), McCleary (1960), and Ingle (1965b, 1968) indicates that visual learning mediated by one eye alone can "transfer" to a test situation where the opposite eye alone is used. This implies that visual memory is shared by opposite brain halves. The purpose of the present experiments was to determine the possible role of the forebrain in such interhemispheric integration of visual memories. In this series of studies, a modification of the training apparatus was introduced (Fig. 2). A swing door

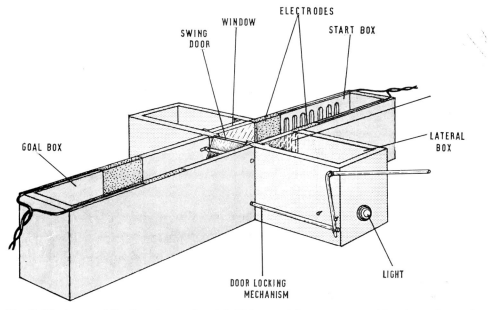

FIG. 2. The box used for Experiments 2 and 3. Fish passed from start to goal box by nosing under a swing door, which was locked in position between trials. Lateral boxes, with windows which could be occluded, allowed stimuli to be presented laterally; note the light in the end wall of the nearer box.

was used in place of the open hole between start and goal boxes. Also, lateral boxes were fitted so that a fish could view a stimulus presented to either side. In one study, the stimulus was a small light bulb at the far end of the lateral box; and in the discrimination study, horizontal and vertical rectangles were bobbed gently within the boxes.

In the first situation, subjects from Group 7 learned to swim through the swing door in response to a 5-sec CS–US interval. Normal fish (trained at the rate of 10 trials daily) learned to avoid on 60–90 per cent of trials within the first 10 days. This ability was not affected by the control operation. Interocular transfer of this task was good for the intact subjects, but lesioned subjects showed a nearly total deficit in retention via either eye. Even when retrained via one eye to a criterion of at least 40 per cent avoidance for 3 days, transfer performance dropped to 10 per cent success for the first 2 days via the opposite eye. With two further training sessions performance rose to the level attained via the first-trained side. As with

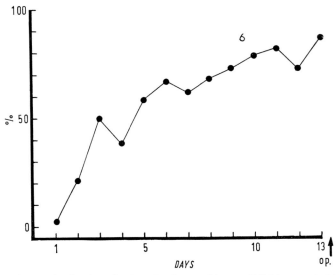

FIG. 3. Preoperative results for six animals trained to avoid a small light presented to one eye. CS–US interval 5 sec. The arrow shows the point of operation: bilateral removal of the forebrain.

previous groups, naïve forebrainless fish took significantly longer to attain the 40 per cent avoidance criterion than had subjects with preoperative training. In this instance, however, interocular transfer tests revealed about 40 per cent performance via the second, untrained eye. The superiority of transfer in subjects trained postoperatively might be attributed to the longer training period required to reach criterion via the first eye.

Not only did these results indicate that the forebrain was involved in interocular transfer, they further reduced the possibility that the deficits observed were due to a change of sensory sensitivity. The stimulus used was much less intense than the overhead light previously employed, so that the change of stimulation of the eye would be correspondingly less. If forebrain removal had raised the threshold of sensitivity, the deficit seen postoperatively should have been much greater than in previous experiments; this was not so. Therefore the suggestion would again be that the forebrain is concerned with more central mechanisms.

In the second training situation, horizontal and vertical rectangles were presented successively in a Gellerman sequence of trials. Subjects were punished for failure to avoid the vertical stimulus and also for making a false avoidance response to the horizontal rectangle. The majority of intact fish took about 100 trials to attain a 70 per cent level of discrimination. Again the control operation had little effect on this performance, and interocular transfer was good in normal subjects. A group of fish that had attained a mean performance of 81 per cent correct for a 5-day period was subjected to forebrain removal and retested for discrimination capacity after the 5-day recovery interval. The level of avoidance responses was much reduced, and no evidence of discrimination retention was obtained. Although avoidance capacity increased slowly, the discrimination level remained at chance for 200 further trials. Interocular transfer tests revealed a significant drop in the frequency of avoidance responses via the second eye.

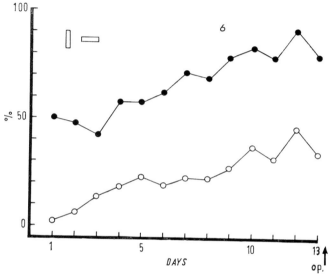

FIG. 4. Preoperative results for six animals trained to avoid ▯, not ▭. CS–US interval 5 sec. ●, percentage discrimination; ○, percentage avoidance (i.e., avoidance irrespective of correctness). The arrow indicates the point of operation; bilateral removal of the forebrain.

As in Experiment 1, naïve forebrainless fish were significantly inferior to preoperatively trained subjects during early sessions. However, after 100 trials their level of avoidances equalled that of the preoperatively trained group. Like the subjects described above, no discrimination ability was revealed during 300 further training trials. But, unlike the former group, these subjects showed no drop in avoidance frequency during interocular transfer tests.

It was of interest that while the ability to avoid ○ dropped, the ability to discriminate ● showed greater falls, and did not rise postoperatively as did the former. If the forebrain were merely facilitating the ability to avoid, without otherwise affecting the memory system, those avoidances which occurred should have been mainly correct ones; an intact memory would only be ordering avoidances in response to the aversive shape. However, since increase in number of avoidances was not followed by increase in discrimination, the suggestion must be that the forebrain is more intimately associated with the input–output channels of the memory.

Because the question of forebrain involvement in the interocular transfer process was not resolved by these initial experiments, I attempted a more direct attack on the question by splitting the anterior commissure. This structure consists of three different tracts: (1) a dorsal commissure which joins the mediodorsal areas of the forebrain, (2) a larger component which connects the lateral regions, and (3) a small ventral olfactory commissure. Severence of the large vessels running over the commissure caused ischemia of the dorsal and lateral forebrain regions and was the chief hazard of the operation. Subjects reported below are those for whom histological examination confirmed a successful operation, without damage to either hemisphere.

Subjects trained preoperatively on either the discrimination or the simple light-avoidance problems showed clear deficits when transfer tests were administered postoperatively. However, relearning via the second eye was faster than the initial, preoperative acquisition. It is possible that the postoperative saving was due to some initial transfer of the visuomotor skill rather than to transfer of specific information about the two shapes. In order to test this, a group of normal subjects was trained to discriminate between rectangles oriented at 45° and 135°. The level of avoidance was only about 30 per cent after 250 trials, and the discrimination itself remained at chance level. Nevertheless, when the horizontal-vertical discrimination was taught via the opposite eye, learning was much faster than that for naïve subjects. It is clear that familiarity with the training situation in some way facilitates learning via the previously untrained eye. It seems that there was little interhemispheric transfer of information in split-brained fish, and that savings were due to their previous experience.

Experiment 3—Unilateral Forebrain Lesions

The results of the previous experiment suggest that some lateralization of memory may occur in goldfish, and several reports indicate that this may happen in certain situations. For example, Schulte (1957) and Ingle (1968) have reported that difficult shape discriminations do not transfer completely from eye to eye in intact subjects. Furthermore, Ingle (1968) has shown that monocular visual "interference" during training via the other eye can abolish subsequent transfer abilities, and that goldfish can be trained to make opposite discriminations via the two eyes. Mark (1967) has concluded that splitting the intertectal commissure in *Astronotus* lateralizes memories controlling a visual discrimination for food reward.

These findings raised the possibility that the same animal might be used as both lesion subject and control subject, following a unilateral brain lesion. Fish subjected to unilateral forebrain removal did indeed show a unilateral visual avoidance deficit similar to the bilateral deficit described above. That is, subjects usually failed to make avoidance responses when the CS appeared on the side contralateral to the lesion. This method proved useful in evaluating effects of partial forebrain lesions. For example, unilateral lesions restricted to the dorsomedial area (the primodium hippocampi of some anatomists) had no effect upon performance in either avoidance level or upon discrimination accuracy via either eye. The results for interocular transfer tests involving this lesion were ambiguous, possibly because interruption of the transverse commissural fibers may have sometimes occurred. Two additional groups of subjects received unilateral electrolytic lesions via stereotaxically held electrodes. Lesions placed in either central or lateral areas produced discrimination performance deficits via the contralateral eye. Some fish showed almost complete avoidance failure via the "bad eye," while others showed variable behavior, and had days in which they failed to inhibit their response to the "no go" shape.

Discussion

The present series of experiments documents a reliable kind of deficit in conditioned avoidance behavior by forebrainless goldfish; but it is not yet evident what kind of mechanism resides within the teleost forebrain. It is likely that this structure, as a homologue of the mammalian limbic system, plays a role in mediating the effects of negative reinforcement. This view is strengthened by the finding of Boyd and Gardner (1963) that goldfish readily learn to avoid stimulation of the forebrain via chronically implanted electrodes. Of course, the results of maze-learning experiments, using food rewards, suggest that positive reinforcement mechanisms may also reside within the forebrain.

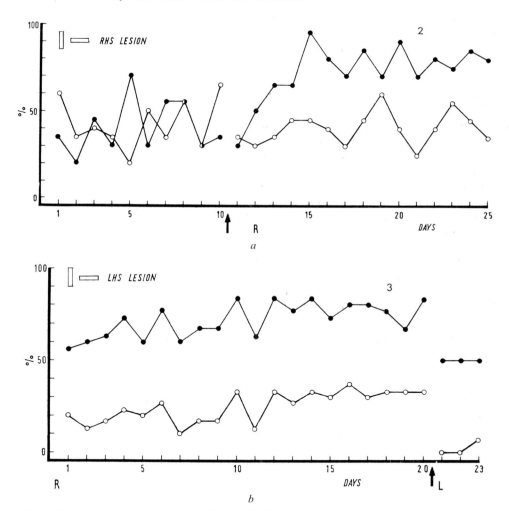

FIG. 5. Results for two animals with unilateral (RHS) forebrain lesions in lateral and central areas (*a*) and three animals with unilateral (LHS) forebrain lesions in the same areas (*b*). All were trained to avoid ▯, not ▭. CS–US interval 5 sec. Letters at base indicate eye trained, arrows show change of side being trained. Note that the side *contralateral* to the lesion gives poorer results than that ipsilateral, whether trained first or second. ●, percentage discrimination; ○, percentage avoidance (i.e., avoidance irrespective of correctness).

Regestein suggests, in another chapter, that forebrainless goldfish are in such a state of fear that they are unable to respond. However, it has been the experience of most workers with forebrainless fish that these animals are peculiarly fearless. This observation would fit with the results presented here, and be interpreted in terms of removal of an area which deals with the incoming signals of pain, and the resultant fear in subsequent such situations. Further, the results of Aronson and Kaplan (1963) and myself show a good measure of agreement for two distinct species, *Tilapia* and *Carassius*.

One of the main differences of method between Ingle (1965*a*, *b*) and Bernstein (1961*a*, *b*, 1962) and other workers is the number of trials given per day, and experiments just terminated in my laboratory suggest that this may be an important variable. Naïve lesioned fish trained at 10 trials per day showed a considerable deficit in learning, but other groups with 20 and 30 trials per day showed higher plateaus. In view of the fact that the large deficits in forebrainless fish have been found with low numbers of trials daily, and little deficit has been found when large numbers of trials have been given, there is perhaps reason to suppose some long-term deficit which is overcome by rapid training. It would be of interest to see the effect on an already trained fish of reducing the trial frequency.

Since forebrainless fish are able to learn to some extent, it is evident that the memory store is organized at lower levels in the brain. Although the optic tectum is often considered a likely candidate for such visual memory processes (see Prosser's article in this symposium), my studies (Savage 1968) indicate that simple avoidances to light or sound onset are well retained following near-total tectal ablation, and that unless transient motor deficiencies develop, learning is also unimpaired. It may be that the locus of reinforcement effects lies within the diencephalon or the midbrain tegmentum. Certainly, Regestein's report (in this symposium) that small unilateral hypothalamic lesions can also result in unilateral visual avoidance deficits supports this suggestion. Of course, the hypothalamus receives descending inputs from the forebrain and from certain areas of the thalamus and midbrain, and it is an area of such general importance that we must expect to find effects on learning subsequent to its removal.

Perhaps the most plausible idea that I can put forward at present is that of the forebrain's "addressing" information about the results of the US (pain or reward) to the memory and motivational systems which directly control the active avoidance response. The forebrain could act to intensify, prolong, or focus the effects of reinforcement, and in this way could greatly facilitate the progress of learning. This might explain the greater effect of lesions on successive than on simultaneous discriminations, and also explain why CR's are not inhibited by forebrain removal. In the latter case a CR can occur, since it is not a directed action, and hence does not need accurate addressing to motor systems. We should avoid the simplistic notion that "memory" is the property of any single structure and attempt to examine the functional properties of various groups of neurons in terms of their role within an integrated "memory system." I hope that the present data justify the study of the forebrain as an important "subsystem" in the memory system of the teleost fish, and hasten us to a better notion of the workings of our own brains.

Acknowledgment

I am indebted to Professor J. Z. Young, F.R.S., for much helpful advice and criticism in the preparation of this chapter.

References

Aronson, L. R., and Kamrin, R. P. 1954. The effects of forebrain lesions on mating behaviour in the male platyfish, *Xiphophorus maculatus. Zoologica* 39:133–40.

Aronson, L. R., and Kaplan, H. 1963. Forebrain function in avoidance conditioning. *Amer. Zool.* 3:21.

———. 1965. Effect of forebrain ablation on the acquisition of a conditioned avoidance in the teleost fish, *Tilapia macrocephala. Amer. Zool.* 5:127.

Behrend, E. R., and Bitterman, M. E. 1962. Avoidance-conditioning in the goldfish: Exploratory studies of the CS–US interval. *Amer. J. Psychol.* 75:18–34.

Bernstein, J. J. 1961a. Loss of hue discrimination in forebrain-ablated fish. *Exp. Neurol.* 3:1–17.

———. 1961b. Brightness discrimination following forebrain ablation in fish. *Exp. Neurol.* 3:297–306.

———. 1962. Role of the telencephalon in colour vision of fish. *Exp. Neurol.* 6:173–85.

Botsch, D. 1961. Dressur- und Transpositionversuche bei Karauschen (*Carassius, Teleostei*) nach partieller Exstirpation des Tectum Opticum. *Z. Vergl. Physiol.* 43:173–230.

Boyd, E. S., and Gardner, L. C. 1963. Positive and negative reinforcement from intracranial stimulation of a teleost. *Science* 136:648–49.

Hale, E. B. 1956a. Social facilitation and forebrain function in maze performance of green sunfish, *Lepomis cyanellus. Physiol. Zool.* 29:93–107.

———. 1956b. Effects of forebrain lesions on the aggressive behaviour of green sunfish, *Lepomis cyanellus. Physiol. Zool.* 29:107–27.

Ingle, D. J. 1965a. Behavioral effects of forebrain lesions in goldfish. *Proc. Amer. Psychol. Assoc.* 1:143–44.

———. 1965b. The use of the fish in neuropsychology. *Perspect. Biol. Med.* 8:241–60.

———. 1968. Interocular integration in goldfish. *Brain, Behavior and Evolution.* Vol. 1 in press.

Janzen, W. 1933. Untersuchungen über Grosshirnfunktionen des Goldfisches (*Carassius auratus*). *Zool. Jahrb. Abt. Allgem. Zool. Physiol. Tiere* 52:591–628.

Karamyan, A. I. 1955. *Evolution of the function of the cerebellum and cerebral hemispheres.* Trans. by U.S. Department of Commerce, Washington, 1962.

McCleary, R. A. 1960. Type of response as a factor in interocular transfer in the fish. *J. Comp. Physiol. Psychol.* 53:311–21.

Mark, R. F. 1967. The tectal commissure and interocular transfer of pattern discrimination in cichlid fish. *Exp. Neurol.* 16:215–25.

Nolte, W. 1933. Experimentelle Untersughungen zum Problem der Lokalisation des Assoziationsvermögens im Fischgehirn. *Z. Vergyl. Physiol.* 18:255–79.

Savage, G. E. 1968. The effect of lesions to the optic tectum on learning and retention in the goldfish, *Carassius auratus.* In preparation.

Scharrer, E. 1928. Die Lichtempfindlichkeit blinder Elritzen. *Z. Vergl. Physiol.* 7:1–38.

Schulte, A. 1957. Transfer- und Transpositionversuche mit Monokular Dressierten Fischen. *Z. Vergl. Physiol.* 39:432–76.

Segaar, J., and Nieuwenhuys, R. 1963. New etho-physiological experiments with male *Gasterosteus aculeatus. Anim. Behav.* 11:331–44.

Sherrington, C. S. 1906. *The integrative action of the nervous system.* New Haven, Conn.: Yale University Press.

Sperry, R. W., and Clark, E. 1949. Interocular transfer of visual discrimination habits in a teleost fish. *Physiol. Zool.* 22:372–78.

Vulpian, A. 1866. *Leçons sur la physiologie générale et comparée du système nerveux.* Paris: Germer-Ballière.

Warren, J. M. 1961. The effect of telencephalic injuries on learning by paradise fish, *Macropodus opercularis. J. Comp. Physiol. Psychol.* 54:130–32.

Young, J. Z. 1964. *A model of the brain.* Oxford: Clarendon Press.

Zunini, G. 1954. Researches on fish's learning. *Arch. Néerl. Zool.* 10, Suppl. 2:127–39.

5

Some Monocular Emotional Effects
of Unilateral Hypothalamic
Lesions in Goldfish

Quentin R. Regestein

Psychiatry Service
Boston City Hospital

Introduction

I wish to report some observations on fear-motivated behavior of goldfish following unilateral hypothalamic lesions. This research—carried out in collaboration with Dr. David Ingle—adds further information to the area of work discussed in this symposium by Aronson and Savage.

Our experiments were designed to answer two different kinds of questions. First, Ingle wanted a more definitive test of his hypothesis that each side of a fish's brain can mediate its own decisions on whether or not to make a conditioned response. This was his interpretation of the fact that goldfish can perform in opposite ways when tested via opposite eyes on the same discrimination problem (Ingle 1965a). We hoped to pin down this idea by making a unilateral lesion that would interfere with the execution of a conditioned avoidance task, but only when the stimulus appeared to the eye projecting information to the lesioned brain half.

Second, my own interest has been focused upon the dynamics of avoidance behavior itself. Making a unilateral lesion in a convenient way to investigate learning phenomena, since the health of the subject is essentially normal, and the intact brain half serves as the best possible control for nonspecific changes in the organism's status over time. Having been schooled in a psychiatric doctrine that counts the rational faculties of an organism mere slaves to its emotional needs, I decided to plunge my lesioning electrodes into the focal point of the teleost psyche—the hypothalamus. This proved to be a good plan, answering Dr. Ingle's question affirmatively and providing a variety of behavioral effects in whose richness a psychiatrist could only rejoice.

139

Experiment 1—Avoidance Conditioning

In our initial study, we conditioned nine large goldfish, 12–16 cm long, to swim from a start box through an opaque swinging door and into an identical goal box (see Fig. 1) on presentation of a standard visual stimulus. Our stimulus, a 2 cm gray square plaque covered with seven black dots, was gently bobbed up and down for 10 sec in a standard position, 10 cm lateral to one eye. Subjects were shocked for failure to swim through the door within this interval.

The relative avoidance capacities of the two brain halves were compared by alternating the stimulus from eye to eye on successive trials. Once the fish avoided consistently with one or both eyes, a score of ocular dominance was obtained by totaling the intertrial comparisons of response latencies. For example, a subject whose latencies via the right eye were briefer than those mediated by the left eye (both preceding and subsequent trials were compared)

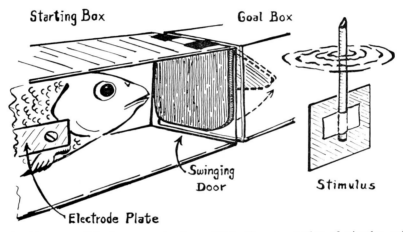

Fig. 1. Avoidance conditioning apparatus for goldfish. On presentation of stimulus, subject swims through door into goal box.

on 70 per cent of occasions, equal on 15 per cent, and longer on 15 per cent would receive a right-eye-dominance score of 70 per cent. When the latency difference was only 1 sec we recorded "no difference" for that comparison. As Figure 2 indicates, most intact fish did show a significant laterality in performance; i.e., most intertrial comparisons favored the same eye for two or more days of preoperative training. For this reason, we routinely placed our lesions in the "faster" brain half, to be certain that any monocular deficits could be attributed to our surgical disruption.

Lesions were made by passing a cathodal current of 1.5 ma for 12–15 sec through a size 00 steel insect pin, insulated except for .05 mm at the tip. These electrodes were slowly lowered into the posterior hypothalamus to a depth of about 3.5 mm from the tectal surface. Histological examination of six fish revealed focal lesions of less than 1 mm diameter, centered in the posterior hypothalamus and sometimes extending a bit into the overlying tegmentum (see Fig. 3). The optic tectum and valvula were not visibly damaged. It is quite unlikely that tectal lesions could account for the observed behavioral changes, since Ingle has found no avoidance decrements for laterally placed stimuli after lesions of tectal afferents or efferents had produced complete scotomata within the upper posterior visual field.

Of the seven subjects trained preoperatively, all showed an avoidance deficit while using the eye contralateral to the lesion. The five fish that showed a preoperative ocular dominance now reversed the relative performance of the two eyes. Furthermore, the two fish that received only postoperative training showed even stronger deficits via the "bad eye." However, of these nine subjects only three had total deficits; these were persistently unable to execute avoidance responses when the stimulus appeared on the bad side. As a partial control for nonspecific brain injury, two fish with anterior hypothalamic lesions and one with a tegmental lesion (2.0 mm deep) failed to show any postoperative deficit in avoidance conditioning.

The exact nature of this avoidance deficit is not easy to specify. We can imagine three plausible interpretations of avoidance failure: (a) subjects could not become sufficiently

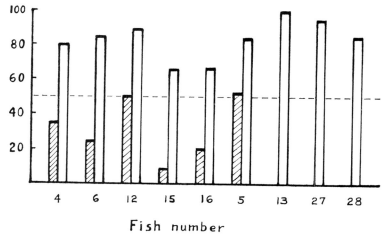

FIG. 2. Percentage of intertrial comparisons for which fish made faster avoidance responses using the intact brain half. The filled bars indicate the preoperative performance for six of these subjects.

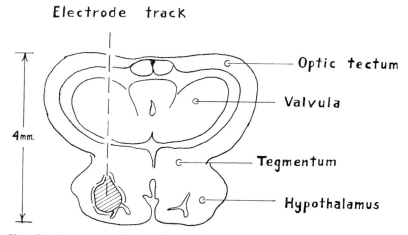

FIG. 3. Site of lesions in posterior hypothalamus. One of the largest lesions is illustrated here in cross section through the midbrain.

aroused by the conditioned stimulus, (b) although aroused they could not translate their implicit fear into an adaptive movement toward or through the door, or (c) they were actually hyperexcitable and were paralyzed with fear by the situation when excited via the lesioned side.

The first two explanations might both apply, since lesioned fish revealed two types of deficit. Some subjects were slow to make an overt response to the stimulus via the bad side and remained quiet for most of the 10-sec stimulus presentation. However, when the stimulus remained for an additional 5 or 10 sec, these fish usually did show arousal and occasionally made a successful, if delayed, avoidance response. This kind of deficit supports the notion that the arousal mechanism is either absent or markedly sluggish on the damaged side. On the other hand, some fish reacted immediately to the stimulus with a startle response and with ineffective writhing or backing movements. These fish seemed to be fully aroused, but could not manage the final propulsive effort toward the door.

A third phenomenon sometimes appeared which may give us some insight into the mechanisms at work. Some subjects showed normal avoidance performances during early trials in a given session, but relapsed to a total unilateral deficit for the subsequent 15 to 20 trials. Careful observation showed that each time the fish made a good avoidance response via the "bad eye," it had been spontaneously active, with preparatory motions toward the door, just prior to presentation of the stimulus. The stimulus never elicited an avoidance response via the damaged side when the fish had been resting quietly. This behavior strongly supports the idea that an arousal deficit can exist for some fish. Clearly, subjects are capable of interpreting the visual cue and making a good avoidance response if already primed during introduction of the stimulus. Such dependence upon prior arousal argues strongly against the "hyperemotionality" hypothesis for these subjects.

Another kind of behavioral test revealed monocular deficits that are compatible with the "motor expression" hypothesis. Free-swimming fish always failed to turn away from a threatening stimulus with the good eye. Although no quantitative measurement of this deficit was attempted, this simple "clinical" evaluation seemed as good an indicator of the lesion as the conditioned avoidance scores. It was clear that these subjects often became aroused by the threatening stimulus, and sometimes swam faster in an effort to escape. However, quite often the subject would turn sharply into the stimulus—a maladaptive expression of its fearful state. We may well suspect that the intact brain half has seized power during the emergency and now guides the fish by its own rules, i.e., turning away from its own half of the visual world.

Experiment 2—Cardiac Conditioning

As a further test of the hypothesis that avoidance failure may reflect a sluggish arousal system, we have trained nine more subjects with a classical conditioning procedure. Heart rate deceleration was recorded as a presumed index of conditioned arousal. The ability to make avoidance responses does not necessarily correlate with the extent of conditioned cardiac response as McCleary (1960) has shown with an interocular transfer task. Therefore, the "motor expression" hypothesis predicts that cardiac deceleration would proceed equally well via either eye, despite the avoidance failure.

In general, fish trained preoperatively showed weaker cardiac deceleration following the lesion. However, in each of eight fish the deceleration was greater as the stimulus appeared via the good eye. Most subjects showed very slight changes of heart rate via the lesioned side, as if their "arousal" capacity were indeed extinguished. However, one fish showed clear increments in heart rate via the bad eye, while decelerating via the good eye. Furthermore, one subject (the only fish initially trained on the active avoidance task) showed strong acceleration to stimulation of either side. Here, the larger increment followed stimulus presentation on the bad side. The unexpected acceleratory responses via the bad eye provide further confirmation that vision is normal.

These two subjects provide suggestive evidence that hypothalamic lesions can unmask a cardiac acceleratory mechanism, which must operate by inhibiting the resting vagal tone and allowing the heart to approach its natural frequency (Randall 1966). Dr. Ralph Ryback, working in Ingle's laboratory, has recently confirmed the existence of the acceleratory system, which reveals itself as a strong tachycardia following the cardiac arrest produced by low-level stimulation of the posterior hypothalamus of goldfish. Incidentally, Ryback also finds that unilateral transection caudal to the stimulated hypothalamus strikingly elevates thresholds for cardiac inhibition. This confirms the laterality of cardiac control that we infer from our lesion effects on the conditioned cardiac response. At higher voltages, some leakage occurs; this fact is compatible with our notion that the second brain half can become indirectly altered even in the lesioned subject.

Forebrain versus Hypothalamic Lesions

Now that we have documented a clear deficit in avoidance behavior consequent to unilateral hypothalamic lesions, we can speculate about the syndrome reported by Savage in the light of our own experiences. At first glance, our lesion effects seem similar; goldfish have trouble making avoidance responses when the damaged brain half receives stimulus input directly. Yet, we suggest that this resemblance is misleading. For one thing, Ingle has completed an analysis of ten unilaterally forebrain-lesioned goldfish, using the same procedures I have outlined above, and has obtained just the opposite effect. Strangely enough, most of these fish respond with shorter avoidance latencies while using the eye projecting to the lesioned side, as if they were unilaterally hypersensitive. Furthermore, two of these subjects readily acquired a horizontal vs. vertical stripe discrimination via the potentially bad eye. This result confirms conclusions reached several years ago wtih bilaterally forebrainless fish, when Ingle was a student in the Chicago laboratory of R. A. McCleary.

Forebrain-lesioned and hypothalamic fish also differ when given spontaneous runs through a continuous Y-maze. Those in the former group tend to turn more often into the arm viewed by the good eye, while the hypothalamically damaged subjects tend—if anything —to turn the opposite way. For the forebrain-lesioned fish, their preference for the good side is enhanced by training on a left-right alternation task, which produces more errors toward the good side. Unfortunately my hypothalamic fish were not subjected to this kind of training, which seems to bring out unilateral deficits more clearly than does training to turn consistently in one direction.

Combining the Y-maze and avoidance results, we come to the tentative conclusion that forebrainless fish are *hyperemotional* when viewing a situation with the eye projecting to the damaged side. They avoid a conditioned stimulus with greater urgency, and they more often avoid swimming down the alley viewed by that eye. This conclusion is supported by Ingle's previous finding (1965b) that bilateral forebrain removal in goldfish can paradoxically enhance learning a simple directional task in the Y-maze, where subjects learn to avoid an invisible barrier placed in one arm.

But why should a hypersensitive fish show the kind of sluggishness or tranquillity that Savage has reported? It seems possible that the level of background arousal may be *too high* for his overwrought subjects, resulting in a kind of catatonic stupor. Occasionally, in our experience, a normal fish takes too many shocks during training and lapses into such a state. Furthermore, we have found that smaller fish—of the size that Savage uses—are more skittish in our apparatus (scaled down for them) than the larger fish, whose emotional stability we have come to appreciate. As a psychiatrist, I am inclined to prescribe a tranquilizer for Savage's anxiety-ridden fish, to test our own hypothesis.

Concluding Remarks

I have emphasized the richness of our hypothalamic syndrome, and have mentioned various possibilities for interpretation. After this hasty sketch (one might even say cartoon) of a kind of psychopathology, I must end with a plea for more comprehensive knowledge of the goldfish's normal avoidance repertoire. A scared fish may dart forward, back up, or flip about, or he may simply go limp when the situation becomes too overwhelming. We should examine lesion effects in terms of changing probabilities of various alternative responses to a variety of situations. Furthermore, we should be more ethologically minded (as a good psychiatrist must be) and consider the viewpoint of the fish as he confronts our contrived situations. We cannot probe too deeply with our cursory culture-bound intelligence tests. Perhaps fish neuropsychologists will begin to carry movie cameras about in the laboratory, in order to capture and analyze the various behavioral pathologies that we so easily inflict with our electrodes and scalpels. If one is determined to analyze behavior by making holes in the brain, however, I can certainly recommend the hypothalamus as a rich lode to mine.

Acknowledgment

The research described in this report was supported by a grant from the National Institute of Mental Health, MH 11555, to Dr. David Ingle, Harvard Medical School, and Psychiatry Service of Boston City Hospital.

References

Ingle, D. 1965*a*. Interocular transfer in goldfish: Color easier than pattern. *Science* 149: 1000–1002.

———. 1965*b*. Behavioral effects of forebrain lesions in goldfish. *Proc. Amer. Psychol. Assoc.* 1:143–44.

McCleary, R. A. 1960. Type of response as a factor in interocular transfer in the fish. *J. Comp. Physiol. Psychol.* 53:311–21.

Randall, D. J. 1966. The nervous control of cardiac activity in the tench and the goldfish. *Physiol. Zool.* 39:185–92.

Part III Physiological Aspects of Fish Behavior

1

Neural Control of Electric Organs

Michael V. L. Bennett

Department of Anatomy
Albert Einstein College of Medicine
Yeshiva University, New York

Electric Fish and Discharge Patterns

Electric organs have originated in at least six different evolutionary lines and provide remarkable examples of convergent evolution. In all but one group the generating cells of the organs appear to be modified from muscle (7, 14, 19, 34, 35, 37, 38, 58). The action potentials of these cells are similar to those in muscle and presumably result from movements of the same ions down their concentration gradients. In the exceptional group, the sternachids (Gymnotidae), the electric organ consists of modified nerve fibers; apparently the original myogenic organ was lost (9, 51). These neurogenic organs are of particular interest because of the high frequency of their activity, in excess of 1,000 discharges per sec in many species (39 and unpublished). How the activities of the single cells summate to give the organ discharge is well understood in all electric fish (3, 6, 7, 9, 12–16, 19, 23, 28, 34, 36). The sometimes very large outputs result from many cells acting together, rather than from any qualitatively different response of the cells themselves. Nonetheless, in maintained impulse frequency and in currents per unit area, these cells may establish the extremes of physiological behavior (e.g. 39, 50), and they are often remarkable in morphological aspects as well (e.g. 15, 59).

Electric fish and their organs can be divided into two types—weakly electric and strongly electric. The strongly electric fish are those where the maximum discharge is considered sufficiently large to discourage predators or disable prey. Included in this group are the electric eel (*Electrophorus*), the electric catfish (*Malapterurus*), both monospecific genera as far as is known, the electric rays (Torpedinidae), of which there are many species, and probably the stargazer (*Astroscopus*), of which there are several species (Fig. 1). To date rather inadequate tests have been applied to determine the effectiveness of strongly electric organs. In the usual test for defensive value, the predator has been the experimenter himself. As far as disablement of prey is concerned, the very large discharges of eels and catfish have remarkably little effect on small fish. No obvious disability is caused such prey, and fairly careful tests will have to be applied to establish any usefulness of the electric organ in this respect. Of course a small increment in effectiveness of predation might provide adequate survival pressure for evolution of the organs. Large prey could well be more severely affected than small, because larger total fields are involved. However, this is not a simple scaling problem, for it involves the site of action of current and the impedances of the two fish and the intervening water. Electric discharges affect frogs much more severely than they

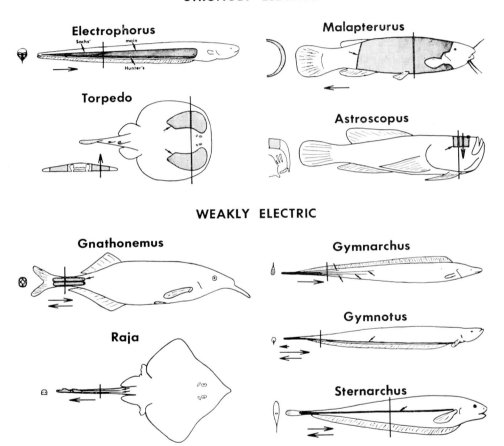

STRONGLY ELECTRIC

Electrophorus

Malapterurus

Torpedo

Astroscopus

WEAKLY ELECTRIC

Gnathonemus

Gymnarchus

Raja

Gymnotus

Sternarchus

FIG. 1. Electric fish. Representative electric fish are diagramed. All but *Torpedo* and *Raja* are shown from the side. The electric organs are indicated by small arrows, and are shown either stippled or solid. Sectional views are also shown that pass through the organs at the levels of the solid lines. The large arrows indicate the direction of current flow through the organs during activity in the generating cells. In *Gnathonemus*, *Gymnotus*, and *Sternarchus* the two or three arrows indicate successive phases of discharge and the relative amplitudes are shown by the length of the arrows. *Electrophorus*, *Gymnotus*, and *Sternarchus* are gymnotids and are found in tropical South America. *Gnathonemus* is a mormyrid and is found in Africa. *Malapterurus* and *Gymnarchus* are also African. The torpedinids and rajids are marine and cosmopolitan. *Astroscopus* is marine but restricted to the western shore of the Atlantic Ocean from Long Island to Brazil.

do small fish, and apparently stunning may result. Whether this greater effectiveness is due to differences in skin resistance, internal structure, or neural sensitivity is not known.

The weakly electric fish include the skates, the mormyrids, *Gymnarchus* and all the gymnotids other than the eel (Fig. 1). In the last three the electric organ functions primarily as the energy source in an electrolocation system (8, 11, 29–31, 33, 38, 40, 48, 49, 61–63). The animal sets up a field around itself, and using its electroreceptors, detects inhomogeneities in this field produced by the environment. Detection of their own fields may be considered an active use of the electroreceptors. Passive use, that is, detection of fields of extrinsic origin, also appears to occur in several groups which have very sensitive electroreceptors but no electric organs (24, 41, 47). The skates have electroreceptors, the ampullae of Lorenzini (48, 49, 65), and presumably the electric organ can be used in electrolocation, although organ discharge has never been observed under conditions where such a use seems likely (7, 56). The receptors may be used passively in most circumstances. It is clear that weakly electric fish are aware of each other's discharges, but the degree to which communication extends beyond mere detection remains to be determined.

Lissman (38) has suggested that the strongly electric organs evolved through a stage where the organ functioned in electrolocation, an eminently reasonable hypothesis that endows the intermediate stages with survival advantage. Darwin himself recognized the difficulty of understanding the gradual evolution of strongly electric organs when an intermediate, weakly electric stage could have no defensive or offensive value. In the eel a weakly electric organ persists, the Sachs organ, and the fish normally emits weak and apparently electrolocating pulses. In at least one torpedinid, *Narcine*, there is also a weakly electric organ, although the normal discharge of this organ is completely unknown (13, 45). There is no known weakly electric organ in the electric catfish, the stargazers, or their relatives, although their strongly electric organs might function in electrolocation. However, the organs discharge only after prey has been encountered and do not function in its initial detection (personal observations on the catfish and ref. 53). Thus, in the last two there is little evidence of a stage of electrolocation, although various catfish are known to be more sensitive to electric fields than other nonelectric fish (41).

The patterns of organ discharge depend on the use of the electric organ. The strongly electric organs are normally inactive, as indeed they must be, for the power outputs are so large that the fish can maintain them for only short periods. The discharges consist of pulse trains of varying length (Fig. 2a, a'). In the electric catfish, in *Torpedo*, and in the stargazer the pulses are all more or less the same size, although a small decrease during a train may occur and an occasional partial discharge may be observed in the last two (14, 19). As far as can be determined, every electroplaque discharges in each full-sized organ pulse. There is a high degree of synchronization, for the individual pulses are usually only slightly longer in duration than the discharges of the single electroplaques. In the eel the first pulse of a train is small, and the discharge does not reach its maximum until about the second or third pulse. This increase is due to recruitment of additional electroplaques, as will be discussed below.

Discharges in skates usually can be evoked only by violent and noxious stimulation, and the responses then are long-lasting pulses of variable amplitude and duration that must involve fused and repetitive responses of the single elements (7, 56). These discharges appear to have no value and their relation to discharges under more normal conditions remains to be established. Studies of the single cells do show that in many species repetitive activity is required to achieve maximum output (7). Discharge of the accessory organ in *Narcine* probably also involves repetitive and fused activity, for single volleys in the efferent nerves produce little output, while repetitive volleys lead to augmentation, prolongation, and fusion of the responses (13).

The freshwater weakly electric fish may be divided into variable and constant frequency types, although this distinction is not as valid as it once appeared to be. Both types emit pulses continually and seem never to stop to rest. Both types have evolved in South America and in Africa, a further convergence in electric fish (7, 38). In contrast to weakly electric organs in the marine fish, activity of the electroplaques is highly synchronous.[1]

The variable frequency species include the mormyrids and some gymnotids. These fish emit brief pulses with a comparatively long interval between them (Fig. 2b, b'; refs. 6, 7, 12, 15, 42). The discharge occurs at a somewhat irregular basal frequency of a few per second in the mormyrids and at a much more regular basal frequency, usually from 5 to 50 per sec,

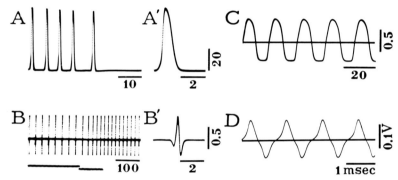

FIG. 2. Patterns of electric organ discharge. *a, a'*, an electric catfish 7 cm long recorded from in a small volume of water with head negativity upward; *a*, mechanical stimulation evoked a train of five pulses which attained a maximum frequency of 190/sec; *a'*, single pulses could also be evoked (faster sweep speed); *b, c*, weakly electric gymnotids recorded immersed in water, head positivity upward; *b*, a variable frequency gymnotid, *Gymnotus*; pulses were emitted at a basal frequency of *ca.* 35/sec: Tapping the side of the fish at the time indicated by the downward step in the lower trace caused an acceleration up to about 65/sec. The acceleration persisted beyond the end of the sweep. The small changes in amplitude are due to movement of the fish with respect to the recording electrodes. *b'*, faster sweep showing the pulse shape; *c*, a constant, low frequency gymnotid, *Sternopygus*. The pulse frequency is about 55/sec. The horizontal line indicates the zero potential level. *d*, a constant, high frequency gymnotid, *Sternarchus*. The frequency is about 800/sec. The horizontal line indicates the zero potential level. Calibrations in volts and milliseconds.

in the gymnotids. The frequency depends on the species and individual as well as on temperature (25, 28). From the basal rate, the discharge accelerates markedly in response to almost any novel stimulus (Fig. 2b). The accelerations result in an increased rate of testing the impedance of the environment, and resemble in some respects an orienting or arousal response. The degree of acceleration varies with the species, but is usually up to a maximum of 100–200/sec. Sometimes, stimuli will cause the fish to cease discharging for brief periods, apparently a response akin to hiding or to cessation of vocalization (cf. 43, 44).

In the constant frequency types, including many gymnotids and *Gymnarchus*, the duration of the individual pulses is of the same order as the interval between them. In *Gymnarchus*

[1] Spike-generating membrane is absent in all known electroplaques of marine fish and present in all those of freshwater fish. Presumably this difference and that in discharge patterns of weakly electric organs represent adaptations to the different properties of the two environments. An obvious environmental difference is in conductivity, but it is difficult to relate this to the physiological properties (7).

the frequency is about 250/sec, as it is in some *Eigenmannia*, which are gymnotids. In the gymnotid *Sternopygus* the frequency is usually from 50–100 sec and the pulse duration is 5–10 msec (Fig. 2c). In sternarchids, where the frequency is *ca.* 1,000/sec, the interval between pulses is about 0.3–0.5 msec (Fig. 2d, 3d).[2]

Gymnarchus has been observed to cease its discharge when surprised or when presented with an electrical stimulus mimicking the discharge of another *Gymnarchus* (32, 38, 64). Similar behavior has not been seen in the constant frequency gymnotids, although both *Eigenmanna* and *Sternarchus* will alter their discharge frequency slightly when presented with a small signal close in frequency (25, 66). Such a change would presumably reduce mutual interference by different individuals of similar frequencies. Sternarchids have also been observed to produce a brief transient acceleration or "chirp" either spontaneously or when presented with electrical stimuli near their own frequencies (25; T. H. Bullock, personal communication). It is tempting to regard this response as a communication signal, for it is so transient and infrequent as to be of little value in electrolocation.

The properties of single discharges are generally constant within one species, but in many cases the pulse shapes are indistinguishable from one species to another. Frequency of discharge differs considerably between individuals of the same species in constant as well as variable frequency types, and individuals of different species with the same pulse shape can overlap in frequency. In short, the experimenter often cannot distinguish species from the discharge alone. It cannot be said that the fish do not, although it would seem that finer points of recognition would require interactions involving alterations of frequency.

In the strongly electric fish, synchronization of discharges appears to be of obvious utility, for it leads to an increased voltage. Presumably the energy delivered to the medium or prey is the most important factor, although the optimum pattern of discharge would depend upon the site and mode of action. Since the organs generate direct current pulses, the question of optimum frequency does not arise in the same way as in stimulation by alternating current. Because in these species activity is accompanied by decreased resistance, energy output is increased when all the series elements are active together. Furthermore, inactive parallel elements would tend to shunt active ones. Similar considerations apply to synchronization in the weakly electric fish, and in the freshwater species it is usually very precise. Moreover, in many species the discharge of the single cells is diphasic, with the two phases about equal in amplitude. In these species out-of-phase activity would lead to partial cancellation of the discharges. The requirement for synchrony is particularly great in the mormyrids, where the discharges of the single cells are as brief as 0.3 msec. In several species, accessory organs or different parts of the main organ operate in different but fixed phase relations. Within each part the same considerations apply as to synchronization.

As it turns out, organ frequency is almost always set in the central nervous system.[3]

[2] A detailed consideration of the pulse forms in the weakly electric fish would be out of place in this presentation. In passing, it may be noted that in all constant frequency species a brief pulse is generated by one "face" of the generating cell and the apposed "face" acts as a series capacitance (7, 16, and unpublished). By pulse duration is meant the duration of the external current during active generation of the pulse. Actually this phase is followed by discharge of the series capacitance with a time constant that is long compared with both the active phase and the period between discharges. In spite of this qualification it seems reasonable to consider the pulse duration as that of the active phase. If one does not, one is led to the confusing proposition that the period between pulses is short compared with their duration.

[3] An exception was studied on the Amazon expedition of the *R/V Alpha-Helix* in collaboration with A. B. Steinbach. One type of sternarchid possesses an accessory electric organ modified from sensory nerve fibers. Reflecting this origin, the discharge frequency is set peripherally in the organ itself.

In the simplest cases a single nucleus fires a single spike which ultimately leads to a single discharge of each electroplaque. This nucleus has been termed the "command" nucleus by Albe-Fessard and co-workers (cf. 2, 26, 60), and in the species where there is constant activity we have called it the "pacemaker" nucleus. In one sense the "decision" to discharge the electric organ is reached at this nuclear level. The problem of control of discharge can be resolved into two parts. One concerns the mechanisms whereby the cells of the command nucleus are brought into synchronous activity. The other concerns the mechanisms whereby all the generating cells fire synchronously, although their distances from the command nucleus vary widely.

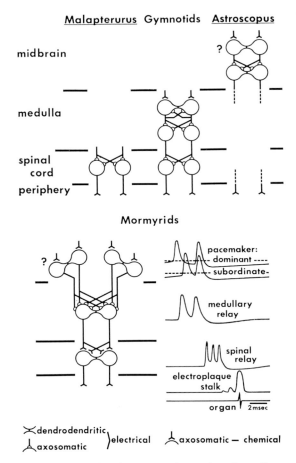

FIG. 3. Neural circuitry controlling electric organs. The modes of coupling and transmission between cells are diagramed. Where axosomatic junctions are indicated, axodendritic junctions are found as well. The mode of transmission to the command nucleus is known only in *Malapterurus*, although it is shown as chemical in the others. Where there is a question mark, the cells have not been definitely localized, but several of their properties can be inferred. In *Malapterurus*, gymnotids, and *Astroscopus*, a single command volley at each level precedes each organ discharge. In mormyrids the activity preceding a single organ response is more complicated and is diagramed at the several levels involved. The dotted lines indicate the thresholds of the cells in the two pacemaker nuclei.

Neural Circuitry Controlling Electric Organs

Malapterurus, *the Electric Catfish*

The simplest control system is that of the electric catfish (Fig. 3, ref. 18). A single giant cell (100–200 μ in diameter) on each side of the spinal cord sends out an axon that innervates the entire electric organ on that side, some 10^6 electroplaques. It is easy to record in the two giant cells, which can be localized by the relatively large electric fields they set up around themselves during activity. When afferent fibers are stimulated by nearby electrodes, depolarizations are produced in the giant cells that increase as the stimulus strength is increased (Fig. 4a). At some point the depolarizations reach threshold, and the cells are excited. There is, however, a feature of this excitation that is markedly different from what would be observed when, say, afferents to two synergistic motor neurons were stimulated; namely, the two cells are always excited or not excited together. A stimulus is never found which is suprathreshold for one cell and subthreshold for the other.

The origin of this identity of threshold is easily demonstrated. The two cells are closely coupled electrotonically; that is, their interiors behave electrically as if they were in different

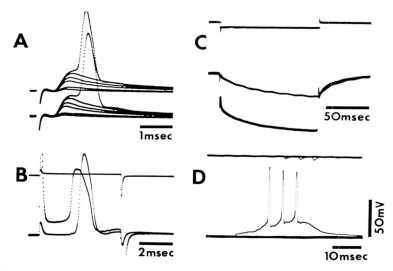

FIG. 4. Properties of the giant electromotor neurons of the electric catfish (*Malapterurus*). *a*, upper and lower traces, recording from right and left cells respectively. Brief stimuli of gradually increasing strength were applied to the nearby medulla (several superimposed sweeps, the stimulus artifact occurred near the beginning of the sweep). Gradually increasing depolarizations were evoked until in one sweep both cells generated spikes. *b*, two electrodes in the right cell, one for passing current (shown on the upper trace) and one for recording; one recording electrode in the left cell. The traces from the recording electrodes are the lower ones starting from the same baseline. When an impulse was evoked in the right cell by a depolarizing pulse, the left cell also generated a spike after a short delay; *c*, when a hyperpolarizing current was passed in the right cell, the left cell also became hyperpolarized, but more slowly and to a lesser degree (display as in *b*); *d*, when the cells were excited by irritating the skin a depolarization gradually rose up to the threshold of the giant cell and initiated a burst of three spikes (lower traces, baseline indicated by superimposed sweeps). Each spike produced a response in the organ (upper trace, recorded at high gain and greatly reduced in amplitude because curare had been used to prevent movement). Modified from Bennett, Nakajima, and Pappas (1967).

(although quite separated) parts of the same cell. Both hyperpolarization (Fig. 4*c*) and de-depolarization spread from cell to cell, and coupling is sufficiently close that an impulse generated in one cell is able to propagate to the other (Fig. 4*b*). Thus, if afferent fibers excite one cell, an impulse will be generated in the other cell whether or not an impulse arises in it independently. (Only one impulse will be generated in each cell even if the stimulus excites both, for the two impulses will collide in the path connecting them exactly as ascending and descending impulses collide in a single axon.)

In every case of electrotonic coupling discussed in this paper, so-called tight junctions have been found between the coupled cells (10, 17, 18, 20–22, 52). A tight junction is a region where the cell membranes come in contact, occluding the extracellular space between them. In cases where the membrane resistivity of the tight junctions could be estimated, it was found to be much lower than that of surrounding, nonjunctional membrane. The loss of extracellular space is not alone enough to produce the electrotonic coupling. The nature of the change in the membrane leading to lowered resistivity is not known. Although in some systems cells are directly coupled by electrotonic junctions between their processes, this is not true of the giant electromotor neurons of the catfish (Fig. 3). Instead, afferent fibers form junctions with both cells, which are thereby coupled to each other by virtue of being coupled to the same structures. From a purely functional point of view this complexity of the connecting path appears to have little or no significance.

When physiological stimuli that evoke organ discharge are applied to the catfish, there is a depolarization in the electromotor neurons that gradually rises to threshold (Fig. 4*d*). This result indicates that the discharge frequency is set in the giant cells themselves, which thus comprise a two-cell command nucleus. The output represents an integration of the afferent excitatory (and inhibitory) inputs just as the discharge frequency of a motoneuron is a resultant of its excitatory and inhibitory inputs. The electromotor neurons "decide" whether there are adequate inputs to call for an output. The two neurons function as a single cell and constitute the final common path for electric organ discharge in the same sense that a single motoneuron is the final common path for its motor unit. It could be said that the cells form a functional or electrical syncytium. However, these terms are somewhat misleading, because impulses in a few of the afferent fibers that are part of the electrical network are not, in fact, able to propagate throughout the system. Of course many instances are now known where impulses in different parts of a single cell fail to propagate to other excitable regions of that cell. For example, antidromic impulses in the axons of the giant cells are unable to invade the cell bodies because of the great disparity in size.

Another way of describing the electrotonic coupling of the giant cells is to say that it provides positive feedback between them. If one cell is more depolarized than the other, current flows between them that tends to excite the less depolarized cell and inhibit the more depolarized one. Although in mediating afferent impulses the junctions are excitatory, their role in coupling the cells cannot be characterized simply as either excitatory or inhibitory. Electrotonic transmission can be very fast, and although it is not in principle infinitely fast, delays less than 0.1 msec have been measured in a number of instances (10). The speed of electrotonic transmission certainly contributes to the synchronization of the giant cells. It might be suggested that the giant cells could be equally well synchronized by chemically transmitting synapses if they were arranged reciprocally. However, chemically mediated transmission has never been found to involve a delay less than 0.4 msec at room temperature (4, 18). The giant cell spikes are never separated to that extent when orthodromically fired, even near threshold, and usually the separation is less than 0.1 msec. Thus, reciprocal chemical synapses could not mediate the observed synchrony.[4]

Weakly Electric Gymnotids

The control of electric organs in weakly electric gymnotids is somewhat more complex than in the catfish (22). The electric organ extends over most of the body length and is innervated by neurons which are distributed along the spinal cord. However, the organ frequency is set in the medulla rather than in the spinal neurons. (From a functional point of view it would be difficult for synchronous activity to arise in a nucleus that was as long as a gymnotid's spinal cord.) There are two midline nuclei in the medulla that control the electric

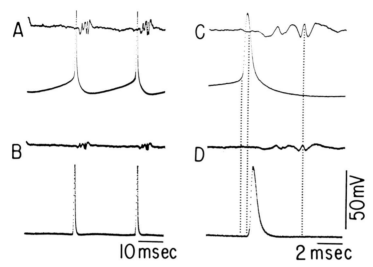

FIG. 5. Responses of pacemaker and relay cells in a weakly electric gymnotid (*Gymnotus*). *Upper traces*, activity in the spinal cord and peripheral nerves leading to the electric organ (recorded at high gain in a curarized animal). *Lower traces*, intracellular recordings in pacemaker (*a, c*) and relay (*b, d*) neurons (gains indicated in *d*). Faster sweep in *c* and *d* where the dotted lines indicate the times of firing of the cells in relation to the descending activity. Taken from Bennett, Pappas, Giménez, and Nakajima (1967).

organ. The dorsal one is a pacemaker and the ventral one is a relay. Their involvement in organ discharge is indicated by the fact that cells in each give a single spike before each organ pulse (Fig. 5). In the pacemaker neurons there is a gradually rising depolarization between spikes (Fig. 5a, c). The depolarization is similar to pacemaker potentials in other tissues, and the cells appear to be spontaneously active. In the relay cells the potential between spikes is quite flat and the discharges arise abruptly from a level baseline (Fig. 5b, d). These cells are clearly activated from a higher level, which is, in fact, the pacemaker nucleus. The interval between pacemaker and relay activity is accounted for by conduction time in pace-

[4] When one cell is directly stimulated, the spike in the other cell may be delayed by 0.5 msec (Fig. 4b). This interval represents conduction time along the connecting path rather than synaptic delay. The conduction time is consistent with the observation that brief potentials are much more attenuated in spread from cell to cell than are long-lasting ones. In orthodromic activation the connecting path is already depolarized by the afferent fibers which end more or less equally on both cells, and conduction between the cells is much more rapid.

maker axons. A single volley descends in the axons of the relay nucleus and this activity excites the electromotor neurons.

That the discharge frequency is really set in the pacemaker nucleus is indicated by the effects of polarization in a single pacemaker cell. Hyperpolarization retards the next spike in the polarized cell and also retards each subsequent spike (Fig. 6*b, d*). The organ discharges are not changed in duration or desynchronized; they are "reset" in phase by the same amount as the pacemaker spikes and follow them at a normal interval. The effects on the organ discharge indicate that the entire pacemaker nucleus is affected by polarization in a single cell. Moreover, since hyperpolarization spreads from cell to cell, the coupling between cells appears to be electrotonic.

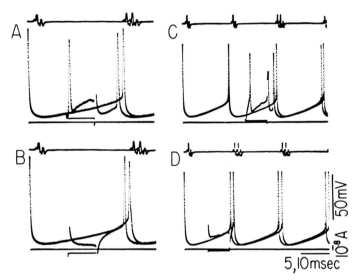

FIG. 6. Effect of polarization in a single pacemaker cell of a weakly electric gymnotid (*Gymnotus*). Recording as in Fig. 3 except that current applied through the recording electrode is indicated on the lower trace. Two superimposed sweeps in each record, one with and one without current application. The sweeps were triggered by the spike of the pacemaker cell. Faster sweep in *a* and *b*. Modified from Bennett, Pappas, Giménez, and Nakajima (1967).

In pacemaker cells of the variable frequency gymnotids, full-sized spikes can be evoked by depolarizing pulses. Such stimuli do not lead to any organ discharge, which indicates that the impulse in a single pacemaker cell is not able to propagate to the others (as has also been shown more directly). Of course some depolarization does spread to the neighboring cells, and this leads to an advance of the next and subsequent discharges (Fig. 6*a, c*).

The electrotonic coupling of the pacemaker cells obviously leads to synchronization of their firing. Each cell is spontaneously active and would get out of step with the others if there were not coupling—or positive feedback—between them. The accuracy of synchronization is again very high, too high to allow mutual synchronization by chemically mediated transmission, with its associated delay. In this system coupling is not sufficiently close to allow impulses to propagate from a single cell to another. However, it is sufficiently close to synchronize the cells, and when all the cells around an impaled one are firing it is extremely difficult to block that cell's activity. While a spike in any one cell affects its neighbors but little, many cells firing together can produce a large and very suprathreshold depolarization in an inactive cell.

As it happens, the medullary relay neurons are also electrotonically coupled and, as in *Malapterurus*, by way of the pacemaker fibers afferent to them. Here the coupling does not serve to keep the cells from firing out of phase, for each cell is always excited once per organ discharge by the large descending volley from the pacemaker nucleus. Presumably the coupling serves to synchronize relay cell firing, either because asynchrony was present in the initial pacemaker volley, or because it has arisen in transmission from the pacemaker nucleus. (The relay neurons in *Sternopygus* are not coupled to each other, but there is less requirement for precise synchronization in this species because the organ discharge is longer lasting.) In the gymnotids, the spinal relay neurons have been adequately studied only in the electric eel (20, 52). These cells, too, are electrotonically coupled and by way of the descending fibers afferent to them. Preliminary experiments indicate a similar organization in *Gymnotus*. Again, coupling would tend to increase synchronization.

The numbers of cells at various levels in the electromotor system are also relevant to the problem of control. There are perhaps 500 electroplaques in the gymnotid *Steatogenys*—about 10 per segment posteriorly, decreasing to 2 per segment at the rostral end of the main organ, a distance of about 80 segments. There is a somewhat smaller number of motoneurons, several per segment. There are yet fewer medullary relay neurons, only about 50, and still fewer pacemaker cells. Similar numerical relations are found in other weakly electric gymnotids, except that in some there are more pacemaker than medullary relay cells (22, 57). The significance of this pyramid of numbers may be in the requirement for synchronization. Presumably, more accuracy can be obtained when fewer cells are involved.

It is seen that in the weakly electric gymnotids the final common path for organ discharge involves not only the spinal relay neurons but the pacemaker and medullary relay nuclei as well. A certain amount of signal shaping may go on in the relays, but this is only a small extension of the Sherringtonian concept. Positive feedback through electrotonic coupling is clearly required at the pacemaker level, and probably functions at the lower levels as well as in several species.

Further Simple Electromotor Systems

Electric organ control in *Astroscopus* appears similar to that in the gymnotids, although it is not as completely studied (17). In *Astroscopus* the electric organ is modified from eye muscles, and the electroplaques are innervated by the oculomotor nucleus. This nucleus is also a relay, and the decision to fire the electric organ is probably reached in a nucleus one level higher than the electromotor neurons. However, synchronization of the command nucleus is imperfect. When a spinal stimulus is given at threshold strength for organ discharge, postsynaptic depolarizations in the motoneurons vary markedly in amplitude from quite small to suprathreshold. This asynchrony is of little importance, because the electric organ discharge is usually either full sized or absent. In few stimulus presentations is the response of the organ of intermediate amplitude. In *Astroscopus* the electromotor nucleus does not integrate inputs from several sources to set the organ discharge frequency. Its inputs appear to come from a single higher-level nucleus, and thus it would be characterized as a relay. Nevertheless, it clearly performs a certain decision function (and perhaps signal shaping as well) in distinguishing between large and small volleys from the higher nucleus. From this example it becomes clear that it may be difficult to distinguish between command and relay nuclei. A relay may itself perform an integrative operation in deciding whether or not there has been a pacemaker volley.

In the skate the electroplaques are innervated by spinal neurons that are apparently innervated in turn by a medullary nucleus (56, 60). Whether the higher nucleus is the command nucleus or another relay remains to be determined. The skates provide a particularly interesting case because of the rather asynchronous firing of their electroplaques (cf. 7). The functional necessity for the speed of electrical transmission is not present and positive feedback between cells could in principle be provided by reciprocal chemically transmitting junctions. If electrotonic coupling did prove to be present, it would suggest that some functional aspect other than speed was the determining factor, for example, ease of formation or metabolic economy (cf. 22).

The rostral centers controlling electric organ discharge in *Gymnarchus* have not been investigated physiologically. From a morphological point of view they appear quite interesting, as there are four interconnected nuclei (60). At this time it can only be said that a single volley descends the spinal cord to initiate each organ discharge (unpublished).

Complications in the Final Common Path

It is obvious that we do not completely understand the control of an effector cell when we find the highest level of the final common path to it. It may be useful to consider the decision to activate the cell as being made at this level, but even in simple cases this concept may be inadequate. For example, an occasional muscle fiber is innervated by two motoneurons, either of which can excite the fiber. The command to contract is impulse activity in either motoneuron, and there is no final common path. Often, a given movement can be produced by many combinations of activity in synergistic (and for that matter antagonistic) muscle fibers. Here the command can be thought of as activity in any one of a number of different and potentially overlapping groups of motoneurons. Similarly the command to activate a single effector cell can be considered either as firing of the highest level of the common path to it or as firing of any of the subsets of afferent fibers adequate to excite this level.

If one considers tension as the output of a muscle fiber, it may be necessary to express the command to reach this tension as a *frequency* of firing in the controlling neuron rather than as merely a single impulse. It will be seen that these examples have relevance to the control of electric organs.

The mormyrid electromotor system perhaps presents the most complexities (21, and unpublished). The electroplaques are innervated by spinal neurons, which are in turn innervated by axons from a small relay nucleus in the midline of the medulla (Fig. 3). This relay is innervated by what are probably a pair of higher, but still unidentified, nuclei that occur one on each side of the midline. Activity in either of the bilateral nuclei excites the medullary relay and ultimately the electric organ. Apparently the bilateral nuclei are similar to pacemaker nuclei in variable frequency gymnotids, although the rate of spontaneous activity is much lower.

Although in the mormyrids the final *common* path ends at the medullary relay, the integrative activity goes on at a higher level. In this case it would seem preferable to consider the higher-level nuclei as the deciding ones, and the command to fire as activity of either of them.

This duality of the command system does not lead to confusion, because activity in one pacemaker nucleus resets the phase of firing in the other. The descending fibers from each pacemaker nucleus form tight junctions on the relay cells, and apparently when one pacemaker nucleus excites the relay, this activity propagates "antidromically" from the relay to the other pacemaker nucleus and thereby resets its firing. (In Fig. 3 the pacemaker nuclei have been termed dominant and subordinate, respectively.)

As in gymnotids, the medullary and spinal relays are coupled electrotonically. The coupling is so close, however, that an impulse set up in one cell body propagates to excite all the other cells. Thick dendrodendritic bridges form extensive areas of tight junction between neighboring cells, and these areas are likely to be the sites of coupling. Presumably the cells within each pacemaker nucleus are also coupled. This point has not yet been directly demonstrated, but the degree of synchronization of the command volley is such as to require the speed of electrotonic transmission.

In the mormyrids also there is a successive reduction in cell numbers at higher levels of the electromotor system which extends at least as far as the medullary relay. There are about 500 electroplaques, 250 spinal neurons, and 25 medullary neurons. The importance of numbers can be illustrated by the effects of directly stimulating single cells of the medullary and spinal nuclei. In the former nucleus the activity rapidly involves all the cells and leads to an organ discharge that is indistinguishable from the normal response. In contrast, propagation through the spinal nucleus requires a much longer time, and only a small asynchronous organ discharge is produced.

There are further complications in the mormyrids that are not well understood. The initial command volley apparently consists of a single spike. In the medullary relay, this volley is transformed into two spikes separated by a short interval. (Probably the second volley propagates antidromically into both pacemaker nuclei, cf. Fig. 3.) This transformation in spike number results from a property of the relay cell membrane, for a brief stimulus also evokes two spikes. A double volley descends the spinal cord and produces a double postsynaptic potential (PSP) in the spinal neurons. However, these cells fire three times. A brief depolarization in the spinal neurons also evokes a three-spike discharge and, as in the medullary relay, the repetitive firing appears intrinsic to the membranes of the postsynaptic cells. The third spike in the spinal neurons is somewhat irregular, and it is synchronized by the second volley from the medullary relay. The three spikes are all propagated out the motor axons. At the nerve-electroplaque synapse the PSP produced by the first volley is very small, and does not initiate firing. There is, however, marked postactivation potentiation, and the second PSP is much larger, although it is usually still subthreshold. Only the third PSP is adequate to initiate a spike. (When the organ is active at high frequencies the second PSP may be facilitated sufficiently to excite the cells.) The reason for all this signal transformation remains obscure. It may be associated with the very high degree of synchronization observed in some mormyrids, but the same mechanisms are seen in others where the organ discharge is much longer lasting and the requirement for synchrony considerably less.

In the torpedinids the electric organ is innervated by the fifth, seventh, ninth, and tenth cranial nerves (45). The electromotor neurons act as a relay of activity from a pair of small nuclei, one on either side of the midline (26, 55). The data available indicate that a command volley arising in either small nucleus can excite the electric organ on both sides of the body, a convergence of commands similar to that in the mormyrids. It is not known whether there is any interaction between the command nuclei. As in the stargazer, the command volleys consist of single impulses at every level, and the PSP's in the relay cells may vary somewhat in amplitude.

Although midline nuclei have developed in a number of control systems, paired command nuclei may be fairly common because of the basically bilateral organization of the nervous system (and they may in fact occur in the stargazer). If either of the two command nuclei can excite an entire effector system, synchronization between the two is not important. However, it appears functional for each command to reset the phase of firing in both command nuclei. Probably this resetting occurs in the mormyrids by actual invasion of the impulses. Mutual inhibition could also be a mechanism. For example, crossed inhibition like that between Mauthner cells (27) would be equally effective in an electric organ system. (Mutual excitation would not work for Mauthner cells since inhibition rather than simple resetting is required.)

The adult eel has three parts to its electric organ (Fig. 1). The Sachs organ generates weak and presumably locating pulses at a low and variable frequency. The main organ acts only during the strong discharges. The Hunter's organ, named after its discoverer, apparently functions like the main organ anteriorly and the Sachs organ posteriorly (1). The separate organs are controlled by a single relay nucleus in the medulla like that in the weakly electric gymnotids (20). A single command volley descends the spinal cord and excites all the electromotor neurons, which then transmit a single discharge out of each ventral root supplying the electric organs. At a low frequency of activity the PSP's in the electroplaques of the main organ are subthreshold and do not excite the cells; only the cells of the Sachs organ become active (1). When there are two or more closely spaced command volleys, the PSP's in the main organ are facilitated enough to fire the cells, and then all the organs are discharged. Thus, control of the main organ is by way of frequency of discharge in the same cells that operate the Sachs organ. As a result only a single bulbospinal relay system is required, rather than two. However, this apparent saving is made at the expense of an increase in the minimum latency with which the main organ can be activated. It seems likely that the dual functioning of the single control system is a result of evolution from an earlier stage where there was but a single, weakly electric organ.

Synchronization of the Electroplaques

Given that a synchronous decision has been reached in the command nucleus, most electric fish are faced with a second problem, that of exciting the electroplaques synchronously. This is not a trivial matter, for the different parts of the organ may be separated from the command nucleus by large and different distances. Even at high conduction velocities, the differences in conduction time would cause marked asynchrony if all the cells were connected by straight line nerve tracts of equal conduction velocity. Several potential kinds of compensatory mechanisms might be proposed as diagramed in Figure 7*a–c*. One would be to make the paths to the closer cells more devious so that the actual conduction paths would be of the same length (Fig. 7*a*). A second mechanism would be to use direct paths, but to make the shorter ones of just sufficiently lower conduction velocity that the impulses would arrive at the ends simultaneously (Fig. 7*b*). This difference is symbolized in the figure by making the shorter paths of thinner lines, for, other things being equal, a thinner fiber has a lower conduction velocity. A third mechanism would be to introduce a compensatory delay at some specific part of the shorter paths. In the diagram this is symbolized by slowly conducting (thin) branches from the main path that are longer at the parts nearer the command nucleus. Synaptic delays at a relay might also differ systematically so as to provide temporal compensation.

It appears that in most instances combinations of the proposed mechanisms are present. The simplest to observe is equalization of path length. This is an obvious feature of the electric organs of *Torpedo*, *Astroscopus*, and *Malapterurus*, in which the efferent nerves enter the organ and run for some distance before giving off small branches which return to end near the point of entry of the nerve. This feature is also seen both in the innervation of mormyrid electroplaques and in their peculiar stalk systems whereby impulses are propagated from the site of innervation to the main bodies of the cells (15). It is probably also present in the innervation of eel electroplaques. Compensatory differences in conduction velocity are more difficult to demonstrate in electromotor systems, for conduction must be accurately measured along paths that are usually highly convoluted. It apparently does occur

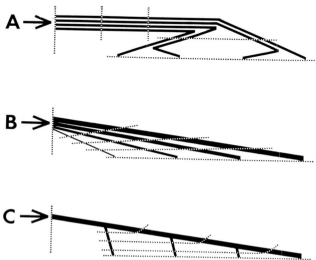

FIG. 7. Mechanisms of compensatory delay. Neural pathways are diagramed leading to terminations in the periphery at different distances from a rostral command center. A command volley arises at the large arrow and the dotted lines represent times of arrival of impulses at equal time intervals afterward. *a*, equalization of path length. The paths to the nearer cells are made more tortuous so that all paths are of nearly equal length. *b*, compensatory differences in conduction velocity. The paths leading to the periphery are direct, but conduction is slower in the shorter, thinner paths. *c*, localized compensatory delays. Thin terminal branches in which conduction velocity is reduced are longer in the paths leading to the nearer parts of the periphery.

in the stalk system of mormyrid electroplaques, where differences in conduction distance are easily visualized and where synchronization is very precise. As would be expected, the shorter paths involve stalks that are smaller in diameter. Probably in most systems equalization of path length is only partial, and synchrony is contributed to by compensatory differences in conduction velocity.

The best example of compensatory differences in conduction velocity is found in the giant axons innervating the mantle of the squid. Here synchrony of contraction is important in generating the maximum propulsive force, and the muscle nearer the stellate ganglion (in which there is a relay) is supplied by thinner axons of slower conduction velocity (54).

In a large electric eel the times to be compensated for are quite large, since the organ may be over a meter in length and the descending fiber tracts have conduction velocities in the range of 50 m/sec (2). At each level about half of the required compensatory delay occurs in activation of the spinal relays and the other half occurs in the periphery. Micro-electrode investigations have shown that transmission between descending fibers and spinal neurons is electrical, and that little delay occurs at the synapses themselves (20). Most or all of the delay is a result of conduction time in terminal branches of the descending fibers.

In the mormyrids firing of the electromotor neurons is highly sychronous, and there is a systematic difference in the delay between arrival of the descending volley close to the cells and their firing (unpublished). Transmission at the synapse is chemically mediated, and it is possible that the delay is in the processes of transmitter secretion or action. However, conduction time in the terminals may be the relevant factor, as it is in the eel. Probably the presynaptic volleys are recorded from the large fibers rather than from the terminals, and the measured delays are actually conduction times in the terminals plus the true synaptic delays. The precise evaluation of these factors is likely to require experimentally difficult measurements on very fine axons. If morphological investigations reveal that the terminals are longer and thinner where the delays are greater, it will be unnecessary to postulate systematic diffrences in synaptic processes. Nonetheless, compensatory delays in either terminal conduction or synaptic processes are clearly present in the mormyrids and also *Malapterurus* (37), and may be found in may sites where precise phase relations of neural activities are important.

Principles of Organization

There are two features common to the organization of the various electromotor systems. First, where a number of cells act together there is likely to be positive feedback between them. In command nuclei, where a highly synchronous volley arises, there must be feedback, and this must be mediated electrically because chemical transmission is too slow. In relay nuclei there is no absolute requirement for feedback, but cells are often coupled, presumably to increase synchronization. Again, the coupling must be electrical if the synchronization is to be precise. Second, there is the tendency toward reduced numbers of cells at higher levels. The decision to fire electric organs is apparently always reached in cells which are few in number compared with the final generating cells. The most striking example is in the catfish, where only two cells do the deciding for all the electroplaques. This aspect of organization is explicable by what may be termed the committee principle. If a group of people must make a decision together, the smaller the group the better. The same applies to neurons, as is simply illustrated by propagation of impulses through the mormyrid relay nuclei.

It might be asked, Could not a command "nucleus" consist of a single cell (a committee of one)? Indeed, each Mauthner cell may be considered a command "nucleus" for the contralateral axial musculature.[5] Several reasons for multicelled command nuclei can be proposed. It might be that a single cell body would have difficulty supplying axon terminals to all the lower level cells. Alternatively, it might be advantageous to avoid the equivalent of putting all one's eggs in a single basket. Evolution may yet progress to single-celled command "nuclei," although in most instances the multicelled nuclei do about as well as required by the electroplaques.

The changes in cell number in relay nuclei cannot be simply related to the committee principle, since the decision is reached at a higher level. Phylogenetic or ontogenetic factors

---

[5] In the hatchet fish each Mauthner fiber also activates the depressor muscles of both pectoral fins. The Mauthner cells constitute a bilateral command system for these muscles and presumably there is crossed inhibition between the two sides (4, 27).

may be responsible for the presence of the relays, particularly where they serve no marked synchronizing function. The progressive increase in cell number may be equivalent to a progressive increase in size as the number of postsynaptic cells to be activated increases.

It is interesting to compare the function of relay nuclei to transmission of impulses along an axon. At a node an impulse that has been attenuated in electrotonic propagation from the preceding node triggers the generation of a new impulse that is of full amplitude. The node acts as a pulse-restoring element, and decrementless conduction is thereby made possible. A relay nucleus potentially does more than this. The volley of impulses in the fibers efferent from the relay may be more synchronous than that in the afferent fibers, or all the efferents may become excited when only a fraction of the afferents are active (as sometimes occurs in *Astroscopus*). These functions do not *require* coupling of the cells; all that is necessary is that a number of afferent fibers converge on each relay cell.

The extent to which firing of an electric organ resembles other decision processes remains to be determined. Several of the systems investigated show ways in which the final common path concept of a decision requires extension. Yet it is reasonable to think that the two features observed in electromotor systems have some general relevance, and, in agreement with this, they have been found in several synchronized muscle systems (4, 10, 52). As Morrell (46) noted in his review on the neural basis of learning, negative feedback is not the only feature of the nervous system. While much of neural control is homeostatic through negative feedback, other phenomena, perhaps including learning, involve a mobilization of large numbers of cells. At least superficially, this recruitment would appear to require mutual reinforcement of neuronal activities, that is, positive feedback.

Learning and Electric Fish

The foregoing material indicates that, in the majority of electric fish, discharge frequency is the primary dimension along which electrical output can be varied. In the electric catfish both electromotor neurons must fire together. In the weakly electric gymnotids and mormyrids, the command and relay nuclei generally fire highly synchronously. Each command volley produces a single discharge of every electroplaque. Although changes in amplitude can occur, these are usually small and appear to be due to refractoriness and to be secondary to changes in frequency. Only slightly less precise synchronization is observed in the relay nucleus of *Astroscopus*. The main organ discharge of the torpedinids is also quite synchronous and constant in amplitude. In many respects these organ discharges are analogous to activity of a single motor unit, although many more cells are involved and the final common path may extend across several synapses. Only the organ of the skates, the main organ of the eel, and the accessory organ of the torpedinids appear to have amplitude as variables. In the eel, and perhaps in the others as well, these changes are secondary to changes in frequency.

It was of interest to see if conditioning techniques could be applied to the control of organ discharge. Since unconditioned accelerations are readily evoked in the variable frequency forms, it seemed likely that experiments on these forms would be successful, and it was hoped that psychophysical investigations of the electrosensory system would be facilitated. In most experiments to date the animal was placed in a restraining box and the organ discharge was picked up by electrodes placed at each end (43). A response was considered a change of frequency to some chosen criterion value. Separate electrodes were used to administer strong shock for aversive or unconditional stimulation. The experimental setup had the feature, aesthetically pleasing to the electrophysiologist, that only wires led to the experimental aquarium. No mechanical devices were involved and the entire system was excellently suited to electronic data processing.

It was found that organ discharge is accessible to both classical and operant conditioning techniques (43, 44). In view of the evolution of electric organs from skeletal muscle, this finding is not startling (cf. 5), but there is still satisfaction in being able to condition a highly quantifiable response that involves neither movement nor secretion. Avoidance conditioning can be obtained using a strong electric shock as an aversive stimulus and light, vibration, weak electric pulses, or a resistance change as a conditional stimulus. In *Gymnotus* the operant response can be either acceleration or cessation of discharge, but in mormyrids only

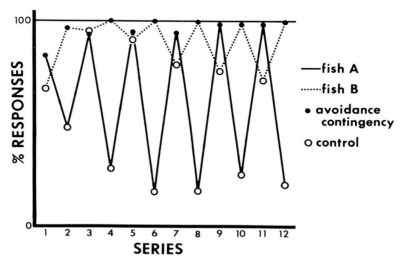

FIG. 8. Operant conditioning of acceleration of electric organ discharge rate in a mormyrid (*Gnathonemus*). A yoked control procedure was used. In a particular series one fish served as the avoidance subject, and the other served as a control. A light signal was presented to both fish at 40-, 60-, and 80-sec intervals. A response by the avoidance subject during light terminated light for both fish and avoided shock. A response was considered to be an acceleration to 2.8 times the average frequency recorded over the terminal hour or so of adaptation to the apparatus. If the avoidance subject did not respond within 5 sec both fish were shocked and light was terminated. The fraction of CS presentations to which the control subject responded within 5 sec was recorded, but these responses had no effect on light or shock.

After each series of about 220 trials the contingencies were reversed, that is the avoidance subject became the control and vice versa. The abscissa shows the successive series. The ordinate shows the percentage of trials in which responding occurred for each fish. The filled circles represent the fish in the avoidance contingency; the open circles represent the control. The solid line traces the fish that was first in the avoidance contingency, the broken line traces the one that first served as control.

accelerations have been brought under stimulus control. An example using a yoked control procedure is shown in Figure 8. In this experiment successive series of about 220 trials were given. In each series one fish was the avoidance subject and the other was its control. The avoidance subject could terminate the light and avoid shock by accelerating its discharge to the criterion frequency. The behavior of the yoked fish had no effect, and it received shocks whenever the avoidance subject did. To control for individual differences the roles of the fish were interchanged in successive series. In all but an early one of the 12 series shown in Figure 8 the avoidance subject responded in a larger fraction of trials than the control subject. It is thus clear that the operant contingency led to a greater incidence of responding.

If each fish is considered separately, in alternate sessions intermittent contingent and noncontingent shocks were given. The rate of responding was always higher when shocks were contingent on responding, again indicating operant conditioning. The control responding of one of the fish (Fish B) was considerably greater than that of the other. Examination of the experimental records shows that when this fish went into the control contingency, it continued to respond before the avoidance subject. This behavior was adventitiously reinforced when the avoidance subject finally did respond, and thus a high level of control responding was maintained.

While present data on conditioning of organ discharge are fragmentary, the feasibility of such studies is clearly demonstrated. An important part of the effector pathway is known in these systems, and they may possibly be useful in establishing a neurophysiological basis for learning. For example, when organ discharges are conditioned to weak electric fields or conductance changes, alterations in the connections between electrosensory and electromotor nuclei could conceivably be demonstrated at the cellular level. Of course, it is possible that all the interesting changes occur in the neuropil, where they are inaccessible to electrophysiological investigation. The success of the studies of the control systems has been greatly facilitated by the large size of the neural elements and the synchronization of their activity. While there is no assurance that conditioning of organ discharge involves neural elements with similar characteristics, these systems seem good places to look. The short latency of unconditioned responses (cf. Fig. 2*b*, ref. 12) does suggest that fairly direct and rapidly conducting pathways are involved.

Summary

The patterns of electric organ discharge can be of several kinds, in part depending on the function of the organ. Strongly electric fish are and can be only intermittently active. All the generating cells become active more or less synchronously to generate trains of pulses. Discharges of weakly electric organs in marine fish are poorly known, but apparently involve asynchronous fused and repetitive activity of the individual generating cells. Freshwater weakly electric fish are usually continually active, and the individual pulses involve very synchronous activity of the generating cells. These fish can be divided into constant and variable frequency types, although individuals of each kind may cease discharging for brief periods.

Several features are common to the different electromotor systems that have been studied physiologically. At the neural level where the discharge frequency is set, the "deciding" neurons are electrotonically coupled. In these cases the degree of synchronization is so great that the speed of electrotonic coupling is required. Chemical transmission is too slow. At lower levels of the control systems, that is, in relay nuclei, electrotonic coupling is often present, presumably to increase synchrony.

The concept of the final common path can be applied quite simply to the electric catfish and the weakly electric gymnotids. In the stargazer, the relay nucleus may perform an integrative function in addition to that of synchronization. In the mormyrids and torpedinids the deciding nuclei are bilateral and a command arising on either side can excite the electric organs on both sides. The final common path thus bifurcates at a level below that where the major integrative or decision functions are found. In the electric eel the main organ is controlled by frequency of discharge in the same neural system that controls the Sachs organ.

Several mechanisms of compensatory delay contribute to synchronization of parts of an electric organ at different distances from the command nucleus. The nerves to the nearer parts may run a more indirect course or may be of lower conduction velocity. A delay may be introduced at a relay, as in the eel spinal cord, where it is known to be due to reduced conduction velocity in the presynaptic terminals.

Two principles of organization appear to apply to electric organ systems; there is positive feedback between the deciding cells, and the number of deciding cells is reduced compared to the number of effector cells. Both features can be related to the need for synchrony. It remains to be determined whether this type of organization is involved in decision processes on a higher level.

Alteration of discharge frequency can be conditioned operantly or classically in several variable frequency species in which the discharge provides a simply quantifiable response depending only on the parameter of frequency. These electromotor systems may prove useful in the study of the electrophysiological basis of learning.

Acknowledgment

This paper is in large part a summary of investigations carried out while the author was in the Department of Neurology, College of Physicians and Surgeons, Columbia University. The work was supported in part by grants from the National Institutes of Health (Career Program Award K3-GM-5828 and Research Grants Grants NB-3728 and NB-3270), from the National Science Foundation (GB-2940), and from the United States Air Force (AF-AFOSR-550).

References

1. Albe-Fessard, D., and Chagas, C. 1954. Étude de la sommation à la junction nerf-électroplaque chez le gymnote (*Electrophorus electricus*). *J. Physiol. (Par.)* 46:823–40.

2. Albe-Fessard, D., and Martins-Ferreira, H. 1953. Rôle de la commande nerveuse dans la synchronisation du fonctionnement des éléments de l'organe électrique du gymnote, *Electrophorus electricus* L. *J. Physiol. (Par.)* 45:533–46.

3. Altamirano, M.; Coates, C. W.; Grundfest, H.; and Nachmansohn, D. 1953. Mechanisms of bioelectric activity in electric tissue. I. The response to indirect and direct stimulation of electroplax of *Electrophorus electricus. J. Gen. Physiol.* 37:91–110.

4. Auerbach, A. A., and Bennett, M. V. L. 1967. Chemically and electrically transmitting junctions in the central nervous system of the hatchetfish, *Gasteropelecus. J. Gen. Physiol.* 50:1090–91.

5. Basmajian, J. V. 1963. Control and training of individual motor units. *Science* 141:440–41.

6. Bennett, M. V. L. 1961*a*. Electric organs of the knifefish, *Steatogenys. J. Gen. Physiol.* 45:590A.

7. ———. 1961*b*. Modes of operation of electric organs. *Ann. N.Y. Acad. Sci.* 94:458–509.

8. ———. 1965. Electroreceptors in mormyrids. *Symp. Quant. Biol.* 30:245–62.

9. ———. 1966*a*. An electric organ of neural origin. *Fed. Proc.* 25:569.

10. ———. 1966*b*. Physiology of electrotonic junctions. *Ann. N.Y. Acad. Sci.* 137:509–39.

11. ———. 1968. Mechanisms of electroreception. In *Lateral line detectors*, ed. P. Cahn, pp. 313–93. Bloomington: Univ. of Indiana Press.

12. Bennett, M. V. L., and Grundfest, H. 1959. Electrophysiology of electric organ in *Gymnotus carapo. J. Gen. Physiol.* 42:1067–1104.

13. ———. 1961*a*. The electrophysiology of electric organs of marine electric fishes. II. The electroplaques of main and accessory organs of *Narcine brasiliensis. J. Gen. Physiol.* 44:805–18.

14. ———. 1961*b*. The electrophysiology of electric organs of marine electric fishes. III. The electroplaques of the stargazer, *Astroscopus y-graecum. J. Gen. Physiol.* 44:819–43.

15. ———. 1961*c*. Studies on morphology and electrophysiology of electric organs. III. Electrophysiology of electric organs in mormyrids. In *Bioelectrogenesis*, ed. C. Chagas and A. Paes de Carvalho, pp. 113–35. Amsterdam: Elsevier.

16. ———. 1965. Electric organ discharge in the weakly electric fish, *Gymnarchus niloticus. Abstr. 9th Meeting Biophys. Soc.*, p. 18.

17. Bennett, M. V. L., and Pappas, G. D. 1967. Control of electric organ discharge in the stargazer, *Astrocopus:* an example of synchronized oculomotor activity. *Abstr. 11th Meeting Biophys. Soc.*, p. 45.

18. Bennett, M. V. L.; Nakajima, Y.; and Pappas, G. D. 1967. Physiology and ultrastructure of electrotonic junctions. III. Giant electromotor neurons of *Malapterurus electricus. J. Neurophysiol.* 30:209–35.

19. Bennett, M. V. L.; Würzel, M.; and Grundfest, H. 1961. The electrophysiology of electric organs of marine electric fishes. I. Properties of electroplaques of *Torpedo nobiliana. J. Gen. Physiol.* 44:757–804.

20. Bennett, M. V. L.; Giménez, M.; Nakajima, Y.; and Pappas, G. D. 1964. Spinal and medullary nuclei controlling electric organ in the eel, *Electrophorus. Biol. Bull.* 127:362.

21. Bennett, M. V. L.; Pappas, G. D.; Aljure, E.; and Nakajima, Y. 1967. Physiology and ultrastructure of electrotonic junctions. II. Spinal and medullary electromotor nuclei in mormyrid fish. *J. Neurophysiol.* 30:180–208.

22. Bennett, M. V. L.; Pappas, G. D.; Giménez, M.; and Nakajima, Y. 1967. Physiology and ultrastructure of electrotonic junctions. IV. Medullary electromotor nuclei in gymnotid fish. *J. Neurophysiol.* 30:236–300.

23. Brock, L. G., and Eccles, R. M. 1958. The membrane potentials during rest and activity of the ray electroplate. *J. Physiol.* 142:251–74.

24. Dijkgraaf, S., and Kalmijn, A. S. 1963. Untersuchungen über die Funktion der Lorenzinischen Ampullen an Haifischen. *Z. Vergl. Physiol.* 47:438–56.

25. Erskine, F. T.; Howe, D. W.; and Weed, B. C. 1966. The discharge period of the weakly electric fish, *Sternarchus albifrons. Amer. Zool.* 6:521.

26. Fessard, A., and Szabo, I. 1953. Sur l'organisation anatomofonctionnelle des lobes électriques de la Torpille. *J. Physiol. (Par.)* 45:114–17.

27. Furukawa, T., and Furshpan, E. J. 1963. Two inhibitory mechanisms in the Mauthner neurons of goldfish. *J. Neurophysiol.* 26:140–76.

28. Grundfest, H. 1957. The mechanisms of discharge of the electric organs in relation to general and comparative electrophysiology. *Progr. Biophys.* 7:1–85.

29. Hagiwara, S., and Morita, H. 1963. Coding mechanisms of electroreceptor fibers in some electric fish. *J. Neurophysiol.* 26:551–67.

30. Hagiwara, S.; Kusano, K.; and Negishi, K. 1962. Physiological properties of electroreceptors of some gymnotids. *J. Neurophysiol.* 25:430–49.

31. Hagiwara, S.; Szabo, T.; and Enger, P. S. 1965. Electroreceptor mechanisms in a high frequency weakly electric fish. *J. Neurophysiol.* 28:784–99.

32. Harder, W., and Uhlemann, H. 1967. Zum Frequenzverhalten von *Gymnarchus niloticus* Cuv. (Mormyriformes, Teleostei). *Z. Vergl. Physiol.* 54:85–88.

168   *Bennett*

33. Harder, W.; Schief, A.; and Uhlemann, H. 1967. Zur empfindlichkeit des schwachelek-
trischen Fisches *Gnathonemus petersii* (Gthr. 1862) (Mormyriformes, Teleostei) gegen-
über elektrischen Feldern. *Z. Vergl. Physiol.* 54:89–108.

34. Keynes, R. D. 1957. Electric organs. In *The physiology of fishes*, ed. M. E. Brown, Vol.
2, pp. 323–43. New York: Academic Press.

35. ———. 1961. The development of the electric organ in *Electrophorus electricus* (L.). In
Bioelectrogenesis, ed. C. Chagas and A. Paes de Carvalho, pp. 14–18. Amsterdam:
Elsevier.

36. Keynes, R. D., and Martins-Ferreira, H. 1953. Membrane potentials in the electroplates
of the electric eel. *J. Physiol.* 119:315–51.

37. Keynes, R. D.; Bennett, M. V. L.; and Grundfest, H. 1961. Studies on morphology and
electrophysiology of electric organs. II. Electrophysiology of electric organ of *Malapterurus electricus*. In *Bioelectrogenesis*, ed. C. Chagas and A. Paes de Carvalho, pp.
102–12. Amsterdam: Elsevier.

38. Lissmann, H. W. 1958. On the function and evolution of electric organs in fish. *J. Exp.
Biol.* 35:156–91.

39. ———. 1961. Ecological studies on gymnotids. In *Bioelectrogenesis*, ed. C. Chagas and
A. Paes de Carvalho, pp. 215–23. Amsterdam: Elsevier.

40. Lissmann, H. W., and Machin, K. E. 1958. The mechanism of object location in *Gymnarchus niloticus* and similar fish. *J. Exp. Biol.* 35:451–86.

41. ———. 1963. Electric receptors in a non-electric fish (*Clarias*). *Nature* 199:88–89.

42. Lissmann, H. W., and Schwassman, H. O. 1965. Activity rhythm of an electric fish,
Gymnorhamphichthys hypostomus, Ellis. *Z. Vergl. Physiol.* 51:153–71.

43. Mandriota, F. M.; Thompson, R. L.; and Bennett, M. V. L. 1965. Classical conditioning of electric organ discharge rate in mormyrids. *Science* 150:1740–42.

44. ———. 1968. Avoidance conditioning of electric organ discharge rate in mormyrids.
Anim. Behav., in press.

45. Mathewson, R.; Mauro, A.; Amatniek, E.; and Grundfest, H. 1958. Morphology of
main and accessory electric organs of *Narcine basiliensis* (Olfers) and some correlations
with their electrophysiological properties. *Biol. Bull.* 115:126–35.

46. Morrell, F. 1961. Electrophysiological contributions to the neural basis of learning.
Physiol. Rev. 41:443–94.

47. Mullinger, A. M. 1964. The fine structure of ampullary electric receptors in *Amiurus*.
Proc. Roy. Soc. Ser. B 160:345–59.

48. Murray, R. W. 1965. Electroreceptor mechanisms: The relation of impulse frequency to
stimulus strength and responses to pulsed stimuli in the ampullae of Lorenzini of
elasmobranches. *J. Physiol.* 180:592–606.

49. ———. 1968. The function of the ampullae of Lorenzini of elasmobranches. In *Lateral
line detectors*, ed. P. Cahn, pp. 277–93. Bloomington: Univ. of Indiana Press.

50. Nakamura, Y.; Nakajima, S.; and Grundfest, H. 1965. Analysis of spike electrogenesis
and depolarizing K inactivation in electroplaques of *Electrophorus electricus*, L. *J. Gen.
Physiol.* 49:321–49.

51. Oliveira, Castro, G. de. 1955. Differentiated nervous fibers that constitute the electric
organ of *Sternachus albifrons* Linn. *Acad. Brasil. Cienc.* 27:557–60.

52. Pappas, G. D., and Bennett, M. V. L. 1966. Specialized sites involved in electrical transmission between neurons. *Ann. N.Y. Acad. Sci.* 137:495–508.

53. Pickens, P. E., and McFarland, W. N. 1964. Electric discharge and associated behaviour in the stargazer. *Anim. Behav.* 12:362–67.

54. Pumphrey, R. J., and Young, J. Z. 1938. The rates of conduction of nerve fibres of various diameters in cephalopods. *J. Exp. Biol.* 15:453–66.

55. Szabo, T. 1954. Un relais dans le système des connexions du lobe électrique de la Torpille. *Arch. Anat. Micr. Morph. Exp.* 43:187–201.

56. ———. 1955. Quelques précisons sur le noyau de commande centrale de la décharge électrique chez la Raie (*Raja clavata*). *J. Physiol. (Par.)* 47:283–85.

57. ———. 1957. Un noyau particulier dans la formation réticulée bulbaire de quatre poissons électriques appartenant à la famille des gymnotidae. *C. R. Acad. Sci.* 244: 1957–59.

58. ———. 1960. Development of the electric organ of mormyridae. *Nature* 188:760–62.

59. ———. 1961a. Les organes électriques des mormyrides. In *Bioelectrogenesis*, ed. C. Chagas and A. Paes de Carvahlo, pp. 20–23. Amsterdam: Elsevier.

60. ———. 1961b. Anatomo-physiologie de centres nerveux spécifiques de quelques organes électriques. In *Bioelectrogenesis*, ed. C. Chagas and A. Paes de Carvahlo, pp. 187–201. Amsterdam: Elsevier.

61. ———. 1965. Sense organs of the lateral line system in some electric fish of the gymnotidae, mormyridae, and gymnarchidae. *J. Morph.* 117:229–50.

62. ———. 1968. Activity in peripheral and central neurons involved in electroreception. In *Lateral line detectors*, ed. P. Cahn, pp. 295–311. Bloomington: Univ. of Indiana Press.

63. Szabo, R., and Fessard, A. 1965. Le fonctionnement des électrorécepteurs étudie chez les mormyres. *J. Physiol. (Par.)* 57:343–60.

64. Szabo, T., and Suckling, E. E. 1964. L'arrêt occasionel de la décharge électrique continue du *Gymnarchus* est-il une réaction naturelle? *Naturwissenschaften* 51:92–94.

65. Waltman, B. 1966. Electrical properties and fine structure of the ampullary canals of Lorenzini. *Acta Physiol. Scand. Suppl.* 264:1–60.

66. Watanabe, A., and Takeda, K. 1963. The change of discharge frequency by a.c. stimulus in a weak electric fish. *J. Exp. Biol.* 40:57–66.

2

Effects of Low Temperature on Conditioning in Goldfish

C. Ladd Prosser / Toshio Nagai

Department of Physiology and Biophysics
University of Illinois, Urbana

Metabolic adaptations to heat and cold in fish are of two sorts—those which are genetically fixed and those which are acquired by individual fish in the process of acclimation. The net effect of metabolic adaptations is to permit biochemical and behavioral activity over a wide range of temperatures, that is, to compensate for cold or heat. In addition to metabolic adaptations, and as a first line of defense against the inexorable limitations of life processes by temperature, there are behavioral adaptations. It may well be that oxygen consumption is determined by behavioral requirements rather than that behavior is limited by available metabolic energy (Fisher 1958). The object of this paper is to summarize some of our experiments on central nervous system compensation during temperature acclimation in fish.

It is well known that species of fish from cold waters are capable of behavior at lower temperatures than are warm-water fish. These differences are partly genetic, partly environmentally induced. The limits within which acclimatory effects can occur are determined genetically. The temperatures of cold block of conduction in peripheral nerves of some leg nerves in birds (Chatfield, Lyman, and Irving 1953) and of tail nerves in rodents (Miller 1965) can be lowered by prior exposure to low temperatures. In catfish nerves, the temperature of cold block of conduction is near $0°$ C and is very little altered by temperature acclimation (Prosser and Farhi 1965). However, spinal reflexes show cold block at higher temperatures (up to $10°$ C) and are affected by temperature of acclimation (Roots and Prosser 1962). This agrees with earlier evidence that transmission at neuromuscular junctions and synapses is more sensitive to low temperature than is nerve conduction (Battle 1926).

Measurements of maximum rate of swimming at different temperatures revealed a low temperature below which swimming failed, a temperature of maximum swimming rate, and an upper temperature above which swimming failed (Roots and Prosser 1962). The cold-blocking temperature for coordinated swimming was higher than the temperatures for block of spinal reflexes, and the swimming temperatures were much altered according to acclimation. The increasing range of variation of limiting low temperatures according to complexity of the nervous function and the corresponding increasing dependence on acclimation are shown in Figure 1.

A higher level of neural complexity was examined in conditioned reflexes (Prosser and Farhi 1965). Conditioned behavior in a shuttle box was shown to be more temperature sensitive than was maximum swimming. Breathing movements of goldfish were conditioned to be interrupted by a flash of light by pairing flashes with a shock as the unconditioned stimulus. When the conditioned fish were then cooled, the conditioned response was lost

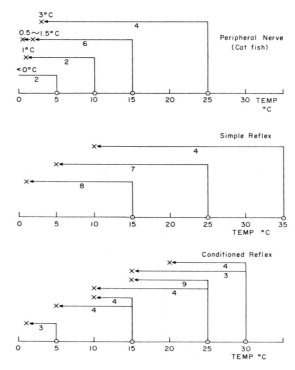

FIG. 1. Representations of blocking temperatures for conduction in peripheral nerves, for spinal reflexes, and for conditioned respiratory reflexes. From data in Prosser and Farhi (1965) and Roots and Prosser (1962). Temperatures on *X*-axis are of acclimation and for conditioned reflexes are also temperatures of conditioning. Blocking temperatures indicated by *X*'s. Numbers of goldfish tested are given below horizontal lines.

at some critical temperature. Some fish became conditioned readily, others less easily. Cold block of the conditioned response was usually reversible. The temperature of cold block was proportional to the temperature at which conditioning had occurred (Figs. 1, 2). Also, a minimum temperature for conditioning was found; this depended upon prior temperature of acclimation (Fig. 2). Thus the three temperatures—acclimation, minimum temperature for conditioning, and temperature of cold block of the response—were related but not proportional.

We then examined electrical responses of the optic tectum of the fish to flashes of light. Preliminary results were reported for *Leuciscus* and *Tinca* (Prosser 1965) and experiments on *Carassius auratus* follow. Evoked potentials were detected extracellularly by either saline-filled capillaries, electrolytically sharpened stainless steel electrodes, or platinized indium electrodes. After an experiment with a steel needle the final position was checked by the Prussian blue reaction and histological examination. Once the normal pattern of response to light was established, the effects of cooling and of conditioning were examined. Light stimuli were provided as spots of variable brightness and of 1 mm diameter on a ground glass plate at the side of the bath, 5 cm from the left eye of the fish. Recording was from the right tectum.

At the surface of the tectum, spikes in afferent optic fibers were recorded, as described by Jacobson and Gaze (1964); these were not examined in detail in this study. At the surface

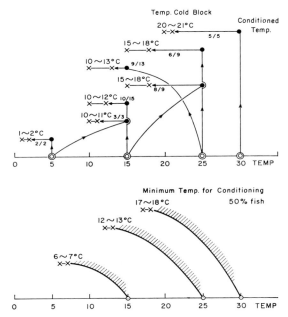

FIG. 2. Representations of relations between acclimation temperatures (on horizontal axis) and minimum temperature for conditioning of 50 per cent of group of fish (lower figure) and blocking temperatures (upper figure). In upper figure open circles represent acclimation temperatures; solid circles represent conditioning temperatures and X's represent blocking temperatures for fraction of fish indicated. From data in Prosser and Farhi (1965).

and in the 200–300 μ granular subsurface layer a negative evoked response was recorded with latency of 50–60 msec to both the "on" and "off" of the light (Figs. 3, 4*f*). At high intensities (approximately 10× threshold) a second negative wave appeared ahead of the first one, as found by Konishi (1960).

When one electrode was at the point of maximal response on the tectum, a second electrode placed at various points surrounding it recorded smaller negative responses (Fig. 3). No positivity lateral to a focus of negativity was found. However, as the active lead penetrated to greater depths (approximately 300 μ) a positive wave replaced part and then mirrored all of the negative wave (Fig. 4*d, c*). Positive responses were recorded throughout the central gray zone. Similar reversal of polarity of evoked responses was observed in the catfish optic tectum by Buser (1955). At greater depths (400–500 μ) the positive response broadened and at approximately 700 μ the sign of the response reversed so that in this region of many neuronal cell bodies a second (deep) negative evoked response appeared (Fig. 4*a*). The deep negative response was less reliably obtained and seemed to be more sensitive to the condition of the fish than the subsurface response. The positivity in the midlayers is broad and serves as an electrical source for both subsurface and deep negative potentials.

The latency of the deep negative evoked response was 10 to 20 msec longer than the latency of the subsurface negative response (Fig. 4*a*). It is postulated that at least one inter-neurone exists in the path between the two responses. When the Prussian blue test was applied at the point where the deep negative response was obtained, a blue spot corresponded to the deposit of ferricyanide at the level of the dense layer of pyriform cell bodies. The region of positivity corresponded to the layer of dendrites where there are very few cell bodies. It is concluded that the recorded evoked responses constitute "field" potentials in a vertical negative-positive-negative orientation.

Cooling of the brain was effected by passing cold water through the mouth and over the gills. Brain temperatures, monitored by thermistors, showed little or no difference between tectal surface and deep layers.

Figure 5 shows the blocking effect of cooling on the evoked responses. Before blocking, the amplitudes decreased and the latencies of the evoked responses lengthened. The deep negative response was more sensitive to cooling than the surface one; it blocked at a higher temperature, and on rewarming it recovered later than the subsurface response.

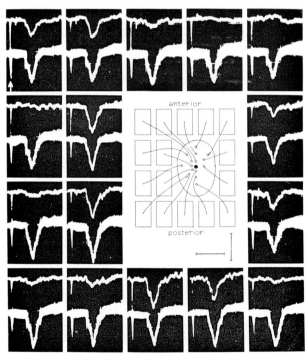

FIG. 3. Map showing distribution of subsurface slow negative "on" response around central focus of maximum response. Lower records from electrode which remained at point of maximum response as indicated by solid dot. Upper records from an electrode which was moved to points indicated in diagram by small circles. Calibrations 100 msec and 0.4 mv. Distance from anterior to posterior limits 3 mm and from medial to lateral limits 2.5 mm.

The temperature for cold block of the evoked responses was influenced by the temperature of prior acclimation of the fish, as shown in Table 1.

Shocks were applied to the flank of the fish simultaneously with termination of the 200–1,000 msec light flash. The intensity of shock was below that needed to elicit a twitch of the tail. Intervals between the paired presentations were usually 30 sec (sometimes 15 sec) and a record of the response to light alone was photographed after every 10 or 20 reinforced trials. After approximately 150 paired presentations of flashes and shocks, the evoked responses changed by the appearance of a second response later than the direct response (Figs. 6c, 7d). Out of nine different fish in which both subsurface and deep negative evoked responses were recorded, in six a conditioned second response appeared at each level, in two it appeared only at the deep layer, and in one only in the subsurface response. Occasionally a second conditioned response appeared after the first one (Figs. 6d, 7e). The principal conditioned response started approximately 105 msec after the beginning of the first response in the subsurface layer, 110 msec later than the direct response in the deeper layer (Table 2).

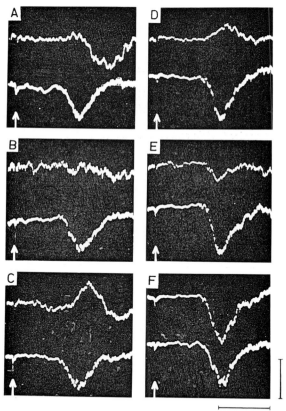

Fig. 4. Deep and subsurface evoked "on" responses to flashes of light. In all records, lower recording is from subsurface electrode and beginning of flash is indicated by arrow. Upper recordings are from an electrode which was raised from the deep layers with responses as follows: *a*, deep negative at 750 μ level; *b*, neutral region at 650 μ; *c*, mid-positive response at 500 μ; *d*, less positive response at 200 μ; *e*, beginning of subsurface negative response at 30 μ; *f*, both electrodes at same subsurface level. Time 50 msec, voltage 0.2 mv.

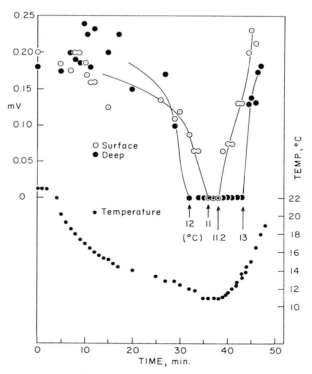

FIG. 5. Brain temperature (lower curve) recorded by a thermistor at surface. Amplitudes of slow negative responses recorded at surface (open circles) and at depth of pyriform cellular layer (solid circles) during cooling. Deep response lost earlier (12° C) and recovered later (13° C) than subsurface response which was blocked at 11° C and recovered at 11.2° C.

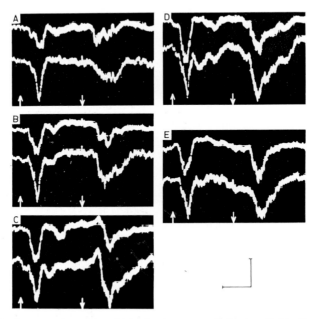

FIG. 6. Conditioning experiment in which shock was applied when light stimulus was terminated. Intervals between paired presentations 20 sec. Records show responses to light alone at various times during conditioning and extinction. Records of "on" and "off" slow negative responses recorded at subsurface (lower records) and deep (upper records) levels. *a*, control; *b*, after 50 paired presentations; *c*, after 150 paired presentations showing conditioned second response at "on" and enhanced "off" response; *d*, after 250 paired presentations; *e*, extinction of conditioned response after 250 flashes without reinforcement. Time 200 msec, voltage 0.2 mv.

TABLE 1

TEMPERATURES OF COLD BLOCK OF EVOKED NEGATIVE RESPONSES

FISH TESTED	ACCLIMATION TEMPERATURE: 15° C		ACCLIMATION TEMPERATURE: 25° C	
	Surface Response	Deep Response	Surface Response	Deep Response
Different fish...................	4°–5° C (5)	5°–8° C (8)	9°–12° C (5)	10°–12.5° C (4)
Same fish: simultaneous records from surface and depth.............	4° C (4)	6° C (4)	11° C (3)	12° C (3)

NOTE: Number of fish tested in parentheses.

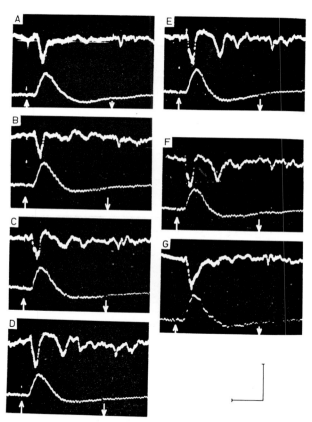

FIG. 7. Simultaneous records of slow negative subsurface "on" responses (upper records) and electro-retinograms (lower records) obtained from wick electrode on cornea and small silver coil at back of eye. Conditioning by shock at end of each illumination; interval between paired presentations 15 sec. *a*, control; *b*, after 60 paired presentations; *c*, 120 presentations; *d*, after 200 paired presentations, conditioned response follows initial response; *e*, after 200 presentations, double conditioned response; *f*, after 60 flashes without reinforcement; *g*, extinction after 250 flashes without reinforcement. Time 200 msec, voltage 0.5 mv for tectal response, 0.1 mv for ERG.

177

If, after a conditioned response was established, the light intensity was increased to give the double direct response, the conditioned response was seen to have a much longer latency (approximately 150 msec) than the second direct response (40 msec). Figure 7 shows that the retinal potential did not change while the conditioned response was established. Hence, the conditioning was not a sensitization to light. Repeated flashes of light alone failed to induce the late response; also, repeated shocks with occasional tests by flashes failed to induce the response. Attempts at reverse conditioning, i.e., with shock preceding or occurring simultaneously with the onset of the flash, did not result in a conditioned response. It seems clear from these controls that the delayed second responses are truly conditioned as a result of pairing light with shock.

When shocks were omitted after the conditioned response was established, extinction occurred after 100–200 flashes (Figs. 6e, 7g). Time for extinction at 3 or 4 flashes per min ranged at room temperature (23° C) from 25 to 80 min. During conditioning trials the latency of the conditioned response declined to a constant value and during extinction the

TABLE 2

AVERAGE LATENCIES AND RANGES OF LATENCIES OF DIRECT
EVOKED "ON" RESPONSES AND OF
CONDITIONED "ON" RESPONSES

(In Milliseconds)

SURFACE		DEEP	
Direct	Conditioned	Direct	Conditioned
55 (40–70)	161 (140–200)	65 (50–80)	176 (140–300)

NOTE: Number of fish tested: surface, 10; deep, 6.

latency lengthened until the response disappeared. Two fish were left in darkness without shocks and were tested for conditioned response at approximately 15-min intervals. The response was lost in one fish at 150 min, while the other continued to give conditioned responses after 200 min. Thus the conditioned response is lost faster on repeated stimulation by flashes than in constant darkness.

When both lobes of the forebrain and thalamus were removed by suction prior to a conditioning series, the conditioned modification of evoked responses occurred much as in normal fish. Also, when a cut was made between the two optic lobes (but not across the floor of the brainstem) the conditioned response was recorded from the right optic tectum when the stimulus was to the left eye. It appears, therefore, that the forebrain and the contralateral tectum are not necessary for the modification. When afferent spikes were recorded by an amplifier of short time-constant simultaneously with the slow evoked response, no burst of spikes corresponding to the late conditioned response occurred. This indicates that the modification of evoked responses occurs within the cortex.

The effect of cooling was to block the conditioned response more readily than the normal unconditioned evoked response (Fig. 8). The deep-layer conditioned response was cold blocked at a higher temperature than the subsurface conditioned response and each of these at higher temperatures than the direct responses. Blocking of the conditioned response by cold was reversible (Fig. 8l). When stimulation by light flashes was continued at 5° C, even though the response was blocked, extinction did not occur and the response was present on rewarming and was then readily extinguished. Thus the conditioned response persisted longer at 5° C than at 20° C. Various combinations of conditioning and acclimation temperatures have not yet been examined, but the conditioned response is clearly more sensitive to low temperature than is the normal evoked response. Blocking temperatures are influenced by acclimation temperature.

The preceding observations show that in fish, those nervous functions which involve synaptic transmission and "higher order" integration are sensitive to cooling. There is no reason to associate the conditioned respiratory response with the conditioned electrical response in the tectum, but both are very sensitive to cooling. The long latency of the conditioned response of the tectum is compatible with the theory of conditioning in reverberating networks. The critical steps which are most sensitive to cooling remain to be identified. Whether the conditioned evoked response is at a site of primary change or whether it is recorded downstream from such a site cannot be decided on present evidence.

In terms of theory of temperature adaptation, the effects of temperature on behavior appear to have a basis in modification of electrical responses in the tectal cortex. It is hoped

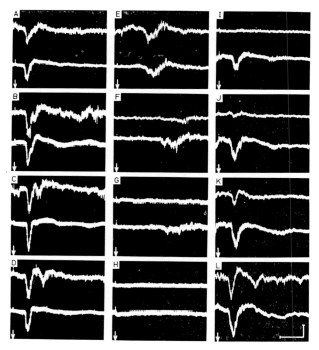

Fig. 8. Effect of cooling on conditioned response in 15° C-acclimated fish. Negative "on" responses recorded from deep cellular layer (upper records) and from subsurface layer (lower records). Unconditioned stimuli (shocks) applied at end of light flashes, interval between paired presentations 30 sec. Reinforcement continued during cooling. Responses *a, b,* and *c* at 22.5° C. *a,* control; *b,* after 130 paired presentations; *c* after 180 paired presentations, deep negative conditioned response, no surface conditioning; *d,* start of cool-ing, brain temperature 20° C; *e,* brain temperature 9° C; *f,* brain temperature 6° C; *g,* brain temperature 5° C; *h,* brain temperature 4.8° C. Warming started between *h* and *i*. Brain temperature at *i,* 7° C, at *j,* 8° C, at *k,* 12° C, at *l,* 19.5° C. Note decreasing sensitivities to cooling in following order: deep conditioned response, deep unconditioned response, subsurface evoked response. Time 200 msec, voltage 0.1 mv.

that, by making use of differences in temperature sensitivity, it may be possible to make a kinetic analysis of both the direct evoked responses and the conditioned responses.

Acknowledgment

This research was supported by National Science Foundation Grant GB-4005.

References

Battle, H. J. 1926. Effects of extreme temperatures on muscle and nerve tissues in marine fishes. *Tr. Roy. Soc. Canada Ser. III* 20:127–43.

Buser, P. 1955. *Analyse des réponsés électriques du lobe optique à la stimulation de la voie visuelle chez quelques vertébrés inférierus.* Paris: Masson.

Chatfield, P. O.; Lyman, C. P.; and Irving, L. 1953. Physiological adaptation to cold of peripheral nerve in the leg of the herring gull (*Larus argentatus*). *Amer. J. Physiol.* 172: 639–44.

Fisher, K. C. 1958. An approach to the organ and cellular physiology of adaptation to temperature in fish and small mammals. In *Physiological adaptation*, ed. C. L. Prosser, pp. 3–49. Washington: American Physiol. Soc.

Jacobson, M., and Gaze, R. M. 1964. Types of visual responses from single units in the optic tectum and optic nerve of the goldfish. *J. Exp. Physiol.* 49:199–209.

Konishi, J. 1960. Electric response of visual center in fish, especially to colored light flash. *Jap. J. Physiol.* 10:13–27.

Leghissa, S. 1955. La struttura microscopica e la citoarchitettonica del tetto ottico dei pesci teleostei. *Z. Anat. Entwicklungsgesch.* 118:427–63.

Miller, L. K. 1965. Activity in mammalian peripheral nerves during supercooling. *Science* 149:74–75.

Prosser, C. L. 1965. Electrical responses of fish optic tectum to visual stimulation: Modification by cooling and conditioning. *Z. Vergl. Physiol.* 50:102–18.

Prosser, C. L., and Farhi, E. 1965. Effects of temperature on conditioned reflexes and on nerve conduction in fish. *Z. Vergl. Physiol.* 50:91–101.

Roots, B. I., and Prosser, C. L. 1962. Temperature acclimation and the nervous system in fish. *J. Exp. Biol.* 39:617–29.

3

The Use of Poikilothermy in the Analysis of Behavior

Paul Rozin

Department of Psychology
University of Pennsylvania

Introduction

Progress in many areas of biology has been contingent upon the selection of an organism ideally suited for the study of the problem at hand. In the study of behavior, and particularly of relatively complex and plastic behavior involving motivation and learning, there has been a great emphasis on the homotherms (mammals and birds). In order to understand this behavior it would be nice to simplify it; that is, to study similar kinds of behavior in simple systems. One way to simplify a system is to damage it, by brain transections or lesions; another is to study an organism at a simpler level of organization. In this regard, the teleost fish offer some unique opportunities. Their behavior is in many ways as complex as that of mammals and birds; notably, they show the same basic phenomena of learning and motivation. They learn with amazing rapidity. It is only through rather sophisticated investigations that it has been possible to show differences in learning abilities in fish, birds, and mammals (Bitterman 1966). Fish, in contrast to the other poikilothermic vertebrates (reptiles and amphibians), are as a group very active and easy to teach and to motivate. They may be the only poikilotherms that show these great similarities to the mammals and birds. It is then possible that some of the complex phenomena of mammal and bird behavior can be studied in the fish with the added advantage that, because they are poikilothermic, wide control over their metabolic rate can be exercised. In this paper, I would like to give four examples of the use of poikilothermy to investigate some general issues in behavior. All these examples deal directly or indirectly with the learning abilities of goldfish. Goldfish have been selected partly because of their availability and partly because they can function well over a very wide temperature range.

Poikilothermy and Motivated Behavioral Temperature Regulation

Poikilothermy puts a fundamental limitation on animals. Their behavioral capacity or potential is under the fairly strict control of environmental temperature. The phenomenon of temperature adaptation or acclimation produces some long-term "independence" of the thermal environment, but over the short run it is fair to say that the activity and capabilities of the fish or other poikilotherms decline with falling temperatures, within the normal range.

It has been shown that rats can learn an arbitrary response in order to increase their body temperature. Weiss and Laties (1960) have trained shaved rats in the cold to press a lever in order to turn on a heat lamp above them for a few seconds. Of course, in the mammal body temperature can be controlled under most circumstances by internal "non-behavioral" adjustments. Over the short run the fish must rely on behavioral means to regulate its body temperature; i.e., it must swim to some place where the temperature is more comfortable. There are some data suggesting that fish will congregate at optimal temperatures and select particular temperatures in temperature gradients (Fry 1947). Some of this behavior might be accounted for as automatic or involuntary (Fisher and Elson 1950); in other words, as a taxis of some sort. It would be particularly adaptive for poikilotherms to be able to *learn* certain responses which would lead to changes in environmental temperature. For example, fish might learn that a certain portion of a lake is characteristically warmer than other portions, and go there when the temperature drops, even if there is no clear temperature gradient leading to this site. The well-developed learning ability of the fish, combined with a motivating effect of certain temperature changes, could provide the fish with a powerful independence of its environment. It should be pointed out that voluntary behavioral thermoregulation can be demonstrated only in an animal capable of learning an operant; among the poikilotherms, fish are certainly best at this.

The first experiment poses the question: If given the opportunity, will a fish regulate its environmental temperature? (Rozin and Mayer 1961b.) In other words, Are fish poikilotherms because they can't help it or because they don't care? Small goldfish were placed in a 1-pt container of water at about 25° C, the temperature to which they were adapted. This small container was placed in a large water bath of the same temperature (see Fig. 1). After the fish were placed in the small container, the temperature of the outside bath was gradually raised over a period of about one-half hour to 41° C, the lethal temperature for these fish. When the temperature in the experimental (small) container reached between 30° and 35° C, training was begun. Measured amounts of cold water were introduced into the container at irregular intervals. Each cold reinforcement consisted of a 1-sec flow of cold water (2 to 3 ml) from a tube mounted above the container, and produced a transient drop in the temperature of approximately 0.3° C (at 35° C). A small light bulb mounted above the container was lighted during the 1-sec reinforcement. Each fish received approximately 50 reinforcements in each of two training sessions.

In the third session, a lever (Hogan and Rozin 1961) was placed in the container, with the lever target located behind a hole in a Plexiglas sheet (see Fig. 1). In order to actuate the lever, the fish had to put its head through the hole and push at the target. The lever guard prevented chance operation by the swimming movements of the fish. When the temperature rose above 30° C, training for lever pressing was begun. The method of "successive approximations" was used: the reinforcement is first given whenever the animal is near the lever, then when the animal touches the lever, and finally only when the animal actually presses the lever. Most fish learned to press the lever within two hours after the onset of training. Seven small goldfish were trained.

The fish were then placed in a "titration" situation. The temperature of the water bath rose gradually and leveled off at 41° C. By pressing the lever for squirts of cold water, the fish could lower the temperature of the water in its container. The temperature in the outside bath was maintained at 41° C for the entire session, once it had reached this level. Thus, a constant temperature stress was provided for the fish.

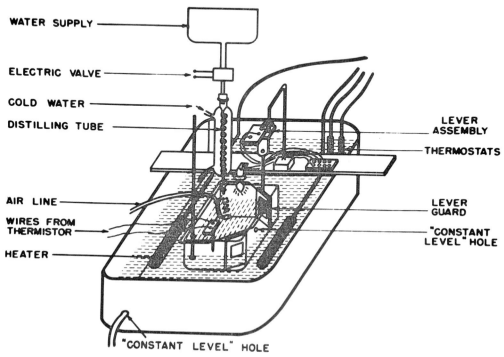

FIG. 1. Device for the study of regulatory behavior in the goldfish. 1, water supply; 2, electric valve; 3, cold water; 4, distilling tube; 5, air line; 6, wires from thermistor; 7, heater; 8, "constant level" hole; 9, lever assembly; 10, thermostats; 11, lever guard; 12, "constant level" hole (Rozin and Mayer 1961b).

Once the fish were trained, they were run in experimental sessions lasting two hours. In the first series of experiments (Experiment 1 in Table 1), the lever was not made available to the fish until the temperature in the small container had reached 38° C. The lever pressing responses and temperature were recorded continuously during the 2-hour period. Under these conditions fish would press the lever rapidly when it was first made available, typically driving the temperature down to about 35° C (see panel B, Fig. 2). After this the fish usually responded sufficiently frequently to maintain the temperature in the range 32°–36° C (see Table 1, fish SG 108 and SG 106, low reinforcement size). The "selected" temperature of around 35° was considerably higher than the temperature selected by goldfish with similar thermal histories but tested in a gradient (Fry 1947). In order to see whether this difference could be due to the increased work required in this experiment as opposed to swimming in a gradient, reinforcement size was doubled, so that fish got twice as much cold water and a drop of approximately 0.5°–0.6° per press (at 35° C), (Rozin 1961). Under these circumstances (see Table 1 and panel *A* of Fig. 2) fish usually maintained a somewhat lower temperature. Therefore, it appears that to some extent the high temperature setting may be influenced by the amount of work required to produce a thermal change in the environment. However, the fish definitely did not halve their response rate in response to a doubled reinforcement (Table 1).

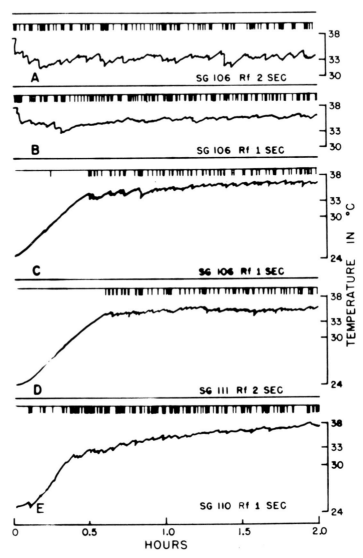

Fig. 2. Some typical records of individual thermoregulation sessions. In each panel, the top line indicates lever presses, as downward deflections, and the bottom line graphs temperature in the small container in ° C. Panel *A*, Fish SG 106, session begins at 38° C, double reinforcement (2 sec); Panel *B*, Fish SG 106, session begins at 38° C, standard reinforcement (1 sec); Panel *C*, Fish SG 106, session begins at 25° C, standard reinforcement (1 sec); Panel *D*, Fish SG 111, session begins at 25° C, double reinforcement (2 sec); Panel *E*, Fish SG 110, session begins at 25° C, standard reinforcement (1 sec); Panels *B, C, E* from Rozin and Mayer (1961*b*); Panels *A* and *D* from Rozin (1961).

A second series of experiments (Experiment 2 in Table 1) explored further the meaning of the particular temperature set by the fish, and particularly the lower limit of responding. In these experiments fish were allowed access to the lever from the beginning of the session at 25° C. In this situation fish were able to maintain their tank at a given temperature with less work than under the first procedure, because they were not required to bring the temperature down initially to the selected level. Furthermore, the procedure allowed determination of the temperature at which responding began. Under these conditions the fish usually did not respond at all (Fig. 2c, d) until the temperature rose to the neighborhood of 33° C. Occasionally a significant amount of responding occurred before this point was reached. The temperatures maintained in the last hour and a half of these sessions were approximately the same as (and if anything, higher than) those selected in the first experiment (see Table 1).

TABLE 1

FISH	EXPERIMENT 1					CONTROL[a]	
	Reinforcement Size	Number of Sessions	Mean Responses	Mean[b] High	Mean[b] Low	Number of Sessions	Mean Responses
SG 108	Low	3	164	36.3	33.2	3	20
	High	3	105	36.5	32.6	3	19
SG 106	Low	4	155	36.3	33.8	4	36
	High	4	124	35.3	30.9	4	32
	EXPERIMENT 2						
SG 106	Low	4	140	36.1	34.2		
SG 109	Low	4	118	37.7	35.2		
	High	4	76	37.2	34.5		
SG 110	Low	4	105	37.6	35.4		
	High	4	78	36.9	33.6		

[a] During control sessions, the temperature in the outside bath was held at 25° C.

[b] In Experiment 1 mean high is the average of the highest temperature recorded over the last 110 min of each of the three or four sessions under each condition. Mean low is the average of the corresponding lowest temperatures. In Experiment 2, the mean high and low were determined for the second hour of each session.

Again, the high level of reinforcement led to slightly lower temperatures (Table 1), but the reduction in responses was not proportional to the change in reinforcement.

Control experiments have indicated that the increased activity of the fish at higher temperatures and the slight increase in oxygen tension of the water associated with reinforcement are not important factors controlling thermoregulatory behavior in this situation.

Apparently, goldfish can be motivated to learn an arbitrary response in order to produce a change in ambient temperature. Given the opportunity, they will function as homotherms.

Poikilothermy and Feeding

The analysis of hunger has been carried out almost entirely in mammals. It would be desirable to understand the parallel processes in fish and other animals in order to get some idea of how the sophisticated mammalian food intake and food motivation system has evolved. In particular, fish offer special advantages in the study of this problem. First, the study of hunger and feeding in mammals has been confounded by complicated interactions (at both the behavioral and neurological levels) between hunger and thirst (behavioral water regulation). If, as seems reasonable, fish do not have a system of behavioral water regulation, they might indeed prove a simpler preparation for studying hunger and feeding. Second, the hypothalamus in fish is in many ways similar to the mammalian hypothalamus (see Aronson [1963] for a recent review of the fish nervous system). Yet in contrast to mammals, fish have only a moderately developed forebrain, so that modulation of the hypothalamic activity by higher centers may be less extensive in the fish. In fact, the feeding of fish seems to be relatively undisturbed by forebrain removal (Rozin, unpublished, and see Aronson [1963] for a review of the effects of forebrain removal in fish), assuming that the species in question does not use olfaction as a primary means of identifying food. Third, fish are poikilotherms, which means that their metabolic rate and food requirements can be manipulated over very wide ranges. The poikilothermy takes on particular importance in light of what are presently believed to be the major factors modulating food intake in the mammal. A variety of metabolic and other signals seem to be integrated and evaluated in the mammalian hypothalamus in order to determine whether eating will or will not occur. It is difficult to dissect out the components of this multiple control system directly, although considerable success has been achieved along these lines in the analysis of the recovery from brain lesions damaging the feeding system (Teitelbaum and Epstein 1962), and in the analysis of the development of feeding (Teitelbaum, Cheng, and Rozin 1967). One of the most well-documented components in mammalian food regulation is "thermostatic." Brobeck (1957) and his colleagues have argued cogently for the importance of internal temperature changes and temperature regulation in controlling food intake. In the fish such factors should not be present. Therefore it might be possible to look at a system of regulation of food intake similar to the mammalian system but lacking a thermostatic component. Indeed, the response of fish to increased temperature is an increased food intake (Rozin and Mayer 1961*a*), while mammals respond to temperature increase by a decrease in food intake.

The characteristics of regulation of food intake in fish, measured as the number of pellets eaten in a lever-pressing situation, seem quite similar to the regulation of food intake in mammals. Notably, both rats and fish respond more or less quantitatively to changes in the caloric density of their diet. They tend to keep their day-to-day caloric intake constant, and therefore more or less double the volume of food intake if the caloric content of the diet is halved (Rozin and Mayer 1961*a*). In contrast to this sophisticated "caloric" regulation, both rats and goldfish show a disappointing response to food deprivation. Both species increase their food intake only slightly following moderately long periods of food deprivation (Rozin 1961; Rozin and Mayer 1964; Bare and Cicala 1960). Also, both maintain food intake relatively constant when the work load (number of presses required per pellet) is varied over a wide range (Teitelbaum 1955; Rozin and Mayer 1964). One might presume that the similarities in fish and rat regulation represent the working of components other than the thermostatic one. That is, it is possible that the mammalian regulation includes the basic components of fish regulation, with the thermostatic and other components added. Further analysis of food regulation in fish is required in order to evaluate the implications of the lack of thermostatic control. It is interesting that forebrainless fish (hypothalamic animals) show the basic features of regulation in normal fish, including caloric compensation (Rozin, unpublished). This seems to be a promising preparation for the analysis of feeding.

Poikilothermy and Timing

Rhythmic phenomena are of great interest and great importance in all organisms. Biological clocks seem to be present wherever they are looked for (Bünning 1964; Harker 1964). The most common appears to have a period of about 24 hours (circadian rhythms). The timing mechanisms responsible for these rhythms are not yet understood. Most workers feel that the rhythm is endogenously generated, though it has been suggested that subtle environmental periodicities may be responsible for this regularity in behavior (Brown 1962). There is no question that the more salient environmental periodicities such as temperature and light cycles cannot entirely account for rhythms. On the other hand, a simple metabolic hypothesis is also not tenable, since a number of circadian rhythms have been shown to be temperature independent, i.e., independent of metabolic rate (Bünning 1964; Harker 1964).

In addition to the massive literature on biological clocks, there is a smaller literature on short-term learned discriminations of temporal intervals in birds and mammals. Here again, the mechanism by which animals discriminate intervals of the order of minutes is unknown. It seems quite unreasonable that periodic environmental cues could be used, as the intervals involved are arbitrary and very short. It is possible that (*a*) a simple metabolic clock is involved, (*b*) a sophisticated temperature-independent clock is involved, or (*c*) short-term timing in mammals and birds is accompanied by some sort of behavioral pacing, such as counting or moving back and forth between two points a certain number of times. The understanding of the basis of these short-term temporal discriminations, with possible fallout to the understanding of biological clocks, would be advanced if such a discrimination could be studied in a poikilotherm, since metabolic rate (temperature) could be varied over a wide range. As of a few years ago there were no good studies on short-term temporal discriminations for arbitrary time intervals in any poikilotherms.

Recently, a short temporal discrimination was reported in a single gourami fish (Wolf and Baer 1963), and further evidence was reported in goldfish (Rozin 1965). Goldfish were first trained to press a lever for food reinforcement. When the fish were responding well the reinforcement was made available only once every minute (fixed interval 1 min or FI–1). After the fish had received a worm (Hogan and Rozin 1961) for pressing the lever, a light above the tank was operated for 5 sec. During this time the lever was inoperative. When the light went off a 1-min timer began operation. While the timer was operating, lever presses were recorded but not reinforced. At the end of 1 min the reinforcement was again made available; the next time the fish pressed the lever, it received one worm. The 1-min timer started again when the light-accompanying reinforcement went off.

Rats and pigeons show a characteristic performance after several sessions of training on this FI–1 schedule. Typically, they do not respond in the period immediately following reinforcement, but afterward show a positively accelerating response rate, terminated by reinforcement. The three fish used in this experiment developed a similar pattern of response after they were exposed to this schedule for 30 to 60 sessions of approximately 30 min each. In order to analyze the temporal discrimination, each 1-min interval was broken up into six consecutive 10-sec periods, and the response frequencies for these periods were tabulated. The three fish responded from three to eight times as often in the last 10 sec before reinforcement (sec 50–60) as they did in the first 10 sec of the 1-min interval.

This clear temporal discrimination allows a partial analysis of the mechanism of short-interval timing. Suppose that the fixed-interval behavior were invariant over a wide temperature range. This would suggest that a simple metabolic clock is not involved. Furthermore, it is untenable that the constancy could depend upon environmental cues, because of the brevity and arbitrariness of the time interval. Finally, it is possible to eliminate behavioral pacing as a mechanism of timing, since temperature changes drastically affect the rate of ongoing behavior and should therefore disrupt (spread out in time) any pacing mechanism.

The fixed-interval behavior of three goldfish was tested for temperature invariance. The fish were stabilized on FI–1 schedules for a period of 30 to 60 days at 30° C. When the discrimination was stabilized, studies of temperature dependence were begun. Two days of performance at 30° C were followed by two at 20° C, and then two at 30° C. These temperature changes were made within three hours following the end of the last session at either temperature. Each of the three fish was run five times on this six-day experimental series. Each six-day series was separated from the next by at least two additional days of regular sessions at 30° C. The temporal discrimination can be evaluated in terms of the relative response rate in each 10 sec of the 60-sec interval. Figure 3 shows these curves averaged over the 20 experimental sessions at 30° C (the number of responses in the first 10-sec period at each temperature was arbitrarily set at 10 and the other values were adjusted proportionally). The comparable curves for the 10 sessions at 20° C for each fish are shown in the same figure. Note that the curves for the two temperatures are in almost perfect agreement. In

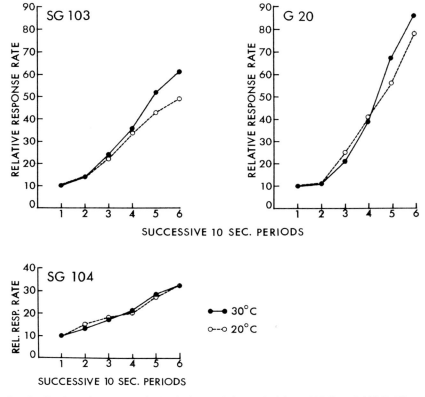

FIG. 3. Distribution of responses in 1-min interval for each fish at 30° C and 20° C. The number of responses in the first 10-sec period at each temperature was arbitrarily set at 10, and the other values were adjusted proportionately (Rozin 1965).

the case of temperature dependence, since the metabolic rate at 20° C is approximately half that at 30° C (Fry 1957), one might expect the 20° curve to rise half as quickly as the 30° curve. Thus it should take 20 sec for the 20° curve to rise the same amount as the 30° curve does in 10 sec. But this is clearly not the case. The correspondence between the curves is most impressive for fish G 20, as the relative response rate-curve shows a sharp inflection point at the same time (20 sec) at both temperatures. Although the relative response rate or temporal discrimination remains invariant, the absolute response rate (total number of responses in a half-hour session) shows clear temperature dependence. The three fish responded 1.86, 1.87, and 2.27 times as frequently at 30° as they did at 20°, so that their response rate approximately doubled along with their metabolic rate.

The temperature dependence of response rate and activity in general strongly suggests that this temporal discrimination is not based on behavioral pacing or counting. It should also be pointed out that the temperature invariance of relative response rate cannot be accounted for as a rapid relearning of a "new" time interval during the two days at 20° C. First of all, it takes a very long time to establish a temporal discrimination in goldfish. Second, in other experiments (Rozin 1965), it was shown that when goldfish are switched from an FI–1 to an FI–2 schedule, their performance on the first few days of FI–2 resembles their FI–1 performance, as opposed to the stabilized FI–2 performance they reach a few weeks later.

In summary, with the use of poikilothermy it has been possible to show that the goldfish times short intervals using an endogenous temperature-independent physiological clock, and that "behavioral pacing" cannot account for the temporal discrimination. This timing ability may depend upon the same mechanism involved in circadian rhythms.

Poikilothermy, Memory, and Forgetting

The study of learning, memory, and forgetting is a major concern of present-day physiological psychologists. One of the most basic issues in this area remains undecided: Are forgetting and learning two aspects of the same process, or are they fundamentally different? The assumption that they are the same is basic to the widely espoused interference theory of forgetting which holds that forgetting is essentially a kind of negative learning. Of course, if their underlying processes are the same, then for the moment they need not be studied separately. There is no question that, under certain circumstances, learning of some materials produces forgetting for other materials. Explicitly provided interference is well known to cause retention loss. New responses incompatible with the old responses will have a deleterious effect on the retention of the older responses (retroactive inhibition). Similarly, incompatible responses learned *prior* to the acquisition of the material to be ultimately tested interfere with the retention of this new material (proactive inhibition). But while there is abundant evidence that explicitly provided retroactive and proactive interference produces forgetting, we have no reason to believe that most instances of forgetting are due to such interference effects. The most likely alternative to an interference or "learning" theory of forgetting is that memory traces *decay* over time. The problem with this theory is that it is hard to formulate it in positive terms. What is decay? Is such an assumption more than an assertion that interference theory is inadequate? I would like to outline an experimental program presently being conducted by Henry Gleitman and myself, which is aimed at clarifying the role of decay in forgetting.

Is long-term forgetting a temperature-dependent process? Davis, Bright, and Agranoff (1965) have shown that consolidation of memory in goldfish is temperature dependent. Although electroconvulsive shock (ECS) does not have an amnesic effect when administered 2 hr after training at 18° C, it produces a significant effect when fish are cooled to 9° C during the 2 hr between training and ECS. We are directing ourselves to temperature dependence of long-term forgetting as opposed to consolidation. If forgetting is temperature dependent it should be accelerated by heating during the forgetting interval. Of course, if it turns out that either forgetting or learning, but not both, is temperature dependent, we would have very strong evidence that they are very different processes. There is some evidence suggesting a temperature dependence of forgetting over a 1-day interval in goldfish (French 1942), and a little evidence for temperature dependence of learning (Hoagland 1931).

In our preliminary experiments, we have trained goldfish to swim across a barrier while a light was flashing in order to avoid an electric shock in a shuttle box apparatus designed by Horner, Longo, and Bitterman (1961). The fish were maintained and trained at a temperature of 26° C. Two days after the goldfish acquired the avoidance response half of them were placed in tanks at 33° C for periods of four or eight weeks, while the remaining half stayed at 26° over the same time periods. Following this forgetting interval the fish were brought back to their original temperature and after a few days of adaptation, tested for retention of the avoidance response (at 26° C). Our preliminary data suggest that fish kept at higher temperatures (33° C) forget more than fish kept at lower temperatures (26° C). Control studies show that pretreatment at the high temperature (33° C) in itself does not interfere with the ability of the goldfish to acquire an avoidance response at 26° C. We are presently confirming and extending this finding.[1]

Of course, this temperature-dependence finding in itself does not provide strong evidence for decay. Although decay theory would certainly predict increased forgetting at higher temperatures (due to the acceleration of metabolism and a consequent increase in rate of breakdown of memory "traces"), interference theory could argue that both learning ability and stimulus input are increased at higher temperatures, so that there is a much greater opportunity for interference. We are attempting to eliminate such an interpretation by immobilizing or anesthetizing fish during the forgetting interval. We hope to show that the temperature dependence of forgetting holds even under circumstances where the fish should be incapable of learning during the interval between acquisition and testing. It is possible that poikilothermy may provide a means of establishing and analyzing the role and mechanism of decay processes in forgetting.

Acknowledgment

The preparation of this paper was aided by National Science Foundation Grant GB 4372 to the author.

[1] A recent repetition of this experiment in our laboratory, using temperatures of 10, 20 and 30° C, has failed to show temperature dependence of forgetting. Should the temperature *independence* conclusion hold true, contrary to our preliminary results, we would change the follow-up experiments described in the last paragraph. However, the basic logic of using poikilothermy to analyze the role of decay in forgetting is unaffected by the particular conclusion of this experiment.

References

Aronson, L. R. 1963. The central nervous system of sharks and bony fishes with special reference to sensory and integrative mechanism. In *Sharks and survival*, ed. P. W. Gilbert, pp. 165–241. Boston: D. C. Heath.

Bare, J., and Cicala, G. 1960. Deprivation and time of testing as determinants of food intake. *J. Comp. Physiol. Psychol.* 53:151–54.

Bitterman, M. E. 1966. Phyletic differences in learning. *Amer. Psychol.* 21:396–410.

Brobeck, J. 1957. Neural control of hunger, appetite, and satiety. *Yale J. Biol. Med.* 29:565–74.

Brown, F. A. 1962. Extrinsic rhythmicality: A reference frame for biological rhythms under so-called constant conditions. *Ann. N.Y. Acad. Sci.* 98:775–87.

Bünning, E. 1964. *The physiological clock*. New York: Academic Press.

Davis, R. E.; Bright, P. J.; and Agranoff, B. W. 1965. Effect of ECS and puromycin on memory in fish. *J. Comp. Physiol. Psychol.* 60:162–66.

Fisher, K. C., and Elson, P. F. 1950. The selected temperature of Atlantic salmon and speckled trout and the effect of temperature on the response to an electrical stimulus. *Physiol. Zool.* 23:27–34.

French, J. W. 1942. The effect of temperature on the retention of a maze habit in fish. *J. Exp. Psychol.* 31:79–87.

Fry, F. E. J. 1947. Effects of the environment on animal activity. *Publ. Ontario Fish. Res. Lab.* 55:5–62.

———. 1957. The aquatic respiration of fish. In *The physiology of fishes*, ed. M. E. Brown, vol. 1, pp. 1–64. New York: Academic Press.

Harker, J. E. 1964. *The physiology of diurnal rhythms*. Cambridge: Cambridge University Press.

Hoagland, H. 1931. A study of the physiology of learning in ants. *J. Gen. Psychol.* 5:21–41.

Hogan, J., and Rozin, P. 1961. An automatic device for dispensing food kept in a liquid medium. *J. Exp. Anal. Behav.* 4:81–83.

———. 1962. An improved mechanical fish-lever. *Amer. J. Psychol.* 75:307–8.

Horner, J. L.; Longo, N.; and Bitterman, M. E. 1961. A shuttle box for fish and a control circuit of general applicability. *Amer. J. Psychol.* 74:114–20.

Rozin, P. 1961. Some aspects of regulatory behavior in the goldfish, *Carassius auratus*. Ph.D. dissertation, Harvard University.

———. 1965. Temperature independence of an arbitrary temporal discrimination in the goldfish. *Science* 149:561–63.

Rozin, P., and Mayer, J. 1961a. Regulation of food intake in the goldfish. *Amer. J. Physiol.* 201:968–74.

———. 1961b. Thermal reinforcement and thermoregulatory behavior in the goldfish, *Carassius auratus*. *Science* 134:942–43.

———. 1964. Some factors influencing short-term food intake of the goldfish. *Amer. J. Physiol.* 206:1430–36.

Teitelbaum, P. 1955. Sensory control of hypothalamic hyperphagia. *J. Comp. Physiol. Psychol.* 48:156–63.

Teitelbaum, P.; Cheng, M.; and Rozin, P. 1968. Stages of recovery and development of lateral hypothalamic control of food and water intake. *Ann. N.Y. Acad. Sci.* In press.

Teitelbaum, P., and Epstein, A. N. 1962. The lateral hypothalamic syndrome: Recovery of feeding and drinking after lateral hypothalamic lesions. *Psychol. Rev.* 69:74–90.

Weiss, B., and Laties, V. G. 1960. Magnitude of reinforcement as a variable in thermoregulatory behavior. *J. Comp. Physiol. Psychol.* 53:603–8.

Wolf, M., and Baer, D. M. 1963. Discrimination, fixed interval and variable interval performance of a fish. *Amer. Psychol.* 18:444.

4

The Use of Fishes in Studies on Memory Formation

Bernard W. Agranoff/Roger E. Davis

Mental Health Research Institute and
Department of Biological Chemistry
The University of Michigan

In order to pursue the biological basis of memory, we require an animal that learns rapidly and that retains new behaviors for a long period of time. Fish appear to be the simplest readily available animals that fulfill these criteria. We have been attracted to the goldfish by the ease with which this species can be conditioned, and because we can train large numbers in the laboratory. Our first attempt at a "memory assay" involved a tracking task in which a fish was required to swim through an annular tank in order to avoid being shocked (Fig. 1) (Davis, Klinger, and Agranoff 1965). However, goldfish trained on this task showed only partial retention, and variability was too great for a convenient analysis of memory formation (Table 1).

We then became aware of the studies of Bitterman (Horner, Longo, and Bitterman 1961; Behrend and Bitterman 1964), who employed an efficient shuttle box procedure in which fish learned to avoid an electric shock paired with a light stimulus. We designed a version of this apparatus (Agranoff and Klinger 1964) consisting of six shuttle boxes with a central barrier and shock electrodes on either side. Trial cycles were programmed by a 1-rpm motor with a set of timing cams. Six fish were placed in individual shuttle boxes. After 5 min in the dark, signal lights were turned on at the end of the box where each animal had initially been placed (Fig. 2). If a fish swam over the barrier during the first 20 sec, an avoidance response was scored. For the next 20 sec, intermittent shock was administered in the lighted end of the shuttle box. Because the water over the barrier was shallow, shock was restricted to one end of the shuttle box. Animals who did not *avoid* the shock almost always *escaped* it by swimming over the barrier when the shock came on. The light remained on during the entire 20-sec shock period. At the end of the fortieth second of the trial, both shock and light were turned off for 20 sec. In successive trials, the presentation of the light and the shock was automatically alternated from one end of the shuttle box to the other. Since we were training fish to swim to the darkened end of the shuttle box, those failing to

193

escape during a trial missed the next trial. Missed trials were infrequent and usually occurred only during the first part of an experiment. A notable departure from the paradigm
described by Bitterman was that our animals were trained not to a criterion of responding,
but for a fixed number of trials over a fixed period of time. In the training session, fish were
in the shuttle boxes for 40 min and they received 20 trials in 4 blocks of 5, spaced by 5-min
intervals of darkness. Retention of the avoidance response was routinely evaluated 72 hr
later, by giving the fish 10 additional trials in a 20-min retraining session.

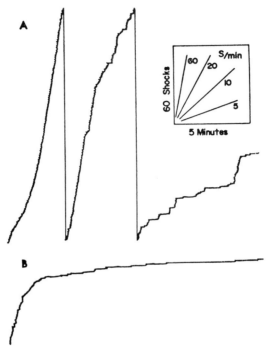

FIG. 1. Tracings of cumulative records of shocks received by goldfish A and B during their first training
session. These data are from a preliminary experiment with shock frequency of 60 per min. The record of A
is typical for naïve subjects. B shows unusually fast learning (from Davis, Klinger, and Agranoff 1965).

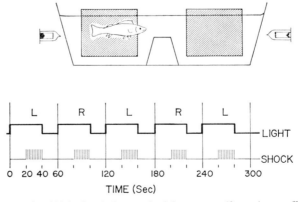

FIG. 2. Diagram of goldfish shuttle box and trial sequence (from Agranoff *et al.* 1966)

In our initial experiments, groups of 20 fish averaged about 2 avoidances in the first 10 trials; 3–4 in the second 10 trials; and about 5 in the 10 retraining trials. The fish showed rapid acquisition in keeping with our requirements for a memory assay. Furthermore, the scores for 21–30 did not appear to vary even when the training-retraining interval was increased to 30 days. That is, animals did not appear to forget the avoidance response.

In order to standardize conditions, incoming animals were kept in 200-gal tanks, then placed in individual home tanks about 12 hr prior to an experiment. They were kept in the home tanks in continuous light, without feeding, for the duration of an experiment. By running several hundred goldfish, we found that we could predict the number of avoidances made in the 10 retraining trials from the score a fish made in his 20 training trials. A prediction equation was obtained from data for control fish. It was used to evaluate the effect of an experimental treatment on retention. The difference between predicted and achieved scores (retention score) is a more reliable estimate of retention than the achieved score alone (Davis, Bright, and Agranoff, 1965). We have not resolved all the reasons for uncontrolled between-group variation in responding, but we have continued to examine the conditions of our behavioral assay.

TABLE 1

LIGHT-TRACKING IN THE GOLDFISH

	MEAN NUMBER OF SECONDS IN LIGHT DURING A 15-MIN SESSION					
	Day 1			Day 3		
	1–5	6–10	11–15 (min)	1–5	6–10	11–15 (min)
50 subjects with shock	52	104	153	97	180	213
F ratios		$F = 27.53$, df $= 2/147$, p $< .01$			$F = 23.47$, df $= 2/147$, p $< .01$	
24 subjects no shock	47	42	43	51	47	41
F ratios		$F < 1$, ns			$F < 1$, ns	

The average scores for trials 1–10 and 11–20 varied during the calendar year 1965 as shown in Figure 3. The data are from groups of 20–40 fish which received different experimental treatments following trial 20. The differences in treatment preclude an evaluation of monthly changes in group scores for trials 21–30. From May to August, when the level of responding is low, irregularities in retention occur which have so far eluded control. This period is correlated with problems in transport and with the breeding season of the goldfish.

As our research project broadened, we arranged shipment of the goldfish through the cooperation of Ozark Fisheries, Stoutland, Missouri. We routinely telephone Ozark weekly and arrange for shipment to be received by rail one to two days later. Plastic bags, each containing 100 goldfish, are shipped in insulated cardboard boxes. In the summer months, a cake of ice in a separate plastic bag is included in each box. Nevertheless, during the summer fish occasionally arrive in poor condition. Animals are selected by Ozark from stocks of common goldfish having a body length of 6–7 cm. After arrival in our laboratory in Ann Arbor, fish weighing between 8.5 and 11.0 gm are used for behavioral studies. Ordinarily the sex of the fish is not established, but we have observed that the gravid female does not fare well in transit or in the shuttle boxes. At some time during the summer, our size requirements will discriminate in favor of the shipment of the current year crop. Age has not been correlated with performance.

When we had a satisfactory assay of memory, we began to experiment with antibiotic antimetabolite drugs. Several laboratories have recently examined the effects of antimetabolites on animal behavior. In 1961, Dingman and Sporn reported that 8-azaguanine injected into rats blocked acquisition of a new swimming maze more than it impaired retention of performance of a previously learned one. These studies were followed by experiments by Chamberlain, Rothschild, and Gerard (1963) in which 8-azaguanine retarded fixation of a spinal asymmetry which otherwise appears after 45 min of central neuronal bombardment

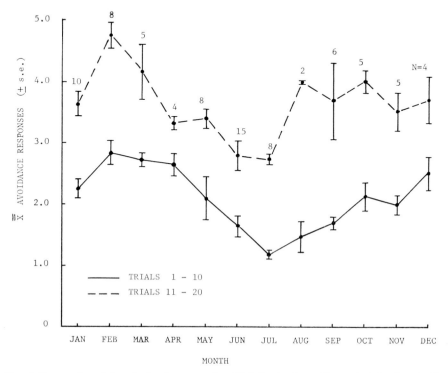

FIG. 3. Seasonal variation in day 1 scores of goldfish in shock-avoidance training (see text)

of the spinal cord. Flexner, Flexner, and Stellar (1963) reported that puromycin, an inhibitor of protein synthesis, could destroy memory in the mouse. We then studied this drug in the fish.

We developed a technique for rapidly injecting drugs into the cranial cavity of unanesthetized goldfish. Ten μl of solution are easily injected into the cranial space over the optic tectum by means of a Hamilton syringe with a 30-gauge needle (Agranoff and Klinger 1964). Some encouraging results with puromycin are shown in Table 2. A control group (72 fish) showed a significant increase in avoidances from the first to the second 10 trials. On retraining, 72 hr later, they performed at the level which was predicted on the basis of scores in their training trials. In practice, a difference between achieved and predicted scores of half a response is near the .05 level of significance. Fish injected with 10 μl of 0.15 M NaCl immediately following trial 20 were not significantly different from the uninjected ones. Another group of 36 fish was given 170 μgm of puromycin intracranially immediately following trial 20 and was then returned to the home tanks. These fish showed a memory loss as reflected in the retention score of -2.7. Since the achieved retraining score was not significantly different from the score for the first 10 training trials, we assume that puromycin obliterated all the memory of the avoidance training. The question can be raised whether the puromycin injection blocked memory or simply impaired the animals' ability to perform the avoidance response for several days. The latter possibility appears to be ruled out by a third group of animals (Table 2) given 20 trials, returned to home tanks, and then injected with puromycin 1 hr later. On retraining, the group showed normal retention. The injection of puromycin 30 min after training causes an intermediate memory deficit. The deficit also varies with the dose of puromycin (Agranoff, Davis, and Brink 1965).

These experiments suggest that puromycin disrupts time-dependent processes in memory storage occurring during the hour following training.[1] The time-dependent effects of puromycin on retention are consistent with the theory that memory is first laid down in a short-term form and that stable long-term memory depends on a fixation (consolidation)

TABLE 2

EFFECT OF PUROMYCIN INJECTED AFTER TRAINING ON MEMORY

NUMBER	TRIALS DAY 1		TREATMENT	TRIALS DAY 4		RETENTION SCORE (A–P)
	1–10	11–20		21–30 A	21–30 P	
72	2.3	3.4	Uninjected	5.3	5.3	0
36	2.5	3.8	Puromycin dihydrochloride 170 μg, immediate	2.7	5.4	−2.7
35	2.5	4.6	Puromycin dihydrochloride 170 μg, 60 min delay	5.5	5.6	−0.1

process which is completed after practice ceases (McGaugh 1966). We propose that puromycin impairs retention of the avoidance response by disrupting memory fixation. Fixation theory was previously based on experiments in mammals showing that long-term memory can be blocked by electroconvulsive shock (ECS) and by other agents which render an animal unconscious. In goldfish, we had obtained evidence not only that fixation occurs in a submammalian form, but that the process can be blocked without causing loss of consciousness.[2]

It has long been proposed that short-term memory is mediated by bioelectrical activity and that fixation represents the formation of structural changes in the brain which constitute long-term memory (Gerard 1961). Agents which cause unconsciousness could act by destroying short-term memory rather than by interfering with fixation. Since fish given puromycin remained alert, we had the opportunity to test its effect on the short-term memory manifested during the training session. We found that puromycin injected before training had no detectable effect on acquisition, but caused a marked loss in memory as seen 72 hr later (Agranoff, Davis, and Brink 1965). It also appears that puromycin injected 20 min before

[1] Fish trained repeatedly over several days did not exceed 80 per cent avoidance responding. Since retraining scores on day 4 average about 50 per cent, we are dealing with partial training. If we should ever find a drug which stimulates memory formation, our method should detect improved retention.

[2] ECS blocks memory in goldfish, and memory is fixed, or invulnerable to ECS, within 2 hr after the training session (Davis, Bright, and Agranoff 1965). Using ECS, we showed that memory storage is slowed by cooling fish following training. We thus confirmed in a poikilotherm the observation of Ransmeier and Gerard (1954) that memory is temperature dependent.

training has less effect. This suggests that the action of puromycin is over within a few hours of injection. More recent studies with another apparatus suggest, however, that the effect of puromycin before training may be of longer duration. We concluded that puromycin blocks long-term memory by interfering specifically with memory fixation. Short-term memory is not destroyed by such treatment. Following puromycin injection, retention is normal for several hours and then decreases over the next two days.

Our original experiments gave rise to still another question. Why is no long-term memory formed during the 40-min training period? This period included four 5-min periods of darkness between trials. In an attempt to answer this question, we allowed animals to remain in the shuttle boxes for an hour following trial 20. They were then injected with puromycin and returned to home tanks. Such animals showed a large memory deficit on day 4 (Davis and Agranoff 1966). Yet a control group allowed to remain in the shuttle boxes for an hour following trial 20 and returned to the home tanks without being injected showed normal memory. These experiments indicate that the training environment prevents the onset of memory fixation. Further research in a recent version of the shuttle box has confirmed

TABLE 3

COMPARISON OF 3 SHUTTLE BOX TASKS

Task	Mode	Trials		
		Train	Retrain	Within Session
I	L→D	20	10	5 min D, 5 trials (repeat)
II	D→L	30	10	5 min D, all trials
III	L→D[a]	30	10	5 min D, all trials

NOTE: The CS:US:ITI sequence was 20 sec:20 sec:20 sec. Recording was manual in I, automatic in II and III. A clear plastic gate was suspended over the hurdle in III.
[a] Response ends CS and US.

and extended the original results (Davis 1968) and suggests further that the environmental effect on fixation is mediated by complex visual stimuli.

We have tried to improve the shuttle boxes to obtain greater automation and greater differences between the initial and the final training scores. We have varied the spacing of trials, whether the animals go into the light or into the dark, the number of trials, and the dimensions of the barrier. A comparison of three tasks we have used is seen in Table 3. The newest shuttle boxes detect the presence of the fish by means of photodetectors on either side of the barrier. The photodetectors register avoidances and escapes and automatically regulate the presentation of the light and shock stimuli so that the animals cannot miss trials. Both of the new shuttle boxes have, in general, confirmed experiments seen in the simpler manual apparatus. While there is not much difference in the retraining scores, it can be seen that tasks II and III show lower day 1 scores (Table 4). In the case of task II, this happens because the animals swim into the light, a more difficult task for goldfish. In the case of task III, this is a result of placing plastic gates over the barrier. An example of results with task III is shown in Figure 4.

The antimetabolite, acetoxycycloheximide, like puromycin, blocks memory fixation (Agranoff, Davis, and Brink 1966). This agent is more desirable than puromycin because it acts at much lower concentrations, about $\frac{1}{1000}$ that of puromycin. In mice, acetoxycycloheximide apparently has a temporary effect on memory, and under specified conditions it can block the effect of puromycin (Flexner, Flexner, and Roberts 1967).

The attraction of puromycin and acetoxycycloheximide is that while they can have many effects, under some conditions, each can block protein synthesis selectively without affecting RNA synthesis. In the goldfish, puromycin and acetoxycycloheximide both block labeled leucine incorporation into protein in the brain (Brink, Davis, and Agranoff 1966). Puromycin aminonucleoside and o-methyl tyrosine, two moieties of puromycin, have no effect on protein synthesis in goldfish, nor do they affect memory (Agranoff, Davis, and Brink 1966). It remains to be answered, however, whether there are agents which disrupt metabolism and do not block memory. Even if protein synthesis is required for storing

TABLE 4

MEAN TRAINING AND RETRAINING SCORES OF CONTROL FISH

		TRIALS			
		Training			Retraining
TASK	N	1–10	11–20	21–30	1–10
I	189	1.86 (.14)	3.03 (.18)	. . . .	5.12 (.20)
II	118	0.64 (.12)	1.95 (.24)	3.08 (.31)	5.39 (.26)
III	141	0.64 (.09)	1.52 (.20)	. . . .	4.91 (.23)

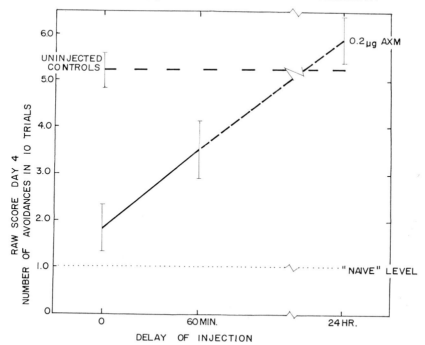

FIG. 4. Raw scores for goldfish treated with acetoxycycloheximide following training in task III

memory in some permanent form, we have not narrowed the possibilities very much. Membrane synthesis, enzyme induction, and formation of new organelles all require protein synthesis. From the behavioral viewpoint, we have found agents that permit acquisition of a response while they block the formation of long-term memory. Further research on the effects of these antibiotics on behavior and brain chemistry should yield further information about the nature of the mental process.

We are studying chemical changes in the brain during acquisition, in the absence of chemical agents. Changes in labeled uridine incorporation into RNA have been observed during training in mice by Zemp, Wilson, Schlesinger, Boggan, and Glassman (1966). Increased labeled leucine incorporation during experimental handling has been observed autoradiographically in the rat by Altman (1966). The exact nature and possible interrelationship of these phenomena require further study.

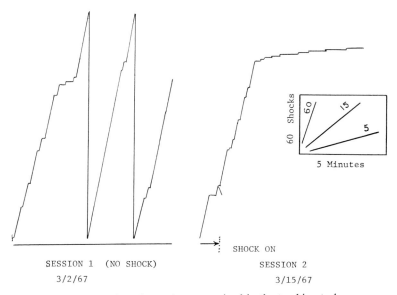

Fig. 5. Tracing of a *P. formosa* trained in the tracking task

Investigations on changes in protein during and after training in different brain regions and subcellular fractions may be fruitful. To facilitate such research, it seems desirable to look for a species with less individual variability than the common goldfish. The extreme variation between goldfish is reflected in acrylamide gel electrophoresis of the brain proteins. Efforts to decrease the variability of our experimental animal have taken two directions. We have looked into the possibility of obtaining an inbred strain of goldfish. In addition we have become interested in *Poecilia formosa*, a parthenogenetic fish found in Texas and Mexico. Acrylamide gel patterns for brain esterases of the soluble proteins showed identical bands. Differences in band intensity are seen, as in assays of protein, among clones of individual cells. We have not yet obtained enough of these animals to study their training performance in detail, but they do learn the tracking task (Fig. 5).

We have reported the use of fishes in research on the biological basis of memory formation. The natural variety among these vertebrates gives promise that we have only begun to recognize their research potential.

Acknowledgment

The authors acknowledge the continued valuable assistance of Mr. Paul Klinger in the behavioral studies. Chemical studies were performed with the aid of Dr. J. J. Brink and, more recently, with Dr. Ramon Lim and Dr. Luigi Casola. This research was supported by the National Institutes of Health and the National Science Foundation.

References

Agranoff, B. W.; Davis, R. E.; and Brink, J. J. 1965. Memory fixation in the goldfish. *Proc. Nat. Acad. Sci. (U.S.A.)* 54:788–93.
———. 1966. Chemical studies on memory fixation in the goldfish. *Brain. Res.* 1:303–9.
Agranoff, B. W., and Klinger, P. D. 1964. Puromycin effect on memory fixation in the goldfish. *Science* 146:952–53.
Altman, J. 1966. Autoradiographic examination of behaviorally induced changes in the protein and nucleic acid metabolism of the brain. In *Macromolecules and behavior*, ed. J. Gaito, pp. 103–26. New York: Appleton-Century-Crofts.
Behrend, E. R., and Bitterman, M. E. 1964. Avoidance-conditioning in the fish: Further studies of the CS–US interval. *Amer. J. Psychol.* 77:15–28.
Brink, J. J.; Davis, R. E.; and Agranoff, B. W. 1966. Effects of puromycin, acetoxycyclohex-imide and actinomycin D on protein synthesis in goldfish brain. *J. Neurochem.* 13:889–96.
Chamberlain, T. J.; Rothschild, G. M.; and Gerard, R. W. 1963. Drugs affecting RNA and memory. *Proc. Nat. Acad. Sci. (U.S.A.)* 49:918–24.
Davis, R. E. 1968. Environmental control of memory fixation in goldfish. *J. Comp. Physiol. Psychol.* 65:72–78.
Davis, R. E., and Agranoff, B. W. 1966. Stages of memory formation in goldfish: Evidence for an environmental trigger. *Proc. Nat. Acad. Sci. (U.S.A.)* 55:555–59.
Davis, R. E.; Bright, P. J.; and Agranoff, B. W. 1965. Effect of ECS and puromycin on memory in fish. *J. Comp. Physiol. Psychol.* 60:162–66.
Davis, R. E.; Klinger, P. D.; and Agranoff, B. W. 1965. Automated training and recording of a light-tracking response in fish. *J. Exptl. Anal. Behav.* 8:353–55.
Dingman, W., and Sporn, M. B. 1961. The incorporation of 8-azaguanine into rat brain RNA and its effect on maze-learning by the rat: An inquiry into the biochemical basis of memory. *J. Pyschiat. Res.* 1:1–11.
Flexner, J. B.; Flexner, L. B.; and Stellar, E. 1963. Memory in mice as affected by intra-cerebral puromycin. *Science* 141:57–59.
Flexner, L. B.; Flexner, J. B.; and Roberts, R. B. 1961. Memory in mice analyzed with anti-biotics. *Science* 155:1377–84.
Gerard, R. W. 1961. Fixation of experience. In *Brain mechanisms and learning*, ed. A. Dela-fresnaye, pp. 21–35. Blackwell Scientific Publications.
Horner, J. L.; Longo, N.; and Bitterman, M. E. 1961. A shuttlebox for fish and a control circuit of general applicability. *Amer. J. Psychol.* 74:114–20.
McGaugh, J. L. 1966. Time-dependent processes in memory storage. *Science* 153:1351–58.
Ransmeier, R. E., and Gerard, R. W. 1954. *Amer. J. Physiol.* 179:663–64.
Zemp, J. W.; Wilson, J. E.; Schlesinger, K.; Boggan, W. O.; and Glassman, E. 1966. Brain function and macromolecules. I. Incorporation of uridine into RNA of mouse brain during short-term training experience. *Proc. Nat. Acad. Sci. (U.S.A.)* 55:1423–31.

5

The Relation of RNA Metabolism in the Brain to Learning in the Goldfish

Victor E. Shashoua

Department of Biology
Massachusetts Institute of Technology

A number of studies (1–11) have correlated the high rates of RNA and protein synthesis in the brain with the acquisition and retention of a learned behavior. Hyden, Egyhazi, and Lange (1–4) were first to point out that a new RNA is synthesized during learning. Moreover, this RNA had a unique base composition, so that it could be detected without radioactive tracers in the presence of the total RNA complement of neurons. Flexner, Flexner, and Stellar (7), in studies of learning in mice, noted that inhibitors of protein synthesis could prevent the fixation of a learned behavior. Similar effects were observed by Agranoff, Davis, and Brink (10) in studies of learning in goldfish. These experiments assume the hypothesis that the establishment of memory is at least a two-step process, the first step being the acquisition phase, which apparently does not require protein synthesis in mice (11) and goldfish (12), and the second being a consolidation step which can be inhibited by drugs which prevent protein synthesis.

The above studies imply that RNA is involved during learning. What is the role of this brain RNA in learning? In particular, it is important to find out if the RNA base ratio changes observed by Hyden and Egyhazi for the rat brain (3) can also occur in other animals. In this paper we attempt to correlate the acquisition and storage of a new swimming skill with the synthesis and composition of RNA in the goldfish brain. Through the use of tritium-labeled orotic acid, as the precursor to uridine and cytidine, the newly synthesized nuclear RNA accompanying the learned task is isolated, and its base composition is determined to give a ratio of uridine to cytidine. The behavioral task for this study was chosen to give a large challenge to the goldfish brain in order to promote maximal changes in RNA synthesis, so that any changes in base composition could be detected in analyses of whole brain extracts.

Experimental Methods

Goldfish (comet variety) 7 to 8 cms in length, weighing 7 to 10 gm were used throughout this study. Orotic acid (10 μc, specific activity 5 mc/mM) dissolved in 10 μl of 0.15 M NaCl was injected into the ventricle of the brain in the region of the optic tectum, similar to the method of Agranoff, Davis, and Brink (11). The animals were generally fed 24 hr before each experiment. Groups of seven experimental and seven control fish were placed in separate five-gallon tanks, each filled with three gallons of water. The tanks were equipped with air bubblers and filters to provide sufficient oxygen and clean water for the fish.

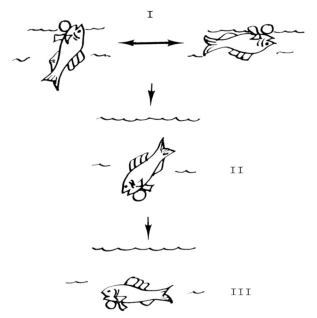

FIG. 1. Stages in the adaptation of a goldfish to the float (19)

The goldfish were trained to swim in a new pattern by attaching a foam polystyrene float to the fish with a suture at the ventral surface, 1 mm caudal to the base of the first pair of lateral fins. A 0.7 cm cube was used for an 8 gm fish. Figure 1 shows the sequence of adaptation of a goldfish to the challenge produced by the float. The animals acquire new swimming skills in the process. In stage I the animal is pulled up to the surface in either of two configurations, one with the head out of the water and the other in an upside-down position. This is apparently a very noxious stimulus and the fish try to escape down to the bottom of the tank, but the float pulls them up. Thus, stage I is characterized by struggling. Stage II is generally attained within 1 hr. Here the animals assume a 45° angle and swim constantly to avoid being turned upside down by the float. At stage III the goldfish have become sufficiently skilful to swim horizontally with the float in a ventral position. Frequently, the tails are bent to one side to compensate for the lateral torque imposed by the float. The fish swim constantly in this position. One can readily observe that the pattern of motion of lateral fins is quite different from that of controls. In each experiment the controls receive a suture at the same position as the experimental groups, but no float. In considering the various aspects of the adaptation of the fish to this task one can postulate influences to various areas of the brain, including motor centers, cerebellum, optic tectum, vestibular regions, and certainly to autonomic controls such as modulation of the air content of the swim bladder.

The use of orotic acid (see Fig. 2) in these experiments results in the formation of labeled UTP and CTP as the precursors of RNA synthesis (13). Under the conditions of the experiment only about 10,000 cpm of the label become associated with each animal brain. Of this, on the average, 1,000 cpm were incorporated into phenol-extracted RNA. After completion of a 4-hr training period the animals were decapitated, and the brains were washed

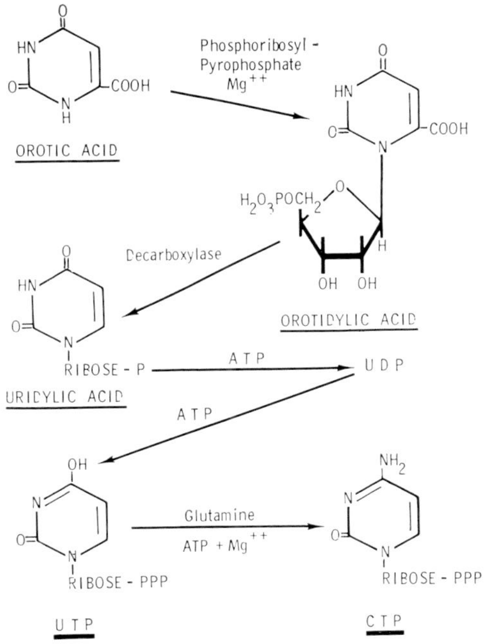

FIG. 2. Metabolic pathways from orotic acid to uridine triphosphate (UTP) and cytidine triphosphate (CTP).

with distilled water and homogenized in a Dounce homogenizer, in 0.02 M phosphate buffer (pH 7.2 combining 0.5 per cent sodium lauryl sulfate). The homogenate was cooled in an ice bath during the brain isolation.

Figure 3 summarizes the extraction procedures for isolation of RNA from pooled brain homogenates using methods adapted from Scherrer and Darnell (14) and Perry (15). The protein and DNA contents of the pools were removed by two 4-min hot phenol extractions at 60° C. After each phenol treatment the mixtures were cooled in an ice bath and then centrifuged to separate the phenol from the aqueous phase. Next the salt content of the aqueous phase was adjusted to 0.1 M NaCl and the solution was mixed with two volumes of ethanol and allowed to stand at $-20°$ C for 18 hr to precipitate the RNA. The RNA ppt was centrifuged off and washed with 95 per cent ethanol. The product, consisting largely of nuclear RNA, was stored under 90 per cent ethanol containing 0.01 M sodium acetate.

The purified RNA was analyzed for total radioactivity as trichloroacetic acid precipitable counts, for total quantity of RNA as absorption at 260 mμ, and for base composition after hydrolysis. The hydrolysis was carried out in 0.3 M KOH for 17 hr at 37° C to give a mixture of the nucleotides as the monophosphates. The excess alkali was removed by ion exchange on carboxymethyl cellulose paper and the product was analyzed for its base composition, using paper electrophoresis (3 hrs at 1400 v and 80 ma) in 20 per cent acetic acid pH 3.0 according to the methods of Wagner and Ingram (16). Figure 4 shows a typical

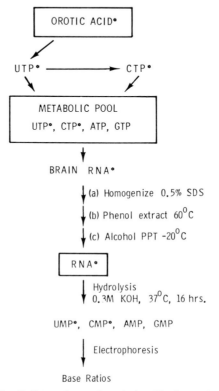

Fig. 3. Extraction and analysis of brain RNA

result for separations of the bases. The distribution of radioactivity was measured with a liquid scintillation counter on consecutive 1.25 × 5 cm strips of the electrophoretic pattern developed on Whatman number 3 paper. Note that a maximum separation of Up and Cp results under these conditions and that there is always one unknown nonradioactive component which absorbs UV but remains at the origin, and another between Gp and Up.

As a check on the possibility of converting cytidine to uridine during the various steps of extraction, hydrolysis, and electrophoresis, a sample of tritiated poly C was processed through the whole sequence shown in Figure 3 and then analyzed. All the radioactivity was found to be at the Cp spot, with no detectable counts at Up, indicating that no U to C conversion occurs during the processing conditions.

Results

Behavioral Studies

Table 1 and Figure 5*a* demonstrate that the behavioral task used in this paper has a learning component which is remembered by the goldfish after 22 hr. These data were obtained on a group of 10 animals (5 per tank), each with a different colored float and suture so that each animal could be identified and rechallenged with the same float on the second trial. The animals were observed at fixed times during the 4-hr training period and those at stage I, stage II, and stage III (see Fig. 1) were arbitrarily scored at 0 per cent, 50 per cent, and 100

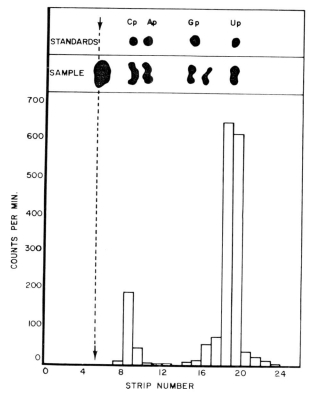

Fig. 4. Typical electrophoretic pattern for separation of the nucleotides. Cp, Ap, Gp, and Up are the monophosphates of cytidine, adenosine, guanosine, and uridine.

per cent trained. At each test time the group score was obtained and plotted to give the learning curve shown in Figure 5*a*. After 4 hr the floats were removed from the fish; 22 hr later, the fish were tested again to give curve II. The faster rate of learning on the second trial clearly indicates that there is a saving. The same data are listed in Table 1 as the time required for each test animal to reach the 100 per cent trained level. Again a saving is indicated, since the mean time for trial II was 21 ± 4 mins as compared with 156 ± 13 mins in trial I. A statistical evaluation of the data in T test ($T = 0$, $N = 10$) gives a p value of less than 0.01, indicating that there is a significant retention of the new swimming skill.

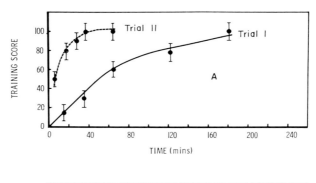

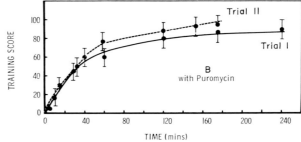

FIG. 5. Learning and retention curves for the goldfish: *a* group received no drugs, *b* group received 120 μg puromycin (intercranial). Trial II was 22 hr after trial I. Ten animals were in each group (19).

TABLE 1

TIMES REQUIRED FOR ANIMALS TO REACH
100 PER CENT TRAINED LEVEL

ANIMAL NUMBER	TRAINING TIMES (MIN)	
	Trial I	Trial II[a]
1	180	15
2	120	15
3	180	25
4	120	15
5	180	35
6	180	15
7	120	35
8	120	25
9	180	15
10	180	15
Mean	156 ± 13	21 ± 4

NOTE: Statistical significance measure: $T = 0$, $N = 10$, $p < 0.01$ for trials I and II.
[a] Twenty-two hr after trial I.

Figure 5*b* and Table 2 show a repeat of the training and testing experiments above with a separate group of animals who received a dose of 120 μgm puromycin each, 1½ hr prior to trial I. The results show that the rate of acquisition of the behavioral task is not significantly different from the control group in Figure 5*a*, i.e., there is a mean acquisition time of 136 ± 13 versus 156 ± 13. Also, there is apparently no saving after 22 hr, since the mean time to reach criterion (100 ± 20 mins) is not statistically different (p value > 0.05 in a T test) from the trial I score of 136 ± 13 mins.

TABLE 2

EFFECT OF PUROMYCIN ON THE TRAINING AND
RETENTION TIMES TO REACH 100 PER CENT
TRAINED LEVEL

ANIMAL NUMBER	TRAINING TIMES (MIN)	
	Trial I	Trial II[a]
1	180	180
2	120	35
3	120	35
4	60	120
5	180	180
6	120	60
7	180	180
8	180	60
9	120	120
10	60	25
Mean	136 ± 13	100 ± 20

NOTE: p value for comparison of trials I and II > 0.05.
[a] Twenty-two hr after trial I.

The dose of puromycin in this experiment has been previously reported by Brink, Davis, and Agranoff (17) to inhibit 80 per cent of the protein synthesis in the goldfish brain. Thus, inhibition of protein synthesis in the behavioral task of this experiment results in no significant retention of the training after 22 hr.

Biochemical Studies

Table 3 summarizes the RNA base ratio measurements for 70 animals—35 experimental and 35 control. The experiments were carried out on groups of seven experimentals and seven controls. The animals were fed 24 hr before the behavioral study. The table depicts the observed uridine to cytidine ratios in the newly synthesized RNA during the 4-hr training period. The results show a consistent increase in the $(U/C)_E$ values for the experimental group over the $(U/C)_C$ control group values. The difference between the average values of $(U/C)_E$ and $(U/C)_C$ gives a result of about 3.30 with a corresponding mean increase of 96 per cent. The data suggest that the new RNA synthesis accompanying the behavioral task has an increased content of uridine (by about a factor of 3) over cytidine.

One very important aspect of these biochemical studies is inherent in the use of a metabolic precursor (orotic acid, see Fig. 2) to give rise to two products, UTP and CTP, which then label the metabolic pools of UTP and CTP. Clearly the composition of this pool will influence the incorporation of UTP and CTP into the newly synthesized RNA to give variable U/C base ratios. The composition of the pool in goldfish brain is not known, but if the values 4/1 for U/C(18) for rat brain can be used as an analogy, then one must expect a similar bias toward labeling of U in goldfish brain. This problem suggests that many factors should influence the labeled base compositions of RNA in goldfish brain. Thus, one might expect the nutritional state, temperature, metabolic rate, and drug effects to give variable U/C base ratios. Table 4 summarizes the results observed for these variables. Each result was obtained from the pooled brains of seven animals. It is clear that one can vary

TABLE 3

SUMMARY BASE RATIO MEASUREMENTS

Expt. Number	Up	Cp	U/C	$(U/C)_E-(U/C)_C$	Per Cent Change
1E	336	44	7.6	4.0	+108
1C	415	114	3.6		
2E	446	69	6.2	3.0	+ 94
2C	116	36	3.2		
3E	501	93	5.4	3.0	+128
3C	726	308	2.4		
4E	560	72	7.8	3.2	+ 70
4C	618	135	4.6		
5E	490	65	7.6	3.3	+ 78
5C	286	67	4.3		
Average E			6.9±.5	3.3±.3	+ 96
Average C			3.6±.2		

NOTE: The animals were starved 24 hr before the experiment. Each experiment had 7 pooled brains for the experimental (E) and control (C) groups.

TABLE 4

FACTORS INFLUENCING THE METABOLIC POOL

EXPT. NUMBER	VARIABLE	C.P.M. Up	CP	U/C	$(U/C)_E-(U/C)_C$	PER CENT CHANGE
6E	Last fed 3 hr	226	27	8.3	3.1	+ 58
6C	" " "	551	105	5.2		
7E	Last fed 24 hr	501	93	5.4	3.1	+139
7C	" " "	726	308	2.4		
8E	Last fed 72 hr	366	54	6.7	1.9	+ 41
8C	" " "	135	28	4.8		
9C	Temp. 23° C	741	230	4.2		
10C	Temp. 9° C[a]	187	33	5.7		
11E	170 μgm puro 1½ hr before expt.	550	294	1.9		
11C	" " "	1222	734	1.7	0.3	+ 10

NOTE: The last feeding time represents the interval (hr) before behavioral experiment.
[a] The experimental group did not try to learn the task, but remained passive at this temperature. Each experiment had 7 pooled brains for the experimental (E) and control (C) groups.

the measured U/C ratios from 1.7 (expt. 11C) to 8.3 (expt. 6E) under different combinations of nutritional state, drug administration, and learning experiments. However, in all learning experiments where control and experimental animals were conditioned identically, the $(U/C)_E$ experimental values showed a consistent increase over the $(U/C)_C$ control values. Thus, the various alterations of the metabolic pool form a background level over which the learning experiment imposes an additional change to higher ratios. The only exception to this was observed in animals which were treated with puromycin, where no significant change occurred as a result of the behavioral task.

Effect of Puromycin

Table 5 summarizes the results for 42 animals—21 controls and 21 experimentals. Each group of seven controls and seven experimentals was studied in parallel on different days. All the animals received 170 µgm puromycin intercranially 1½ hr before the behavioral experiment. The results show that there is no significant increase in the U/C base ratios of the

TABLE 5

EFFECT OF PUROMYCIN ON RNA BASE RATIOS

Expt. Number	Up	Cp	U/C	$(U/C)_E - (U/C)_C$	Per Cent Change
11PE	550	294	1.9	0.2	+10
11PC	1222	734	1.7		
12PE	489	64	7.7	0.1	+ 2
12PC	228	30	7.6		
13PE	895	157	5.7	0.4	+ 8
13PC	351	67	5.3		
Average				0.24	+ 7

NOTE: Puromycin dose was 170 µgm (intercranial) 1½ hr before training.

experimental group over the control group; i.e., values for $(U/C)_E - (U/C)_C$. Also, the maximum percentage increase of $(U/C)_E$ over $(U/C)_C$ was no more than 10 per cent. The data suggest that no change occurs for the U/C values after administration of puromycin in this behavioral experiment. Since the drug was given 1½ hr before the training, and since it is known that protein synthesis (17) is inhibited by about 80 per cent at this stage, it follows that inhibition of protein synthesis prevents the formation of an RNA with a unique base ratio. Moreover, since during these experiments the total new nuclear RNA synthesis as measured by incorporation of label is not significantly different from controls without the drug, protein synthesis is implicated as a possible primary factor in obtaining the base ratio changes.

Discussion

In the behavioral experiment of this paper the goldfish in the experimental group are under a constant stress. They also perform much more work, in addition to learning a new swimming skill. Thus, any of the variables—stress, work, or learning, or all three—could be the responsible factor in promoting the observed RNA base ratio changes. Since the animals under the influence of puromycin seem to acquire the swimming skill at about the same rate as those without the drug, they must necessarily have been exposed to approximately the same level of stress and work as those without the drug. Moreover, these animals, on testing 22 hr later, showed no significant evidence of remembering the task. In addition the puromycin group showed no significant base ratio changes after the acquisition of the new swimming skill. It follows therefore that the RNA base ratio changes are related to the learning component of this behavioral experiment and not to general factors such as work or stress.

These data suggest that RNA base ratio changes can accompany the acquisition stage of learning and imply that normal protein synthesis rates are a requirement for the establishment of these changes. The results are similar to Hyden's and Egyhazi's (3) findings in the transfer of handedness experiments in the rat brain.

There are many possible explanations for the RNA base ratio changes observed as the concomitant biochemical change with the acquisition of new swimming skills by the goldfish. These range from factors which control the brain metabolism to provide changes in the concentration of glutamic transaminase, which governs the conversion of UTP to CTP (see Fig. 2), to a possible induction at the genome level of a special RNA (19) required in promoting the biochemical consequences of the consolidation step in learning, and finally to the specific instructional changes in the newly synthesized RNA. In addition we must also consider the possibility that the results are due to some unusual coupling of stress effects to protein synthesis which can be inhibited by puromycin. Only further experimental evidence can distinguish which of these mechanisms or what other alternatives are the biochemical correlates of learning.

Acknowledgment

This work was carried out during tenure of a Resident Scientist Appointment at the Massachusetts Institute of Technology's Neurosciences Research Program. I wish to thank Professor F. O. Schmitt for providing the opportunity for carrying out this work. Acknowledgment is gratefully given for grants from the National Institutes of Health and the United States Public Health Service.

References

1. Hyden, H. V., and Egyhazi, E. 1962. *Proc. Nat. Acad. Sci. (U.S.A.)* 48:1366.
2. ———. 1963. *Proc. Nat. Acad. Sci. (U.S.A.)* 49:618.
3. ———. 1964. *Proc. Nat. Acad. Sci. (U.S.A.)* 52:1030.
4. Hyden, H. V., and Lange, A. W. 1965. *Proc. Nat. Acad. Sci. (U.S.A.)* 53:948.
5. Dingman, W., and Sporn, M. B. 1962. *Biochim. Biophys. Acta* 61:164.
6. ———. 1964. *Science* 144:26.
7. Flexner, J. B.; Flexner, L. B.; and Stellar, E. 1963. *Science* 141:57.
8. Flexner, J. B., and Flexner, L. B. 1966. *Proc. Nat. Acad. Sci. (U.S.A.)* 55:369.
9. Flexner, L. B.; Flexner, J. B.; and Roberts, R. B. 1966. *Proc. Nat. Acad. Sci. (U.S.A.)* 56:730.
10. Agranoff, B. W.; Davis, R. E.; and Brink, J. J. 1965. *Proc. Nat. Acad. Sci. (U.S.A.)* 54:788.
11. Barondes, S. H., and Cohen, H. D. 1966. *Science* 151:594.
12. Davis, R. E., and Agranoff, B. W. 1966. *Proc. Nat. Acad. Sci. (U.S.A.)* 55:555.

13. Potter, Van R. 1960. *Nucleic acid outlines*, Vol. I, Minneapolis, Minn.: Burgess Publishing Co.
14. Scherrer, K., and Darnell, J. 1962. *Biochem. Biophys. Res. Commun.* 7:486.
15. Perry, R. P. 1962. *Proc. Nat. Acad. Sci. (U.S.A.)* 48:2179.
16. Wagner, E. K., and Ingram, V. M. 1966. *Biochemistry* 5:3019.
17. Brink, J. J.; Davis, R. E.; and Agranoff, B. W. 1966. *J. Neurochem.* 13:889.
18. Mandel, P.; Edel, S.; and Poirel, G. 1966. *J. Neurochem.* 13:885.
19. Shashona, V. E. 1968. *Nature (Lond.)* 217:238.

Part IV   Behavioral Processes in Fish

1

Ethological Units of Behavior

George W. Barlow

Department of Zoology and
Museum of Vertebrate Zoology
University of California at Berkeley

Relation of Behavioral Units to Neurophysiology

Behavior may be subdivided into a variety of units. Depending on the objectives of a given study, one might find the appropriate unit at almost any level of integration. Thus for the sociologist, and for some psychologists, the important measure might derive from interindividual responses, or from patterns of behavior of whole groups. Moving down the scale, the behavioral measure could equally well involve some integrated yet arbitrary end point, such as that produced in bar-pressing devices. Such instrumental responses have proved of value in studies of learning, and they have also gained usage in a few ethological studies. An instrumental response, although an arbitrary end point, can still have a great deal of behavior behind it; animals may approach the target differently, and may activate the instrument in a variety of ways. In most cases, however, it will be a useful measure of relatively complex behavior.

The ethologist has by and large resorted to studies of what have been termed "Fixed Action Patterns," the molar unit of ethology. At a still finer level there is the functional unit, as defined by Liem (1967); this is doubtless the smallest unit that could be used as a measure in behavioral studies, consisting of the simplest coaction of a group of muscles, ligaments, bones, and nerves.

Any unit is appropriate if it fits the needs of the study. The more complex and broadly defined units may be adequate for general studies involving relatively broad treatments, such as those which might result from gross manipulation of the endocrine system or extensive ablations of the central nervous system. On the other hand, the finest unit of behavior, for instance the functional unit, obviously has the most direct relationship to neural events. The study of such fine units may overlook the more highly integrative aspects of behavior, however; and these are often of great interest.

217

Somewhere between these extremes lie the instrumental responses and the fixed action patterns. While the instrumental response is excellent for some purposes, it tends to have limited application. Moreover, it is frequently an indirect index of the behavior of interest rather than a direct measure of it.

Many ethological problems have at their center a reliance on the concept of the fixed action pattern. As a unit of behavior it has the advantage that it refers to behavior that is directly observable, and thus no instrumentation is required in order to record it. This also means that the decision about the occurrence of the event has the disadvantage of containing a subjective element, decreasing the precision. Rarely, as in the case of a fish attacking a mirror, the fixed action pattern can be automatically and objectively recorded.

If behavior studies are to have meaning to neurophysiologists, the models that result from the studies must be translatable into neurophysiological language. This means the behavior must be quantified, yielding mathematical models that can be compared with the models produced by the neurophysiologist.

There have been relatively few mathematical models generated by the ethologists. Such models are found largely in the province of the neurophysiologists. I cite, for example, the stimulating work done by Gerstein and his associates (reviewed in Moore, Perkel, and Segundo 1966) involving auto- and cross-correlations of the activity of one or a few neurons. The shape of things to come, however, is more comprehensively communicated in an article by Ashby (1966). These models have been more important in thinking about behavior than the study of behavior has been useful in illuminating neurophysiology. Although stimulating, these models are little more than that; they have not provided us with an understanding of the mechanisms underlying the behavior. The neuron, moreover, is inherently different from the complex fixed action pattern. Models based on the behavior of individual neurons can only be regarded as starting points.

These statistical models contain assumptions that are seldom adhered to in ethological studies. For one, the unit, the event, should be all-or-nothing. Where one is dealing with trains of spikes along a nerve fiber this condition appears to be met, although even here the assumption bears examining.[1] When dealing with fixed action patterns this requirement is seldom fulfilled.

Another limitation of the statistical models is that the phenomenon under study should exhibit "stationarity." This means the statistical parameters should remain unchanged from one sampling point in time to another. As Moore, Perkel, and Segundo (1966) pointed out, this assumption is seldom tested in neurophysiology. The same holds for ethological studies. There have been a few attempts to test for stationarity, however, as in the creeping-through model of Nelson (1965) and in the distribution of attacks to a mirror by a cichlid fish (Skaller 1966).

The Fixed Action Pattern

Lorenz (1950) made a strong case for the importance of units in the development of all branches of science. And he has rightfully pointed to the central role our notion of fixed action patterns has played in the progress of ethology. But just as the atom was once thought to be indivisible and above questioning, much the same attitude prevails toward the fixed action pattern in current thinking in ethology. If the fixed action pattern is to be used to generate models of use to the neurophysiologist, we must examine it closely to see if it qualifies as a basic unit of behavior.

[1] C. H. F. Rowell: personal communication.

As mentioned, there are indeed instances when fixed action patterns exhibit stationarity in time. However, it is also clear that in most instances they do not (Nelson 1965).

It is also obvious that fixed action patterns do not behave as all-or-nothing responses. Marler and Hamilton (1966) reflect this well when they refer to them as "modes of action patterns." Their development of the topic makes it clear that they are referring to events that are statistically definable rather than to absolute events. Surprisingly, there has been no real effort to study the variation in the several parameters of the fixed action pattern, if indeed we can speak of *the* fixed action pattern.

One study, however, has attempted to come to grips with the degree of stereotypy along one dimension. Dane, Walcott, and Drury (1959) filmed the courtship displays of goldeneye ducks, then analyzed them in detail. The only parameter considered was duration. They made no attempt to delimit units other than trying to work with repeatedly recognizable events. They soon discovered they were dealing at times with units nested within units. This was particularly revealing. It led them to identify the sources of variation, as well as the least variable components.

Some students of behavior seem to have drawn from their publication that the displays of the goldeneye duck, and presumably of most anatid ducks, are essentially invariant. The data of Dane, Walcott, and Drury, however, show that the standard deviation is commonly of the order of 10 per cent to 20 per cent of the mean value; occasionally it is less, but sometimes it is considerably more. (The range of values, of course, is usually much greater.) The one nonsignal movement measured, the wing stretch, was extremely variable yet, importantly, readily recognizable as a distinct category of behavior. The significant point is that this is of the proper order of magnitude for variability in most biological measures. One reason the displays seem so fixed is that they happen so quickly.

Theirs is the only systematic quantitative study in ethology, employing films, of the temporal dimensions of what are commonly regarded as fixed action patterns. As is so often the case, it seems necessary to start with an extreme example in order to make a point. The machine-like fixed action patterns of anatid ducks are probably representative of the more sterostyped displays found among animals, as are certain grooming actions of passerine birds (Rowell 1961). Whether or not all the movements we commonly call fixed action patterns exhibit this degree of stereotypy is far from certain.

The Interrelation of the Parts of the Fixed Action Pattern

When an ethologist speaks of a fixed action pattern he usually has in mind a small piece of behavior, but one that is already complex. Russell, Mead, and Hayes (1954) attempted to come to grips with this problem by defining the action pattern in terms of its components, called *acts*. At the risk of oversimplifying, an act is the least divisible unit of behavior making up the fixed action pattern. Several acts together constitute a superact, the fixed action pattern of contemporary usage. These more complex superacts are then arranged into bouts wherein the event is repeated several times, or into sequences wherein they are related to other fixed action patterns. In practice, it often becomes difficult to decide between a very complex fixed action pattern as opposed to a sequence of simple events. Thus it is meaningful to have a definition for the fixed action pattern that will enable one to distinguish it from a sequence of different fixed action patterns. Such a definition is not easy to come by.

It is generally recognized today that the fixed action pattern is indeed a graded response. The word "fixed" refers to the nature of the gradation itself, expressed as "intensity" or "completeness." If a fixed action pattern consists of several components, say *A*, *B*, *C*, and

D, these will occur in some predictable sequence which relates to their thresholds for expression. At a relatively incomplete, or low-intensity, state one would observe only *A*. At increasing levels of completeness, arrangements such as *AB, ABC,* and *ABCD* would occur, but never sequences such as *ACD* or *DCA*. We can imagine a fixed action pattern as a film strip containing the complete performance, which must be started at the beginning each time it is run through. Any variation would consist in the variable distance that the film is allowed to travel, but the sequence of pictures would be fixed. The emergence of new components in a pattern as "intensity" increases is entirely predictable, according to this view. Such specificity implies a fixed organization within the central nervous system, as Hinde (1966) has forcefully argued. This argument finds support from the work reviewed by Weiss (1950), who postulated "scores" within the brain according to which complex motor patterns can be orchestrated.

The Relation of Causal Factors to the Components of the Fixed Action Pattern

Hinde (1966) has further argued that, according to this view of a fixed action pattern, "the components all depend on the same causal factors." This statement can be given the status of a definition, and can be used to guide our judgment as to which behavioral chains we should call fixed action patterns. Presumably, a different set of causal factors would be required for a transition to the next fixed action pattern.

Russell, Mead, and Hayes (1954) have attempted to resolve this problem by pointing out how a definition could be achieved. In practice, this might consist in varying all conceivable stimuli that could influence the expression of the particular behavior. However, this would be difficult for two reasons. First, the influence could be only statistically defined, because of the spontaneous underlying variability of the behavior. Second, the number of factors to test is almost infinite; one might be confronted ultimately with the uncomfortable task of attempting to prove a null hypothesis.

The Relation of the Fixed Action Pattern to the Trigger

Another salient characteristic of the fixed action pattern is said to be its independence from environmental control; the trigger that sets it off plays no role in the further expression of the behavior. I quote again from Hinde (1966, p. 17–19): The soliciting posture of the female chaffinch "is remarkably constant in form: although it involves most of the muscles in the body, the relations between their contractions vary little, and they are presumably independent of immediate environmental control." Such variations in the "intensity" of the response may be due to the recent history of the animal, sometimes said to be due simply to its motivational state.

Hinde says further, on page 19, that "each [F.A.P.], although it may consist of a quite complicated spatiotemporal pattern of muscular contractions, cannot be split into successive responses which depend on qualitatively different external stimuli (Lorenz 1935, 1937; Tinbergen 1942). Since such movements depend upon external factors only for their elicitation, they vary in degree of completeness, but not in the relation between their parts." It is not clear from this what constitutes a qualitatively as opposed to a quantitatively different external stimulus. Nonetheless, the reader is left with the impression that the essential feature of a fixed action pattern, with relation to the stimulus that elicits it, is that the stimulus is only important as a trigger, not as a modulator of the behavior that ensues. The distinction here is between peripheral modulators and some organization of the fixed action pattern in the central nervous system. Two separate mechanisms are implied.

Testing the Hypothesis

When the chairman for this session introduced this paper, he felt compelled to respond to some earlier remarks by Professor Arthur Hasler, who had drawn to the attention of the audience a new device for protecting downed pilots from sharks. The apparatus consisted of a float with a sack around the pilot to keep the sharks from detecting chemicals in the water. The chairman, Dr. Arthur Myrberg, described the testing of this apparatus as he had observed it. Shortly before the experiment was to begin, Dr. Myrberg transmitted sound signals into the sea, which resulted in the appearance of many large sharks. Upon seeing so many sharks in the water the experimenters decided to defer testing the apparatus until another day when the sharks were not so abundant.

In many respects we ethologists have been guilty of the same sin. We have tended to pick the examples that will confirm our hypotheses. This is reasonable and understandable in the early stages of development when one needs to stand by ideas of value. But as the field progresses the time comes when hypotheses must be tested in the spirit of attempting to disprove them, rather than the other way around. If the ideas are sound, they will survive the sharks.

In brief, there are three diagnostic properties of a fixed action pattern. (1) It has common causal factors different from those of other fixed action patterns. (2) The stimulation triggering, or releasing, a fixed action pattern ceases to exercise futher control over it. And, (3) the components appear in a predictable sequence in time; while the "intensity" or completeness may vary, the interrelation of the parts may not. (In the literal sense then, a fixed action pattern is not fixed.) The third criterion is relatively easy to deal with. It requires only a careful quantitative analysis of many occurrences of the event. The first and second criteria, however, present formidable difficulties. They require considerable control of the environment and of the animal in a complex interaction.

A closer look at what have been thought to be good fixed action patterns in many animals may well reveal that the fixed action pattern is a special case along a spectrum of behavior leading back to relatively unstructured movements. Even in the instances of those fixed action patterns which seem to fulfil all the requirements so nicely spelled out by Hinde (1966), critical inspection may show that the postulates do not necessarily hold. A good example from my own experience comes from the courtship displays of the cichlid fish *Etroplus maculatus*, the orange chromide.

The central courtship movement of the orange chromide consists of a rapid quivering of the head from side to side, coupled with a pronounced flickering, an opening and closing, of the black pelvic fins. This display can be thought of as having two components, quivering and flickering. Ordinarily the two components occur together and produce a readily recognizable display. The triggering stimulus is the approach of the mate, particularly when the fish is near the presumptive spawning site. In a typical situation the male, or the female, will start quivering and flickering at the same time, the flickering will drop out while the quivering continues, then flickering will reappear shortly before quivering stops. All in all, this looks like a fixed action pattern fitting all the criteria.

Quite by accident I discovered that the coupling of the flickering and the quivering is not fixed. If the relative size of the mate is varied, the quivering and the flickering are influenced differentially. Also, the duration of quivering itself varies. This example indicates that the nature of the stimulus differentially influences the components of this behavior pattern.

As a further example, it sometimes happens when one orange chromide is quivering that the mate will indicate by subtle movements that it intends to groom the animal that is quivering. Without interrupting the quivering the actor changes slightly the amplitude of the movement and prolongs the duration of the quivering, often while deleting the flickering. Thus while the behavior is running its course it is still subject to external modulation by the stimulus that started the behavior in the first place.

It could be argued that quivering and flickering are separate fixed action patterns. Most likely they are. The point is that they nearly always occur together. Most observers would recognize them as a unitary display, ascribing variations between the components to threshold differences.

I purposely dealt with courtship movements because displays such as these are so commonly used as examples in illustrating the nature of fixed action patterns. To the best of my knowledge, there is no single case where all the criteria have been properly tested and fulfilled.

When we direct our attention to other signal movements, particularly those involved in aggressive behavior, it becomes increasingly difficult to apply the criteria for the fixed action pattern. The displays of aggressive behavior are notoriously subject to continuing modulation from the trigger. The hostile behavior of the teleost fish *Badis badis* (Barlow 1962) serves as a good example. A given display preceding a damaging fight consists of many components which may or may not be superimposed one upon the other. As the fight begins, these components tend to occur in a predictable sequence, the *ABCD* situation. But after the fish have been displaying for a while the components become scrambled. As the animals reverberate between the different displays the order may become *ACDB*. Furthermore, under certain circumstances some of the seemingly high threshold components may be seen in the absence of the low threshold components.

It can be argued that all the displays share common causal factors. For instance, Sevenster described how a male stickleback will go through a complete fight in front of an inanimate model that presents a constant feedback.[2] One could argue from this that the elaborate sequence of displays share common causal factors. Certainly the ability to run off a series of displays in the presence of an unchanging stimulus indicates there must be some central patterning responsible for this behavior.

On the other hand, it is equally obvious that the hostile displays are under continuing modulation during their expression. The degree of the spreading of the fins, the angle at which the body is held, the presence or absence and timing of head jerking, are all responsive to the continuing changes in behavior of the opponent.

A similar situation occurs in feral chickens. The degree to which the hen erects the tail feathers and lowers the wing in aggressive display is inversely proportional to the distance from the other chicken. (On the other hand, the display is the same whether it be to another hen, a cock, or an immature fowl.) The nearer the other bird, the more complete the display.[3]

[2] Piet Sevenster: personal communication.
[3] Glen McBride: personal communication.

The display is thus continually modulated, and is expressed as a function of the strength of the stimulation.

The nonsignal movements should also be discussed. There are many examples of stereotyped behavior which have no known signal function. Good examples among fishes are parental fanning of the eggs and larvae, or feeding behavior. The movements vary considerably, both in their amplitude of movement and in the duration of the ongoing event. Sevenster (1961) demonstrated the sensitivity of fanning to immediate environmental stimulation. When *Badis badis* feeds on small worms (*Tubifex*) it employs a predictable sequence of movements for extracting them from the gravel (Barlow 1961). But the precise form of this movement varies in response to the strength of attachment of the worm. If the worm is loosely anchored the fish merely swims forward and upward in a smart movement. If the worm is securely fastened in the bottom, the fish turns on its side as it meets resistance and levers the worm out of the bottom. All intermediates exist depending on the feedback received from the worm. Yet for any degree of attachment by the worm, the nature of the motor pattern is predictable. There is thus a core motor pattern, but one which is continually modulated by the immediate environmental situation.

The essential point I have been attempting to make in this critique is that we need a finer analysis of fixed action patterns. It will doubtless come as a surprise to most non-ethologists, that most of our thinking about the fixed action pattern has been done in the absence of hard data. Thus I do not feel embarrassed stressing my point of view in the absence of good data, since this has been the rule. The main issue here is that there are so few data, one way or the other, to support what has been widely accepted as a well-proved and established category of behavior.

I would particularly like to appeal for the use of film analyses in studying the nature of the fixed action pattern. Some surprising results might be obtained. For instance, one might learn more about feeding action patterns than has been previously suspected. It is well known that the action pattern of striking in the praying mantis, once triggered, is no longer under control from the environment (Rilling, Mittelstaedt, and Roeder 1959). When a snake strikes at its prey, one might presume that much the same holds. It is done with blinding speed. One could hardly imagine that a poikilotherm would have the quickness of response necessary to modulate the strike, once triggered. Yet in some films by Frazzetta, which he was kind enought to show me, a python is able to slow the strike in mid-flight when the rat moves, to compensate, to take fresh aim, and to continue in the strike (Frazzetta 1966). This all occurs in just a few frames taken at a high speed, undetected by the eye of the observer. Without the use of film analysis one would have assumed this is a fixed action pattern running its course, immune from further environmental modulation.

Just analyzing behavior on film is not enough. One would have to select a variety of kinds of action patterns, ranging from those seen in courtship displays to aggressive behavior, and on into nonsignal movements. In addition, such an analysis would have to be combined with an experimental approach. A given action pattern would have to be observed in various contexts, and also as it was being influenced by the environment, to determine the degree to which it was or was not independent of continuing environmental cues.

As a note of caution, films are not perfect. Much information is lost and difficult problems of analysis arise.

Of course there are other ways of objectively measuring action patterns. I mention as one example the problem of vocalization. Here the motor pattern may be captured conveniently in three dimensions—duration, frequency, and amplitude. The concept of fixed action pattern would profit from a comparison, say, of vocalizations expressed in the highly stereotyped songs of some birds with the graded responses of primates. There is now evidence to suggest that, even among birds, what appear to be stereotyped vocalizations may be highly graded (Dixon and Stefanski 1965). This problem has not been touched in the vocalization of fishes.

The Separability of the Fixed Action Pattern from Its Orientation

One of the tenets of ethological thinking is that the fixed action pattern has a basic pattern of coordination that is separable from its orientation, usually termed its taxic component. Hinde (1966, p. 20) stated, for instance, that "By definition, the form of a fixed action pattern is independent of the environment."

This concept emanated from the classic experiments on the gray-lag goose conducted by Lorenz and Tinbergen (1939). The goose retrieves a displaced egg by placing her bill just beyond the egg; then with the underside of her bill she prods the egg toward her breast, all the while gently weaving the bill from side to side. If the egg is removed during the process of retrieving, or if a symmetrical cylinder replaces the egg, the head-weaving component disappears and the head comes smoothly back to the breast. The core motor pattern is the bringing of the bill back to the breast. The egg triggers the behavior. The weaving is a response to the erratic path of the eccentric egg. Hence the aiming and the weaving of the head are determined by peripheral input, and are separable from the spatiotemporal coordination of the fixed action pattern.

The question that must be asked is whether all fixed action patterns are so neatly separable into structural and taxic components. In practice a fixed action pattern is usually defined by its form, not necessarily by its coordination. As a consequence it is often difficult to split off the taxic component. For instance, in Hinde's treatment of the problem he cited two examples of the fixed action pattern from many that might have been chosen. One of these is the soliciting posture of the female chaffinch, which seems to fit his criteria rather well. The other example is the response of the young of a mouthbreeding cichlid fish, *Tilapia mossambica*, to the mother when danger threatens. They swim to her, entering her buccal cavity through the mouth or opercular openings. This is a taxic response lacking a distinctive coordination. Not only is the response dependent on the environment, it is unrecognizable in the absence of a mother object. There is no way this simple swimming can be distinguished from any other type of swimming, except by its orientation. In all fairness to Hinde, he does point out several cases where the orientation may be more intimately a part of the fixed action pattern.

Inspection of a wide variety of behaviors should convince one that a number of fixed action patterns are recognizable exclusively by their orientation. The often cited case of the head-standing display of the three-spined stickleback, *Gasterosteus aculeatus*, is a good example. The female Florida flagfish, *Jordanella floridae*, about to spawn responds to the circling male by keeping her tail pointed directly at him, giving rise to a display called T-formation (Mertz and Barlow 1966); there is nothing to distinguish this motor pattern from simple hovering and turning except the orientation itself. When two *Badis badis* engage in hostile displays they characteristically pitch forward at an angle of about 45° while maintaining a head-to-tail orientation; this behavior is recognized through its orientation to the substrate and to the rival (Barlow 1962). As a final example, the orange chromide frequently performs a tailstand in front of its mate, particularly in the early stages of pair formation (personal observation); again, this display is distinguished only by its orientation.

I am convinced that if we study a number of displays, under a variety of situations and in a variety of animals, in many cases the orientation and the form of the fixed action pattern will not be separable. I would further predict that there will be a smooth intergradation from inseparability to separability, as in the case of the gray-lag goose. We must be prepared to visualize the C.N.S. counterpart of a fixed action pattern as more than an undirected core independent of the environment. The taxic component must be regarded in many instances as just as centrally determined as the pattern of coordination. Frequently they will be inseparable. What is determined is not necessarily a precise expression of a movement, but rather a stipulated relation between the organism, its behavior, and key stimuli.

Factors Favoring Stereotypy versus Those Favoring Variability

Two possible reasons for the development of stereotypy, the fixed action pattern, immediately come to mind. One of these is the efficiency of the performance. It is common knowledge from studies of learning that conditioned responses tend to become parsimonious (Adams 1931). (It would be interesting to know if "superstitious behavior" also becomes parsimonious.) Conditioned responses move toward the least expenditure of energy consistent with the problem; in so doing they become relatively stereotyped. Conceivably natural selection may follow a similar path, leading to the simplification of fixed action patterns.

Another factor contributing to the development of stereotypy of behavior is the signal function. Morris (1957) treated this problem lucidly in an article on "typical intensity." He was concerned with the difficulties inherent in the concept of ritualization.

To make his point, Morris offered two simple models. In one of these, the fixed action pattern remains relatively unchanged over a wide range of causal factors (sometimes termed motivational changes). Such a signal has the advantage that it is unambiguous, though relatively poor in information. What has not been sufficiently emphasized is that such a system would be favored when the animals in question mate quickly, or when fights are typically brief and sporadic. Under these circumstances the signals should be unambiguous, facilitating rapid recognition.

The other model put forth by Morris resembles a simple dose-response curve. The "intensity" of the response is directly proportional to the strength of the causal factors. Consequently the intensity or completeness of the behavior reflects the motivation of the sender; the system is said to be rich in information. However, there immediately arises the possibility of ambiguity because of the fine gradations between the various degrees of expression of the behavior. This is just the situation we might expect in pairs of animals that have sustained pair bonds. It might also be expected in animals that engage in complex fights, requiring that each animal continually and accurately assess the state of its opponent. As a corollary, such a system should convey information along many channels and be highly redundant, to minimize the chances of error. And this seems to be the case (Barlow 1962).

The foregoing contained the tacit assumption that the system is deterministic even if the response is graded. What is seldom discussed when considering signal movements is the possibility that there may be selection for a degree of nonpredictability. This might be particularly true in animals that remain paired for long periods preceding copulation or spawning. Under these circumstances the animals could be expected to habituate to one another. Faced with this monotony effect, novelty might be advantageous.

Novelty is commonly associated with arousal and attention (Berlyne 1960). Now there are several ways an animal can introduce novelty into a sequence of courtship movements; it does not require variability in the basic motor pattern. Conceivably, however, the action pattern itself might be variable. On the other hand, the animal could "have its cake and eat it" by keeping certain parameters of the motor pattern constant while varying others. For instance, in the courtship quivering of the orange chromide the fish holds the amplitude and basic form of the movement relatively unchanged while varying such parameters as the duration, the phasing of the pelvic fin movements with the head quivering, the posture (whether horizontal or vertical), and the orientation to the mate.

Another way of reducing monotony is to vary the sequencing of the motor patterns. This is probably more the case than is commonly realized. The numerous flow diagrams given in the literature (e.g., Neil 1964) indicate that the variability in sequencing is much greater than would have been predicted from the original notions of chains of releasers and instincts (e.g., Tinbergen 1951). This is particularly the case among those species where courtship is a relatively continuous event (e.g., Baerends, Brouwer, and Waterbolk 1955; Nelson 1964). (For a similar argument about bird song, see Hartshorne [1958].)

Another hypothesis about fixed action patterns that is often intuitively appreciated but seldom stated is that those movements used in communication are less variable than those which are not. Here again there are few data. If there is some selective advantage in doing movements in the most economical way, therefore in a stereotyped way, then we might expect some of the nonsignal movements to be just as relatively fixed as signal movements. Particularly good examples are to be found among the elaborate grooming movements of mammals (Eisenberg 1963), as well as among activities involved in parental care (Barlow 1964).

Quantitative Models of Behavior

From the introduction one might conclude that I am unduly pessimistic about the application of formal statistical models to behavioral phenomena. Quite the contrary. Those caveats were advanced to create an awareness of the limitations of the models.

The same shortcomings can be found in the application of statistics to almost any real-world problem. It is not so much a question of the identity of the units involved as it is a matter of having an arbitrary criterion so that there is uniformity in the decision-making. In drawing marbles from a bag, for example, it is of little consequence if the marbles are of different colors. The main point is that the differences do not affect the choice.

The application of statistics regularly embraces quite heterogeneous units. In gathering data on accidents involving automobiles and bicycles no great violation of assumptions is done by regarding all automobiles as the same and all bicycles as the same. Useful statistics can be garnered in this way. Indeed, one frequently reads of comparisons between various countries based on such data. On the other hand, an insurance broker would find this gross level of analysis inappropriate to his needs. He would want to segregate the automobiles by age and sex of driver, past history of driver, horsepower of automobile, age of automobile, and so on. As his units become more refined and homogeneous, the power of his predictions increases. Eventually the point of diminishing returns is reached. The same is true with models as they apply to behavior studies. The difficulty again is that if the units are too small and homogeneous, the major phenomenon of interest is lost sight of.

Any quantification of behavior that arrives at some general conclusion is a model. But for fruitful comparisons with neurophysiological investigations the models that seem most promising are those involving the temporal patterning of behavior. This area of study is receiving increasing attention, and we can expect to see growth in this direction in the ethological literature.

The simpler of these models employ only one unit as the measure of the behavior. The number of attacks delivered to an opponent (Heiligenberg 1965a) or to a mirror image (Skaller 1966) are examples of particularly convenient units of measure that lend themselves to temporal analysis. A more complex movement is that of parental fanning where several measures may be made of the same event (Barlow 1964; Mertz and Barlow 1966).

More commonly several units are observed jointly. Then the units are analyzed separately to determine their probability of occurrence and distribution in time, or together, largely by means of cross-correlational analysis (Nelson 1964). A particularly popular approach has been the analysis of sequences of behavior without regard to their distribution in time. These are frequently portrayed using flow diagrams, but occasionally they are subjected to multifactorial analysis (Wiepkema 1961; Baerends and van der Cingel 1962).

Verbal Models of Behavior

Much of the recent literature in ethology has been devoted to the elaboration of verbal models of behavior. Most of these arise from a tripartite notion of behavior, building on three major categories of motivation—aggression, sex, and fear. This literature and its conceptual methodology have been well reviewed by Tinbergen (1959), Hinde (1966), and Marler and Hamilton (1966). There is no merit in elaborating further on what has already been said so well.

I bring in verbal models because the need became so obvious during the discussions at this symposium. People working at the neurophysiological level should be aware of some of the thinking of ethologists about problems broader than those involving just the fixed action patterns. I hope my comments will form a bridge between the fixed action pattern and what are commonly referred to as motivational analyses.

In simple terms, the question might be put, Do shared effectors mean shared C.N.S. mechanisms? As an example, the effector system that moves the jaws of a fish is employed in courtship displays, aggressive displays, digging, eating, retrieving larvae, and in many respiratory movements such as yawning and perhaps even coughing. Albrecht (1966) has argued that many of these behaviors in fishes have more in common at higher levels than is commonly suspected. Clearly, biting, digging, and eating are reciprocally influenced in one cichlid fish (Heiligenberg, 1965b). And parental retrieving of larvae is remarkably like hunting in *Badis badis* (Barlow 1964). Albrecht has extended this to include courtship displays, arguing that most courtship displays have been derived from aggressive behavior.

It is possible to look at even smaller pieces of behavior and to discover that the same movement is used in many different contexts. Thus the pelvic-fin flickering of the orange chromide may occur in the same way in many different situations, such as during courtship, at the end of a fight, during grooming, and when the parent signals to the young (in the latter case the coordination may be slightly different). Yet all of these seem to have certain causal factors in common; they occur at a time when one could readily hypothesize a strong conflict between fleeing and remaining. In this context, all of these pelvic-fin flickerings might be regarded as displacement grooming.

Much the same could be said of the quivering in the orange chromide. This movement is basically the starting action of swimming. It is highly ritualized into a courtship movement and an invitation to grooming, and it serves as a means of ejecting objects or distasteful substances from the mouth. Starting to swim, courtship, and interindividual grooming all have similar causes, the approach of another orange chromide. On the other hand, it is difficult to relate the head shaking employed when rejecting objects to that seen in courtship and grooming.

It is well to keep in mind that a fish is living in a medium that makes great demands on its locomotory abilities. A fish is highly streamlined and, unlike a bird, is typically relatively devoid of large appendages that can move independently of the body. In a fish, as in most animals, locomotory demands take primacy. Thus the basic coordination upon which most of the display movements are built is fundamentally one that must be a primary part of the locomotory apparatus.

A good example of the primacy of locomotory demands comes from Magnus' (1958) study of the fritillary butterfly. The female flaps her wings at a rate of about 8 beats per sec. The male recognizes the female by the flapping of her colored wings and pursues her. Yet the male will pursue preferentially models that flap at a rate up to tenfold that of the female. One might ask why the female has not evolved a higher rate of wing flapping in order to be more attractive to the males, since such females would have been selected for. The most likely answer is that the locomotory demands have primacy over the signal value.

Other factors must also be considered. Additional primary kinds of behavior are those involved in respiration and in feeding, both of which require the participation of the buccal apparatus. Thus jaw structure will be determined mainly by feeding habits and respiration, usually not by modes of fighting or displays. Some interesting exceptions do nonetheless occur, as in the case of the bizarre jaws of the salmons of the genus *Oncorhynchus;* but in this case the males no longer feed.

The difficulty with such an argument, that common effector means common motivation, is that it reduces all to one. Thus in the end everything is locomotion, respiration, or feeding. Clearly the motivational world of the animal is more structured than this. And yet the arguments are, when more narrowly viewed, quite persuasive. Unfortunately, proof is lacking in most instances. There should be more direct testing of hypotheses as to the degree to which movements expressed by a given effector system share causal factors at some higher level. A good example of such an approach is the recent work done by Heiligenberg (1965*b*) relating eating, digging, and attacking in a cichlid fish.

Such experiments on the causation of behavior should include a detailed analysis of the form and dynamics of the behavior in question and of its temporal patterning. This should be done both with regard to its own expression, and with regard to the interaction with other movements and its equivalence to other movements. Thus if two actions share the same motivation and effector, say biting and eating, then in a study of the bouting of either of these, one should substitute for the other. This is an easy assumption to test by interrelating the probability density functions of the two when both occur.

The other side of the coin must also be examined. That is, Do different effector systems indicate different mechanisms in the central nervous system? It is common knowledge that many animals use different groups of effectors in aggressive behavior, depending on the context. Thus a fish may fight with its mouth, or turn and beat with its tail. These are not controlled the same way, however, biting being much more indicative of attack, and tail beating more related to fleeing.

A better and more provocative example is that of the aggressive responses of a rattle-snake. When two males engage in aggressive behavior, they intertwine their necks as though to test each other's strength; they do not bite one another (Shaw, in Eibl-Eibesfeldt 1961). The aggressive behavior in response to attack by a potential predator is extremely different, however (Bogert 1941). If the putative predator is a large mammal the rattlesnake coils, rattles, strikes at the mammal, and bites it. But if the intruder is a king snake, which feeds on rattlesnakes and is immune to their bite, the rattlesnake shows a remarkably different aggressive behavior. It hides its head under the coil while it raises up one coil and slaps at the king snake with it. The adaptive significance of protecting the head is obvious. The important point is that in all three instances aggressive behavior, as conventionally defined, is obviously involved. Just as obviously, there are differences in the motivational state of the snake.

At the heart of the matter, of course, is the problem of defining aggressive behavior. The simple criterion of doing harm, or attempting to do harm, lumps many kinds of behavior that are otherwise separable by form and by context. The most suitable arrangement may be a hierarchical organization of behavior that at some point joins all the aggressive behaviors, but further down separates them out according to their causation. Thus one might conclude that different effectors do indeed indicate different motivational sources. But at some point, at a more general level, different effectors may be thought of as being determined by the same motivation.

Conclusions

I am not optimistic that behavioral models will soon lead to the discovery of C.N.S. correlates. At present our quantitative models of behavior are useful in that they lead to more precise, tangible descriptions of behavior, facilitating the search for their counterparts in the nervous system. These models are more important, however, in testing behavioral hypotheses inherent in verbal models.

It is essential to the development of reliable models that more attention be given to the units of behavior. In particular we need to understand better the basic nature of the so-called fixed action pattern. Even the most highly stereotyped of the fixed action patterns will probably always be graded to some degree and, if slow enough, controlled to some extent by the environment.

The ideas behind the fixed action pattern remain useful in thinking about behavior, and in formulating models to describe behavior. But as currently conceived, most motor patterns would be excluded if the criteria outlined in this article were rigidly adhered to. Most likely a gradation exists between the most highly stereotyped behavior patterns and those that are so variable as to defy characterization.

It may be important in the early stages of inquiry to pursue ideas, to select the example to support the hypothesis. But at some juncture good science demands that the effort be devoted to attempting to disprove the hypothesis. By examining a number of behavioral events, a more meaningful conceptualization of behavioral units will emerge.

As a final, and to some a rather minor, point, it might be wise to drop the term fixed from action pattern. In its present usage it is applied uncritically to almost any behavior that has a degree of regularity sufficient to permit one to recognize it. The term appears to have gained popularity as a replacement for innate motor pattern; this term was unfortunate because it contains an explanation that extends beyond the appearance of the behavior. Fixed action pattern is an improvement in that it was meant to derive solely from the appearance of the behavior. As I have argued, however, the behavior is seldom known to be fixed in the way the criteria demand.

Until there is a better understanding of the mode of expression and control of such behavior it would be preferable to have a less encumbered terminology. As a more general term, I would suggest modal action pattern. This conveys the essential features of the phenomenon: there is a spatiotemporal pattern of coordinated movement, and the pattern clusters about some mode, making the behavior recognizable. (I have purposely avoided the use of the word normative because we know so little about parameters such as central tendency and variance.) Furthermore, the modal action pattern (M.A.P.) is common to the species. The degree of variability and the role of peripheral input remain to be determined in each case. In the meantime, the classification of behavior should be based on the structure of the behavior. With increasing knowledge an articulated classification should evolve. Whether discrete "taxa" or a continuum will emerge remains to be seen.

Acknowledgment

I am grateful to Mildred Eley and to C. Hugh Fraser Rowell for reading the manuscript and offering critical comments. It should be apparent that I am also indebted to Robert Hinde for his timely and lucid restatement (1966) of the problem of the fixed action pattern as well as for his comments.

The writing was done during the tenure of Grant GB-5314 from the National Science Foundation.

References

Adams, D. K. 1931. A restatement of the problem of learning. *Brit. J. Psychol.* 22:150–78.

Albrecht, H. 1966. Zur Stammesgeschichte einige Bewegungsweisen bei Fische, untersucht am Verhalten von *Haplochromis* (Pisces, Cichlidae). *Z. Tierpsychol.* 23:270–302.

Ashby, W. R. 1966. Mathematical models and computer analysis of the function of the central nervous system. *Ann. Rev. Physiol.* 28:89–106.

Baerends, G. P.; Brouwer, R.; and Waterbolk, H. T. 1955. Ethological studies on *Lebistes reticulatus* (Peters): I. An analysis of the male courtship pattern. *Behaviour* 8:249–334.

Baerends, G. P., and van der Cingel, N. A. 1962. On the phylogenetic origin of the snap display in the common heron (*Ardea cinerea* L.). *Symp. Zool. Soc. London* 8:7–24.

Barlow, G. W. 1961. Ethology of the Asian teleost *Badis badis*. I. Locomotion maintenance, aggregation and fright. *Trans. Ill. Acad. Sci.* 54:175–88.

———. 1962. Ethology of the Asian teleost, *Badis badis*. IV. Sexual behavior. *Copeia* 2:346–60.

———. 1964. Ethology of the Asian teleost *Badis badis*. V. Dynamics of fanning and other parental activities, with comments on the behavior of the larvae and postlarvae. *Z. Tierpsychol.* 21:99–123.

Berlyne, D. E. 1960. *Conflict, arousal and curiosity*. New York: McGraw-Hill.

Bogert, C. M. 1941. Sensory cues used by rattlesnakes in their recognition of ophidian enemies. *Ann. N.Y. Acad. Sci.* 41:329–44.

Dane, B.; Walcott, C.; and Drury, W. H. 1959. The form and duration of the display actions of the goldeneye (*Bucephala clangula*). *Behaviour* 14:265–81.

Dixon, K. L., and Stefanski, R. A. 1965. An evaluation of the song of the black-capped chickadee. *Amer. Zool.* 5:693 (Abstract).

Eibl-Eibesfeldt, I. 1961. The fighting behavior of animals. *Sci. Amer.* 205(6):112–22.

Eisenberg, J. F. 1963. The behavior of heteromyid rodents. *Univ. Calif. Publ. Zool.* 69:1–100.

Frazzetta, T. H. 1966. Studies on the morphology and function of the skull in the Boidae (Serpentes). Part II. Morphology and function of the jaw apparatus in *Python sebae* and *Python molurus*. *J. Morph.* 118:217–96.

Hartshorne, C. 1958. Some biological principles applicable to song-behavior. *Wilson Bull.* 70:41–56.

Heiligenberg, W. 1965a. The effect of external stimuli on the attack readiness of a cichlid fish. *Z. Vergl. Physiol.* 49:459–64.

———. 1965b. A quantitative analysis of digging movements and their relationship to aggressive behavior in cichlids. *Anim. Behav.* 13:163–70.

Hinde, R. A. 1966. *Animal behavior*. New York: McGraw-Hill.

Liem, K. F. 1967. Functional morphology of the head of the anabantoid teleost fish *Helostoma temmincki*. *J. Morphol.* 121:135–58.

Lorenz, K. Z. 1935. Der Kumpan in der Umwelt des Vogels. *J. Ornith.* 83:137–213, 289–413.

———. 1937. Über die Bildung des Instinktbegriffes. *Naturwissenschaften* 25: 289–300, 307–18, 324–31.

———. 1950. The comparative method in studying innate behaviour patterns. *Symps. Soc. Exp. Biol.* 4:221–68.

Lorenz, K. Z., and Tinbergen, N. 1939. Taxis und Instinkthandlung in der Eirollbewegung der Graugans: I. *Z. Tierpsychol.* 2:1–29.

Magnus, D. 1958. Experimentelle Untersuchungen zur Bionomie und Ethologie des Kaisermantels *Argynnis paphia* L. (Lep. Nymph.): I. Überoptische Auslöser von Anfliegereaktionen und ihre Bedeutung für das Sichfinden der Geschlechter. *Z. Tierpsychol.* 15:397–426.

Marler, P., and Hamilton, W. J., III. 1966. *Mechanisms of animal behavior*. New York: Wiley.

Mertz, J. C., and Barlow, G. W. 1966. On the reproductive behavior of *Jordanella floridae* (Pisces: Cyprinodontidae) with special reference to a quantitative analysis of parental fanning. *Z. Tierpsychol.* 25:537–54.

Moore, G. P.; Perkel, D. H.; and Segundo, J. P. 1966. Statistical analysis and functional interpretation of neuronal spike data. *Ann. Rev. Physiol.* 28:493–522.

Morris, D. 1957. "Typical intensity" and its relation to the problem of ritualisation. *Behaviour* 11:1-12.

Neil, E. H. 1964. An analysis of color changes and social behavior of *Tilapia mossambica*. *Univ. Calif. Publ. Zool.* 75:1–58.

Nelson, K. 1964. The temporal patterning of courtship behavior in the glandulocaudine fishes (Ostariophysi, Characidae) *Behaviour* 24:90–146.

———. 1965. After-effects of courtship in the male three-spined stickleback. *Z. Vergl. Physiol.* 50:569–97.

Rilling, S.; Mittelstaedt, H.; and Roeder, K. D. 1959. Prey recognition in the praying mantis. *Behaviour* 14:164–84.

Rowell, C. H. F. 1961. Displacement grooming in the chaffinch. *Anim. Behav.* 9:38–63.

Russell, W. M. S.; Mead, A. P.; and Hayes, J. S. 1954. A basis for the quantitative study of the structure of behaviour. *Behaviour* 6:153–205.

Sevenster, P. 1961. A causal analysis of displacement activity (fanning in *Gasterosteus aculeatus* L.). *Behaviour Suppl.* 9:1–170.

Skaller, P. G. 1966. *Temporal patterning of the response to a mirror by a cichlid fish.* Master's thesis, University of Illinois, Urbana, pp. 1–41.

Tinbergen, N. 1942. An objectivistic study of the innate behaviour of animals. *Biblioth. Biother.* 1:39–98.

———. 1951. *The study of instinct.* Oxford: Clarendon Press.

———. 1959. Comparative studies of the behaviour of gulls (Laridae): A progress report. *Behaviour* 15:1–70.

Weiss, P. 1950. Experimental analysis of co-ordination by the disarrangement of central-peripheral relations. *Symps. Soc. Exp. Biol.* 4:92–111.

Wiepkema, P. R. 1961. An ethological analysis of the reproductive behaviour of the bitterling. *Arch. Neerl. Zool.* 14:103–99.

2

Motivation and Learning in Sticklebacks

P. Sevenster

Zoological Laboratory
The University of Leiden

Introduction

There is a growing mutual interest between ethologists and experimental psychologists. The approach which is considered characteristic for ethology has always been the study of behavior as it occurs in nature. Only recently the role of experience has come to the foreground —but mainly as a factor in shaping the animal's behavior in its natural surroundings. The ethologist, therefore, starts his research by carefully observing his chosen animal in a situation which copies the natural environment as closely as possible. The learning theorist, on the other hand, is mainly interested in the general process of assimilating experience. He therefore tries to eliminate the variables which he considers irrelevant, and tends to reduce the situation to the minimal requirements of his animals. Very few studies have been carried out in which the two approaches are combined and related to one another. The present paper is an attempt to show that such a combination can be fruitful and can bring to light phenomena which would not otherwise be easily discovered. In particular it will be shown that the ethological approach may both profit from and contribute to the analysis of a type of experiment which is usually connected with learning theory. I am going to discuss a case of instrumental conditioning in the male three-spined stickleback (*Gasterosteus aculeatus* L.). The experiments are still at an early stage and the analysis is by no means exhaustive. Yet some aspects have come out fairly clearly, and these may be of interest to this symposium. Obviously, with my approach, a brief description of the stickleback's natural behavior has to precede the analysis.

Some Aspects of Courtship Behavior

The observations were all made in tanks of $60 \times 35 \times 35$ cm, with a sand bottom, a row of plants, and tufts of green algae to provide nesting material. To the best of our knowledge (based on observations in nature) a male stickleback will show the full repertoire of reproductive behavior in this environment. Once a male has established a territory and built a nest in a shallow excavation in the sand, any intruding conspecific will be attacked, i.e., approached in a straight line and bitten. All intruders will eventually flee from the territory. However, a gravid female will turn toward the attacking male and adopt a special upright posture, displaying her swollen, egg-laden belly to the best advantage. This courtship posture of the female and the corresponding orientation toward the male are maintained even if she is bitten a few times. She will flee, however, if biting continues or is repeated too often. But the courting female also induces in the male a tendency to return to the nest. After the performance of various activities at the nest, with which we will not be concerned, the male will approach the female anew, and if the female keeps courting, the male will oscillate between the female and the nest. This will continue until the female follows and a sequence of activities is started which eventually leads to her spawning in the nest and the male's subsequent fertilization of the eggs. We can, however, easily prevent the female from following by confining her to a glass tube, and under these circumstances the male's oscillating courtship behavior may go on for very long periods indeed, and may thus be conveniently studied. For more detailed accounts I refer to the studies of Ter Pelkwijk and Tinbergen (1937), van Iersel (1953), and Sevenster (1961). Here only the following points are relevant.

Once the characteristic oscillation between nest and female has set in, most of the male's approaches no longer follow a straight course but show more or less pronounced lateral deviations. The typical approach takes the form of the well-known "zigzag-dance," in which each zigzag comprises a forward as well as a sideways component. These zigzags are clearly connected with the tendency to return to the nest which the courting female evokes in the male. At the same time, however, biting is much reduced. It is especially unlikely to occur at the end of a zigzag-dance, as compared with a straight approach. This relative incompatibility of zigzagging and biting is not due to some complicated interaction between male and female, for the same relationship is found when a model with some female characteristics is used as a substitute for the live female. Since biting may in fact follow zigzagging, a simple incompatibility of muscle contractions is probably not involved. A central inhibitory relationship therefore seems the most likely possibility. It is further important to note that the number of bites at a female in courtship is proportional to the number of bites in a fight against a rival male presented shortly before or after the courtship test. This is evidence that the same (aggressive) motivation underlies biting in both contexts. I conclude that the tendency to bite (evoked by any conspecific) is inhibited or interfered with by the tendency to zigzag (evoked by a courting female).

A striking demonstration of this phenomenon is seen in the period immediately following fertilization. If we allow the female to spawn in the nest the male is no longer willing to court for some time. In this situation the appearance of eggs is the effective factor (Sevenster-Bol (1962). Any gravid female is now approached in a straight line and severely bitten. After a while the readiness to court gradually recovers and it may regain its former level in about an hour. During some transitional stages in this process, we can observe interesting intermediates between purely aggressive behavior and fully developed courtship behavior. One of these intermediates is especially relevant for the present purpose. The male still approaches the female in a straight line and comes up very close to her with open mouth, clearly about to bite as he did at earlier approaches. However, he now stops just short of her and starts making slight zigzag-like jumps around her, all the time keeping his mouth open toward her, or snapping at her without actually touching her. Often the jaws are shut in a peculiar slow fashion on these occasions. The scene may yet develop into a bout of real biting, or else the male may stop circling around the female and slowly turn away. The ordinary oscillating pattern of courtship behavior is then resumed. Since during the circling nothing physically prevents the biting, a motivational interference from the growing tendency to zigzag again seems the most adequate explanation.

Aftereffects of Courtship

Even a short presentation of a female has a profound influence on the male's subsequent behavior, as Nelson (1965) has shown in detail. When the female has been removed there occurs a period of "excitement," in which the male still performs zigzags and characteristic searching behavior between the visits to the nest. Sometimes these zigzags are clearly aimed at visible stimuli (in particular, moving objects like snails, air bubbles, or flies in the room, etc.); sometimes no obvious stimulus can be identified. These zigzags in the absence of the female are therefore called vacuum zigzags, for the sake of convenience. Their frequency of occurrence, after the disappearance of the female, gradually decreases with the decay, following a more or less exponential course (Nelson 1965). Finally a nearly constant, low level is reached, which remains fairly stable until the next presentation of a female. Even at this level, however, temporary increases are found from time to time, notably when the male has wriggled through the nest. This activity of creeping through the nest shows a cyclical occurrence (Nelson 1965), and it is typically followed by a bout of vacuum zigzagging and increased locomotion, very similar to the behavior shown after the disappearance of the female. For some time after this creeping through the nest the male not only shows an increased tendency to zigzag to a female model, but also is less likely to bite a male model (Sevenster 1961). This is quite possibly another demonstration of the motivational interference which I have discussed, though in this case no correction has been made for the number of approaches.

Summarizing this section, we may note that a pronounced tendency to zigzag occurs either immediately after the presentation of a female or immediately after the occurrence of creeping through the nest.

Leaf-Biting

Among other activities of the stickleback's repertoire I shall mention only leaf-biting, which plays some part in the experiments I want to discuss. The activity is usually aimed at leaves protruding from the vegetation into the open space of the territory. Such a leaf is taken in the mouth and pushed away or pulled sideways. Sometimes it seems that the animal simply finds his path blocked by the leaf and that this sets the occasion to remove the obstacle. Functionally speaking, the activity may well serve to keep the area around the nest free from obstacles, and so to ensure unhindered courtship. At other times, however, one rather gets the impression that males are specifically motivated to push leaves, since the activity occurs in bouts and the animals go back repeatedly to leaves which do not seem to obstruct their movements at all. Often the response is very vigorous indeed, and occasionally a leaf is torn off; yet in some males it is not seen at all. Though a proper analysis has not yet been made, there are indications that the frequency of leaf-biting is correlated with the male's aggressiveness. Recently we had a group of fish which (probably owing to pretreatment) were exceptionally aggressive and in fact rapidly killed one another in the storage tank.

When a few survivors, still fighting, were separated and put in planted tanks, they could not be induced to build nests, but they were leaf-biting at a frequency which I had never observed before. One male in particular did almost nothing else. Since these were obviously pathological cases (all died soon afterward), a definite conclusion cannot be drawn. It seems likely, however, that leaf-biting is facilitated by aggressive motivation.

The Role of Learning

Observations on sticklebacks raised in complete isolation in glass beakers (with water only, except for the unavoidable food and dirt) revealed no deviation in any of the behavior features which I have described. On their introduction into a planted tank they behaved as normal individuals, showed leaf-biting, built nests within the usual time, and courted perfectly normally on their first confrontation with a female (see also, Cullen 1960). At least qualitatively the usual relationship between zigzagging and biting in courtship was observed, as well as the usual increase in zigzagging following creeping through the nest. Social experience therefore does not enter into the development of these characteristics. On the other hand, courtship behavior does provide an excellent opportunity to study situations in which learning processes play an important part, and to these we will now turn.

So far I have discussed courtship in a situation where the female was permanently in sight. If, however, an opaque screen separates the nest from the glass tube with the female, the male very quickly learns to make the detour. From then on he oscillates back and forth as usual, with only an occasional mistake or hesitation. This shows that at the end of his nest visit the male is in fact motivated to approach the female, and is not simply reacting to the visual stimulation. After removal of the female, the male will go on visiting the screened-off compartment of the tank more frequently than before her first appearance. In addition, the performance of vacuum zigzags is strongly facilitated in this compartment, compared with elsewhere in the tank.

Obviously the sight of a female or the performance of courtship behavior can be used as a reward in conditioning experiments. In the following I will present the results obtained with one male. However, the same experiments have been carried out with seven other males although with inferior equipment. The features which I will presently discuss were, both qualitatively and quantitatively, remarkably similar from one individual to another.

Swimming through a Ring

At one end of the tank a compartment was completely screened off by an opaque partition. The area left for the experimental male was 40×35 cm. In the case presented the nest was situated in the middle near the front pane. In the partition a sliding door could be moved electrically to uncover a glass window of about 15×15 cm, behind which a gravid female was kept in a glass container. After 10 (sometimes 20) sec the door automatically fell back to shut the window. This presentation of a female will be called a *reward*, if it follows the response to be conditioned in the experimental male; otherwise it will be called an *exposure*. The first step was to accustom the male to the sudden movement and noise of the door. After a while, depending on his initial shyness, he would rush to the window and start courting. In the process the female also became conditioned and turned toward the window immediately when the door shot up, thus providing a fairly constant stimulation. Once this had become firmly established, instrumental conditioning began.

In some experiments swimming through a ring was the response to be reinforced. A gray plastic ring was suspended somewhat below the water surface, at a distance of about 28 cm from the nest (other positions with other males gave equivalent results). To get at the ring, the male, starting from the nest, had to swim obliquely away from the door, since the angle door–nest–ring was about 120°. A series of 4 rings was used with inner diameters of 101, 77, 50, and 26 mm. To facilitate the training the widest ring was used first, and during the process the width was gradually decreased by presenting rings 2, 3, and 4 in succession.

It was surprising how strongly sticklebacks avoided swimming through a ring, even a comparatively wide one, like 2 or 3. Only with ring 1 was there a reasonable chance that the male would spontaneously go through it shortly after it was presented, so that one could soon start reinforcing the proper response and no laborious "shaping" would be required. Every time the animal swam through the ring, a reward was given by the observer pressing a button. When the response rate was increasing rapidly, it was not difficult to proceed with

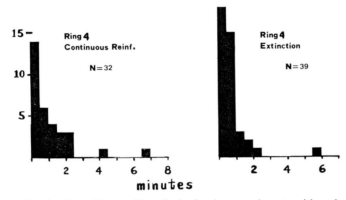

Fig. 1. Frequency-distributions of interval lengths in the ring experiments, with and without reward

rings 2 and 3. The transition to 4, however, remained a difficult step even at the end of the sequence. There was a considerable break in the response rate before the fish went through eventually. However, once the initial reluctance had been overcome, the response rate reached quiet a high level, and there seemed to be no difference between the ultimate response rate with ring 4 and those with the wider rings. In the following we will be concerned only with results obtained with ring 4, since these are the most important for the present purpose.

The stable response rate finally reached when each response is rewarded is represented in Figure 1, as the distribution of interval lengths between responses. Most intervals, including the 20-sec period of the reward, are shorter than one min. Also, it should be noted that during this period the nest is visited as is usual in courtship. Quite often such a nest visit starts very near the end of the reward period, e.g., when the male turns toward the nest as soon as the door comes down. Everything indicates that such a nest visit and the activities performed at the nest are rigidly connected with the preceding courtship and are best considered as its inevitable continuation. The time spent at the nest immediately after the reward is thus unavailable for the response; the fish simply cannot respond again before he has left the nest.

To some extent the same argument applies to the short period of "excitement," which follows the disappearance of the female. The wild locomotion of this characteristic searching behavior seems to develop from a disoriented zigzag dance. For example, if the male happens to be at the nest when the female disappears, he usually turns around and starts a new zigzagging approach, which then loses its orientation and disintegrates. These observations suggest that the excitement period does in fact delay the next response so that this period also could be said to be unavailable for the response, but in this case it is impossible to draw a line objectively, since there is no way to define the end of this period.

The only objective measure for the male's readiness to respond again is the time elapsing after he leaves the nest until the next response. Thus defined, the average "latency" of swimming through ring 4 is only 55 sec. When allowance is made for some delay caused by the excitement period it can be said that on most occasions the male responds again as quickly as could be expected. This is in accordance with the detour experiments with the screen, and the ring can be looked upon as a more drastic detour.

When no reward is given, the intervals tend to become somewhat shorter. Often the fish goes through the ring twice or more in succession, without going away in between. Apparently he perceives immediately that the reward is not forthcoming the first time. Apart from these double responses, however, the intervals are still somewhat shorter in the very first phase of extinction (see Fig. 1). No doubt this is due (at least partly) to the absence of an excitement period, and to the fact that the animal need not move so far away from the ring. In any case the intervals soon increase after this first phase.

The experiments with ring 4 can be summarized by three conclusions: (*a*) the response of swimming through ring 4 is initially a difficult one for the animal; (*b*) the ultimate response rate is as high as could be reasonably expected in view of other evidence; (*c*) at the onset of extinction the response rate increases only slightly.

Biting a Rod

The second response chosen for conditioning was biting the tip of a rod. A transparent rod with a diameter of 4 mm was inserted in the middle of the compartment where the male had his nest, and was mounted perpendicularly with its tip about 18 cm above the sand. This tip was provided with an opaque, bright green knob of 5 mm width. The tip was about 15 cm from the nest, and 20 cm from the door so that the angle between nest, rod, and door was about 90°. Some other positions of the rod relative to the nest and the door were tried, but results were again the same.

It was arranged that a slight bending of the rod away from the vertical automatically caused the door in the partition to open. A displacement at the tip of about 1.5 mm, irrespective of the direction, was sufficient to trigger the apparatus. The reward was the same as with the ring. The object of the training was to make the male bite the green tip of the rod with sufficient force to open the door. In several cases this required considerable shaping; at successive stages in the training, responses more and more approximating the one required were selected to be rewarded. Although it was easy to make the animal approach the rod, it was a difficult step to make him come very close and with his snout pointing at the tip. Sooner or later the animal would suddenly jump forward out of this position and bite at the tip, usually with a rather vigorous thrust. When this had happened a few times, further training was comparatively easy and only occasionally an additional "shaping reward" was required when the proper response had failed for some time.

All animals so far trained have learned this task, though some only after considerable effort. Some individuals, on the other hand, can be said to have learned the trick spontaneously (though they had been subjected to a brief shaping session). By automatic continuous recording in tanks with naïve males we found that quite a few showed the response spontaneously. The male here discussed made one spontaneous response a day previous to his training.

Our study thus far suggests a connection between this spontaneous rod-biting and the leaf-biting which I have mentioned above. The frequencies of these two activities seem to be positively correlated. Fish which learn the response spontaneously showed a great deal of leaf-biting, whereas those which required considerable shaping were seldom seen leaf-biting. Two of the pathological cases which I mentioned for their exceptionally severe fighting and

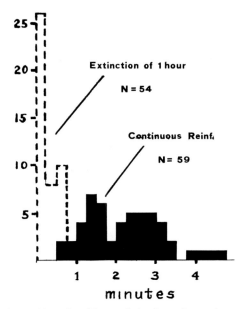

FIG. 2. Frequency-distributions of lengths of intervals in the rod experiments, with and without reward

their high frequency of leaf-biting also showed extremely high rates of spontaneous rod-biting—about 10 and 40 responses per hour. I think the shaping procedure merely serves to bring the male to a position where leaf-biting is easily provoked. This is the case when the fish is very close to the rod, pointing at it. In the preliminary experiments we found that a piece of Vallisneria leaf tied to the rod seemed to facilitate this final step in the training, and hence the green tip was later added. Thus, according to this view, the first rod-biting responses are in fact reactions to a leaflike obstacle.

Once the rod-biting has been established, the response rate increases rapidly, but the stable level ultimately reached with continuous reinforcement is surprisingly low compared with the screen or the ring experiments. The distribution of interval lengths between rewarded bites is given in Figure 2. The majority of intervals last longer than 2 or 3 min, and the average duration is 5.8 min. This poses an interesting problem: Why does the animal in this experiment respond so infrequently?

Since the rewarding presentation of the female includes the rather noisy slam of the door, we originally supposed that this had a frightening effect, which had to wane before the next response could be made. However, silent working of the door by hand with a string did not make any difference. The experiments with the ring also made it quite clear that the low response rate is not related to the particular reward.

Is the low response rate inherent in the response? In other words, Does biting limit rate of performance by some kind of self-inhibitory process? As Figure 2 shows, the rate of biting during the first phase of extinction increases quite spectacularly. Moreover, during extinction, bouts of several bites in rapid succession can be delivered at the rod, with intervening intervals (not included in the distribution in Figure 2) of only a few seconds. Leaf bites may also occur in bouts with short intervals. Furthermore, the rate of biting against another

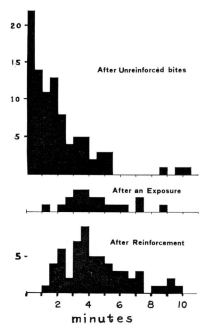

FIG. 3. Frequency-distributions of lengths of intervals in rod experiments with a variable ratio schedule of rewards and with intervening exposures.

male in a glass tube can be considerable: 10–50 bites per minute, including bouts of much higher frequencies. Finally, it seems important that in the male under discussion extinction was not yet complete after almost a month without a single reward. The frequency decreased slowly from 159 responses on the first day to 29 on the last. The evidence argues strongly against any self-inhibitory effect of biting and points to the conclusion that a low response rate is not inherent in the response.

Since the low response rate is not simply related to the reward or to the response, it may reflect their interaction, and this view is supported by the evidence. In some experiments we did not reward continually, but with a variable ratio schedule of one rewarded response to two unrewarded. In addition, "exposures" were given at arbitrary times (the door was opened by the observer). Figure 3 shows the distribution of the intervals after each of these events. It appears that rewards and exposures have identical effects on the length of the subsequent intervals, whereas the effect of an unrewarded bite is quite different. Thus it seems that the presentation of the female, whether as a reward or as an exposure, is the effective factor in producing the long intervals. This fact emerges most clearly if we separate the exposures into two groups: those where the last preceding event was a rewarded bite, and those where the last preceding event was an unrewarded bite. The average interval after a reward is 6.7 min (as compared with 4.9 min without an intervening exposure); the average interval after an unrewarded bite is 6.0 min (as compared with 2.2 min without an intervening exposure). So in both cases the intervals measured in this way are much longer than the corresponding ones without an intervening exposure, whereas the intervals between an exposure and the following response (4.7 min) are practically identical to those between a reward and the following response (4.9 min). This shows convincingly that the exposure does in fact restart the process which determines the length of the interval. I conclude that the presentation of the female (or the performance of courtship) delays the rod-biting response.

For a further analysis of this phenomenon, we must examine the behavior which actually takes place in these long intervals. At the beginning there is, of course, the usual short excitement period after the disappearance of the female. During the remaining part of the interval the rod is not ignored. On the contrary, the male again and again returns to it and, in fact, the first visit to the rod is made very soon after the excitement period. It is difficult to distinguish when the fish is actually paying attention to the rod and when he simply happens to pass it. To avoid a subjective criterion we defined a rod visit as an occasion on which the male's head was within 2 cm of the rod tip. This may have included some accidental rod visits. However, with this criterion it is possible to calculate the latency of the first rod visit (after the door is shut or after the male has left the nest) in the same way as we did for the ring response. This average latency of the first rod visit is 0.9 min, as compared with 0.6 min for the first ring visit, defined by the same criterion (male's head within 2 cm of the ring's center). Thus it appears that, as far as these intervals are concerned, the performance is similar in the two situations. The characteristic difference obviously is the fact that the response to the rod does not occur on the first visit, whereas with the ring it usually does. Something seems to prevent the biting response; analysis of the behavior during the rod visits throws some light on this factor.

As soon as the training process is effective and the response rate starts increasing, rod visits are sometimes accompanied by zigzags aimed at or near the tip. As a stable response rate is attained, zigzag-like jumps clearly directed at the tip become a very regular feature of rod visits. Frequently the male circles around the tip with small jumps while pointing at it. The mouth may be open during the performance and a slow biting movement is usually seen just short of the tip (Fig. 4). Occasionally the rod is actually touched, but not pushed sufficiently to trigger the apparatus. All intermediates are found between shortly fixing the rod tip and persistently circling around it with the mouth open. These performances are very reminiscent of the behavior of a male toward a courting female in the period shortly after fertilization, as was described earlier. It was concluded that biting in that situation is prevented by the motivational interference from the growing tendency to zigzag induced by the courting female. From the similarity of the behavior it seems a plausible inference that biting at the rod is also prevented by the tendency to zigzag.

Throughout each interval the tendency to zigzag gradually decreases, as is the general rule after the disappearance of the female (see above). During intervals of 3 min or more after a reward (24 cases) the average frequency of vacuum zigzags decreases from 4.7 in the first half minute to 0.3 in the last. These figures do not include zigzags directed at the rod, and are calculated per minute away from the nest, i.e., per minute of available time. Thus a cyclical process is started, since each reward has an aftereffect on the tendency to zigzag, which has to wane before the male is able to bite again, which if rewarded increases the tendency to zigzag, etc. During the aftereffect the tendency to respond is still present, as shown by the regular rod visits and the accompanying biting intentions. Because actual biting is suppressed, the response rate remains low in these experiments. This explains why, as soon as the reward fails, the response rate increases to a high value before extinguishing.

The results of the rod experiments can be summarized in the following conclusions: (a) the response of biting the rod is not difficult for the species and is often shown spontaneously; it is not quickly extinguished and can occur at a high frequency; (b) the ultimate response

FIG. 4

rate is very low as compared with the ring experiments, but at the onset of extinction the response rate increases considerably before the slow decrease begins; (c) even though the response rate is low, the rod is often visited, but on these visits biting appears to be suppressed by the aftereffect of the previous reward.

Discussion

Several workers have studied instrumental conditioning in fish. For example, Thompson (1963) trained Siamese fighting fish to swim through a ring, using the sight of a conspecific male as a reward, while Haralson and Bitterman (1950) taught a cichlid to push a lever by rewarding with food. Neither report mentions an increase in the response rate when the reward is no longer given. I take it for granted, therefore, that such an increase was absent or at most only slight and short-lasting. Performances must have been rather similar to those in my ring experiments in this respect.

The distinctive features of the stickleback's performance in the rod experiments, therefore, are the comparatively low response rate with continuous rewarding and the conspicuous increase in the response rate when rewarding is terminated. These indicate that the response rate is suppressed by the reward. In the present paper this suppression is ascribed to the motivational incompatibility of the aftereffect of the reward and the response. This incompatibility is obviously related to the suppression of biting in courtship, which I have described above. The experiments, therefore, point to the conclusion that this suppression of biting is not due to an interaction with the female (nor to stimulation by female traits of the models).

The interaction of the waning aftereffect of the reward with the biting response can be interpreted in a number of ways, depending on the interpretation of the behavior at the rod:

1. The zigzag-like jumps at the rod have to be considered as anticipatory responses, which are facilitated by the aftereffect of the reward. Only when the aftereffect has waned sufficiently can this anticipatory zigzagging no longer suppress the permanent tendency to bite at the rod.

2. The zigzag-like jumps at the rod could be considered simply as vacuum zigzags, which are directed toward the rod only because the male has been trained to visit the rod. For the rest, biting is suppressed generally during the aftereffect, regardless of the object at which it is aimed.

3. The zigzag-like jumps at the rod are actually elicited by the rod, since it has become associated with the female, in the sense that it has acquired female properties and is now treated like a dummy. Biting is specifically suppressed at the rod.

It is not at present possible to decide between these alternatives. A more refined analysis of the behavior at the rod is needed. Even then, it is questionable whether a clear distinction between (1) and (3) can be made. It should be possible, however, to establish whether biting in general or only biting at the rod is affected by the aftereffect. This question is presently being investigated.

If our interpretation is correct, the choice of a particular response or operant (swimming through ring or biting rod) has a profound influence on the subsequent performance in a conditioning experiment. This view contrasts with the implication of many studies on learning that this choice is arbitrary and not of much consequence to the results.

However, since most of these studies deal with higher vertebrates (especially with the rat) it might well be that in these animals the trained response can more easily be detached from its original motivation. For according to the interpretation discussed here the stickleback is not capable of using the biting response as a "motivationally neutral" means to attain the reward. In spite of prolonged training, the biting response remains incompatible with the aftereffect of the reward.

It would be interesting to try a similar, incompatible combination of reward and response in other fish, as well as in higher vertebrates, to establish whether this lack of flexibility is associated with the relative simplicity of the teleost central nervous organization.

In order to test our interpretation of the rod-biting experiments it would be very important to know what would happen if a rival male were presented instead of a female, so that fighting was elicited instead of courting. Since the aftereffect of the fight would presumably be perfectly compatible with the rod-biting response, the prediction is that the interresponse intervals would be short and the response rate correspondingly high. However, so far we have found that our trained males soon stopped responding when the female had been exchanged for a rival male. Our attempts to train males from the beginning with a rival male behind the door were not successful, even though other evidence suggested that the opportunity to fight another male can (sometimes) be a rewarding event. Shortly after the symposium, however, we finally succeeded in training one male, using the appearance of a rival male as reinforcement. In this case the prediction was confirmed: the male usually went back to the rod as soon as the door fell down and he bit the rod without any hesitation. For long stretches the male thus oscillated back and forth between the door and the rod. Typically there is no nest visit following a fight, nor is there a clear "excitement" period. Therefore the response rate was often even higher than in the courtship experiments with the ring (Fig. 5). Longer intervals were found when the animal entered a period of collecting

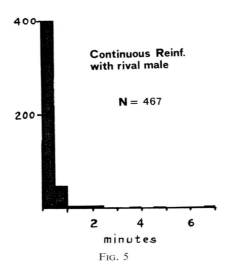

Fɪɢ. 5

material or intensive fanning. This brought the average interval up to 0.6 min. This single experiment therefore strongly supports the interpretation of the courtship experiments with the rod which I have discussed in this paper.

Acknowledgment

I am very grateful to G. Veldhuyzen, F. Körner, and O. Tissing for devising and constructing the apparatus used, and to Ans Jongsma for her aid in making and working out the observations.

References

Cullen, E. 1960. Experiment on the effect of social isolation on reproductive behaviour in the three-spined stickleback. *Anim. Behav.* 8:235.

Haralson, J. V., and Bitterman, M. E. 1950. A lever-depression apparatus for the study of learning in fish. *Amer. J. Psychol.* 63:250–56.

Nelson, K. 1965. After-effects of courtship in the male three-spined stickleback. *Zeits. Vergl. Physiol.* 50:569–97.

Sevenster, P. 1961. A causal analysis of a displacement activity (fanning in *Gasterosteus aculeatus*). *Behaviour* Suppl. 9:1–170.

Sevenster-Bol, A. C. A. 1962. On the causation of drive reduction after a consummatory act (in *Gasterosteus acvleatus* L.). *Arch. Neerl. Zool.* 15.(2):175–236.

Ter Pelkwijk, J. J., and Tinbergen, N. 1937. Eine reizbiologische Analyse einiger Verhaltensweisen von *Gasterosteus aculeatus* L. *Zuits. Tierpsychol.* 1:193–200.

Thompson, T. I. 1963. Visual reinforcement in Siamese fighting fish. *Science* 141:55–57.

Van Iersel, J. J. A. 1953. An analysis of the parental behaviour of the male three-spined stickleback (*Gasterosteus aculeatus* L.). *Behaviour* Suppl. 3.

3

Memory in Homing of Migratory Fishes

Arthur D. Hasler

Laboratory of Limnology
The University of Wisconsin

Among the memory feats of nature, not the least mysterious is the migration of fishes. The homing of salmon illustrates an unusually dramatic example. The Chinook salmon of the northwestern United States is born in a small stream, migrates downriver to the Pacific Ocean as a young smolt and, after living in the sea for as long as five years, swims back to spawn in the stream of its birth. Its determination to return to its birthplace is legendary. No one who has seen a Chinook salmon of 45 kg fling itself into the air again and again until exhausted in a vain effort to surmount a waterfall can fail to marvel at the strength of motivation that sends the salmon upriver in search of that stream where it was born.[1]

How do salmon remember their birthplace, and how do they find their way back from as far as 6,000 km away? This enigma, which has fascinated naturalists for many years, continues to challenge the experimenter. The question is of economic as well as scientific interest, because new dams which stand in the salmon's way have cut heavily into salmon fishing along American and European coasts. Already, nearly every stream of any appreciable size in the American West is blocked by dams. It is true that the dams have fish lifts and ladders, but none has been constructed which effectively enables the descent of the seaward migrants.

There are six common species of salmon. One, the Atlantic salmon, is of the same genus as the steelhead trout. These two fishes go to sea and come back upstream to spawn year after year. The other five species, all on the Pacific coast, are the Chinook (or king salmon), the sockeye, the coho, the humpback, and the chum. These Pacific salmon spawn only once and then they die.

In a typical salmon species the young fish sees the light of day when it hatches and wriggles up through the pebbles of the stream where the egg was laid and fertilized. For a

[1] For a more detailed account of salmon migration, see Hasler 1966.

247

few weeks, the fingerling feeds on insects and small aquatic animals. Then it answers its first migratory call and swims downstream to the sea. It must survive many hazards to mature. Indeed, an estimated 15 per cent of young salmon are lost at every large dam on the downstream trip. Still others die in polluted streams, and many are swallowed up by bigger fish in the ocean. After several years in the sea, the sexually mature salmon responds to the second great migratory call, and finds the mouth of the river by which it entered the ocean. It swims steadily upstream, choosing the correct turn at each tributary fork with amazing precision, until it arrives at the stream where it was hatched. Generation after generation, stocks of salmon return to the same rivulet so consistently that populations in streams not far apart follow distinct evolutionary lines.

The homing behavior of the salmon has been documented by many studies since the turn of the century. One of the most elaborate was made by Clemens, Foerster, and Pritchard (1939) in Canada. They marked 469,326 young sockeye salmon born in a tributary of the Fraser River, and later recovered nearly 11,000 of these in the same parent stream after the fishes' migration to the ocean and back. Not one of the marked fish was found to have strayed into another stream. This remarkable demonstration of the salmon's precision in homing has presented an exciting challenge to investigators.

Donaldson and Allen (1957) switched salmon stock and allowed the eggs to develop in different waters. The adult fish, after their sojourn at sea, returned to the waters in which they had lived as fry, rather than to the parent stream. In this way, Donaldson has built up a run of salmon in the new hatchery on Lake Union, at the University of Washington. It is common practice in Sweden, where streams are blocked by dams, to raise salmon in southern hatcheries, transfer the fingerlings to the north, and later recover these fish in the mouth of their adopted river.

At our Wisconsin Limnological Laboratory we have studied the sense of smell in fish during the past decade, beginning with minnows and going on to salmon. Our findings suggest that the salmon finds its way home from the sea by literally smelling out the stream of its birth. This ability is one of many discriminative abilities of fish which attest to their keen sense of smell.

In the bony fishes the nose pits have two separate openings. The fish takes in water via the front opening as it swims or breathes (sometimes aided by the movement of cilia), and passes water out through the second opening, which may be opened and closed in synchrony with the respiratory rhythm. Any odorous substances in the water stimulate the nasal receptors chemically, and the resulting neural impulses are relayed to the brain via the olfactory nerve.

The human nose, like that of other land vertebrates, can smell a substance only if it is volatile and soluble in fat solvents. Yet in the final analysis, smell is always aquatic, since the substance cannot be sensed until it passes into solution in the mucous film of the nasal passages. For fishes, the odors are already in solution. Nevertheless, they can follow an odor through their watery environment to its source as a hunting dog tracks the scent of an animal on land. It is likely that the quality of the odor changes as the fish approaches its goal, since the concentration increases. We know from our own experience that an odor may be pleasant at one concentration and unpleasant at another.

We initially undertook experiments to determine whether fish could distinguish the odors of different aquatic plants. We used a specially developed aquarium with jets which could inject odors into the water (Fig. 1). Fish were rewarded with food for moving toward one odor source, but for moving to the wrong odor they received a mild electric shock.

After fish were trained to make choices between odors, they were tested for discriminatory capacities with dilute rinses from 14 different aquatic plants. These subjects could distinguish odors of all these plants from one another.

The odors of plants may play a natural role by guiding fish to their feeding grounds when visibility is poor. Or they may keep young fish from straying away from from familiar protective cover. Odors may also have a negative value, and warn fish of poisons. In fact, we have discovered that fish could be used to assay industrial pollutants: our minnows were trained to detect phenol, a common pollutant, at concentrations below those detected by man. These facts make plausible our working hypothesis that salmon use olfactory memory to find their way back to their native stream.

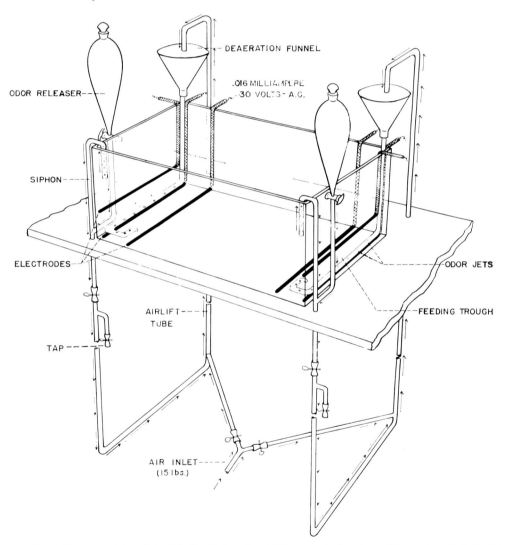

FIG. 1. Experimental tank built in the University of Wisconsin Laboratory of Limnology to train fish to discriminate between two odors. The fish are trained to receive food or avoid electrical shock at either scoring zone upon perceiving correct odor. Young fish have been shown to retain learning longer than older ones.

Of course, there are quite a few "ifs" in this theory. We first determined whether each stream really has its own distinctive odor by taking water from two creeks in Wisconsin and training fish to discriminate between them. Our subjects—first minnows and later salmon—were indeed able to detect the difference. As a control procedure, we destroyed the olfactory tissue and found our fish no longer able to discriminate between the two samples of water. Chemical analysis indicated that the only major difference between these samples lay in the organic materials. By testing the fish with various fractions of water, separated by distillation, we determined that the material detected was some volatile organic substance.

The idea that fish are guided by odors during migrations was then supported by a field test. From each of two branches of the Issaquah River in the state of Washington, Warren Wisby and I took ripe coho salmon that had come home to spawn. We then plugged with cotton the nares of half of each group of fish and placed all fish in the river below the fork, to make the run upstream again. Most fish with unplugged nares swam back to the stream that they had already selected, but the "odor-blind" fish migrated back randomly between the two streams. These results have recently been confirmed by Japanese workers (Sato, Hiyama, and Kajihara 1966).

In our own laboratory, we tested the olfactory memory of fish (Hasler and Wisby 1951), and found that they retained an odor discrimination habit for six weeks after their initial training. Furthermore, the young fish remembered these odors better than did their elders. The finding that young fish were superior in these tests agrees with much comparative ethological data that animals remember very well certain conditions to which they have been exposed in their early stages. For example, an ichneumon fly larva that normally eats the host larvae of the flour moth will eat beeswax moth larvae as well, and when mature will seek out this species on which to lay its own eggs (Thorpe and Jones 1938).

Thus far we have shown that different streams have distinct odors; that salmon can actually respond to these odor differences; and that they remember odors to which they have been conditioned. We then asked whether the salmon's homeward migration is guided solely by its sense of smell. If we could decoy homing salmon into a stream other than their birthplace, by means of artificial olfactory conditioning, then we might solve a puzzling riddle and also devise a practical means of guiding salmon to breeding streams unobstructed by dams.

We needed a substance which would at first be neither attractive nor repellant, but which would become attractive upon appropriate training. Eventually we found that dilute solutions of morpholine, detectable at concentrations of as little as one part in a million, served our requirements. Our collaborators are now conducting field tests in Alaska to learn whether salmon fry and fingerlings that have been conditioned to approach morpholine can be decoyed into a stream other than that of their birth, as they return to spawn. However, if the salmon are not successfully decoyed to the new stream it might simply mean that they cannot, in nature, be attracted by a single substance alone. Perhaps the adding of one substance such as morpholine to the water is like adding the screeching whistle of a freight train to the quiet strains of a violin, cello, and flute. The salmon may still seek out the subtler harmonies of an odor combination to which they have reacted for millenniums. But, as experimenters, we hope they may respond to the call of our whistle.

Various students—notably Powers (1939)—have proposed that specific carbon dioxide concentrations in rivers may serve as guideposts for migrating fishes. However, if fishes were found to be attracted or repelled by a substance such as carbon dioxide, that would not indicate that they respond to it while homing. Indeed, it seems unlikely that a common substance could provide the basis for homing, since salmon would follow such a chemical track regardless of its origin.

In the ocean, it seems to me, odor might play a role mainly by giving the fish a sign stimulus by which they recognize home. If the fish were swimming within a water mass, it would have no sense of being displaced as the water moved unless there were fixed visual or tactile features in the environment. The problem of orienting a balloon in a cloud provides a comparable example.

Home Finding from the Sea

Recently, Canadian, Japanese, and American scientists captured and marked thousands of salmon on the high seas (Neave 1964). When they were recording the sites where the fish were captured in their home streams, it was clear that sockeye salmon had been intermingled as maturing adults in the Gulf of Alaska. Yet after attaining sexual maturity they had sorted themselves out and returned to home streams in British Columbia or Washington; some even cross the Pacific in returning to northern Asia. How do they navigate over such distances as 2,000–5,000 km?

While home finding in a stream might well depend upon the recognition of a familiar odor, it seemed to me that this hypothesis was inadequate to explain movements of salmon in the ocean. Other cues must be used as well. Since it was clear that our Wisconsin team would have difficulties conducting a field study on salmon at sea, I asked myself whether there might be a freshwater fish at hand which also finds its spawning ground from open water. If so, the study of open-lake migration in such a species might give us a clue as to how the salmon accomplishes these feats at sea.

Our initial attack on the problem involved a simpler type of homing than that found in salmon. For several years my students and I have studied the natural history of the white bass (*Roccus chrysops* Raf.) in Lake Mendota, Wisconsin. We have been able to locate only two major spawning sites in the entire lake, and these are of very limited area. These spawning grounds—Maple Bluff and Governor's Island—are both on the northern shore of the lake and are separated by a distance of 1.6 km. Here white bass congregate at spawning time in late May and early June, when temperatures range from 16° to 24° C.

During several spawning seasons (beginning in 1955) white bass were captured in fyke nets, marked with numbered disk tags, and transported in open tanks to different release stations in the lake for daytime release. To date, over 15,000 have been displaced and 15 per cent of these have been subsequently recaptured and tallied. From the start, we observed that a large proportion of fish returned to their spawning sites. As observations accumulated we were impressed with the high precision of homing among the Maple Bluff and the Governor's Island spawners. Of fish recaptured, 89–96 per cent had returned to their original spawning site from the release point located 2.4 km from the spawning grounds, in a lake with a 39-square-km area, and a 32-km shoreline. The percentage return from the release points was actually as high as that of fish released on the spawning ground itself. This indicates a complete return of displaced fish, assuming their mortality to be the same as the control group. In addition, over 900 specimens have returned in subsequent years to spawn at the home site—good evidence of specific "recognition" of the spawning place.

The "take off" direction of displaced white bass was observed after attaching a white plastic float which could be seen as the fish towed it along. From the many fish released, recorded since 1958, we see that the initial course taken is generally north toward the spawning ground, on sunny days. On cloudy days, however, the fish swim randomly. It appears that celestial cues guide the tendency to swim north, bringing the fish to the general vicinity of their spawning area. Once there, they may locate their specific sites by using other local cues.

We have attempted to avoid the possible irritating effects of the float marker by outfitting our fish with a miniature sonic transmitter carried within the body. In 1963, my associates, H. Francis Henderson and Gerald Chipman, constructed a cylindrical unit 0.9 by 4.0 cm, which could easily be inserted with a plunger into the stomach of the fish, or into the body cavity via a small incision (Henderson, Hasler, and Chipman 1966). This transmitter sends a signal at 70 kc continuously for about 15 hr before the miniature battery is exhausted, and it can be detected by a receiver as far away as 1,000 m. Our tests with dummies of the same size indicate that they do not in any way restrict the behavior of the fish. On the basis of over 100 releases of white bass in Lake Mendota, using sonic tags, we have confirmed our previous findings that the fish return to their spawning grounds by a direct route. We have

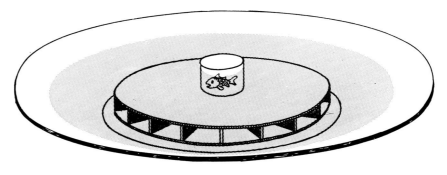

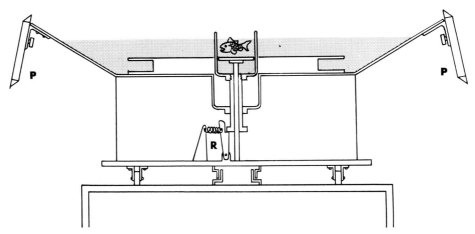

FIG. 2. Tank for training fish to a compass direction. *Top*, as seen from above showing the hiding boxes. *Bottom*, side view showing periscopes (*P*) for indirect observation and the release lever (*R*) to permit the cage to be recessed by remote control when fish is released to score.

begun a similar study of salmon using such transmitters, under the auspices of the National Science Foundation and the Office of Naval Research. Salmon will be followed considerable distances on the high seas in order to determine just how they correct for the displacement.

A compass mechanism would certainly be an aid in navigation, although current drift could displace salmon hundreds of kilometers from their home river if this were the sole source of guidance. In exploring the important possibility that the sun-compass mechanism does operate in fish, we developed a new type of experimental procedure. Fish were tested under the open sky in a specially designed tank (Fig. 2). During training, fish were placed in a cage at the center and released. The fish was then given a small shock to frighten it, which resulted in its seeking cover in one of 16 small compartments along the periphery of the tank. Only one container, invisible to the fish at the center of the tank, could be entered, and this always lay in the same compass direction.

When a fish had learned the location of the "safe" training compartment well, it was tested with all 16 boxes open. Tests conducted between 0800 and 0900 and between 1500 and 1600 hr usually revealed the fish's preference for boxes that lay in the compass direction where it had been trained to seek shelter. However, on overcast days, when the experimenter could not detect the presence of the sun, these trained fish were completely disoriented.

We must conclude that the sun was in fact the fish's point of reference, and that in seeking the same direction at different times of the day, the fish could allow for the movement of the sun (see Fig. 3). The crucial test of this interpretation involved the substitution of an

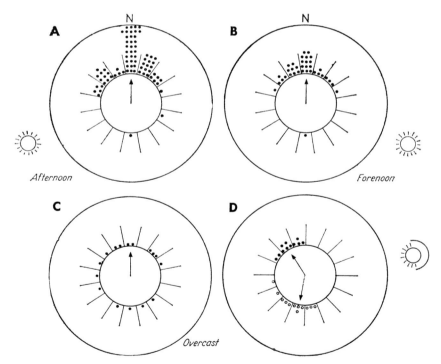

FIG. 3. Scores of fish trained to seek cover in the north compartment: *a*, tested in the afternoon with 16 possible choices; *b*, tested in the forenoon with 16 possible choices; *c*, scores of fish tested under completely overcast sky on two different days; *d*, scores of fish using an artificial light, where the altitude was the same as that of the sun (*solid dots*, scores of fish trained to north and tested in the forenoon; *circles*, scores of same fish tested in the afternoon).

indoor artificial sun for the actual sun. The fish responded as though they were responding to the real sun as it would have been at that time of day by choosing a hiding box at the appropriate angle to the artificial sun. We have thus established the existence of an orienting mechanism which is coupled with a circadian rhythm.

Possible Influence of Sun Altitude

In seeking an understanding of the mechanism of the sun compass in animals, the application of laboratory methods has been extremely illuminating. Yet the whole story of navigational abilities is complex. Such ability, as established in field tests with birds, involves factors other than sun orientation (Matthews 1955). In order to test the relevance of sun altitude for fish, Horst Schwassmann and I flew some sunfish (*Lepomus cyanellus*) that had been trained in orientation to the sun for several weeks at Madison, Wisconsin (43° N), to the equator at Belém, Brazil (1° S), where we tested them out-of-doors in our circular sun-orientation tank (Hasler and Schwassmann 1960). These fish did not adapt to this new and radically different daily sun movement, but continued to make the compensation for the azimuth curve of the sun that would have been "correct" for Madison. One of these sunfish, when flown to Montevideo (30° S) and retrained briefly under the sun (which appears to move counterclockwise in the Southern Hemisphere), continued to make the adjustment that would have been correct for the Northern Hemisphere. What would have been the response of a sexually mature salmon that had moved from one latitude to the other at a normal and gradual rate?

Under the equinoctral sun at the equator a rapid deterioration of the oriented behavior of the trained but displaced fish occurred, and all the fish showed an increasing tendency to maintain the same angle to the azimuth position of the sun throughout the day, suggesting that altitude changes are at least perceived. Later experiments in attempting to fool the fish by changing the altitude with mirrors add credence to this view.

It is clear that other types of studies must be undertaken in order to solve the riddle of the salmon's migratory accomplishments. Certainly we must be boldly imaginative in approaching the problem by going to sea with new techniques and logical hypotheses to be tested and returning to the laboratory to elaborate on the mechanisms used by the fish to find its way. Recently it has been proposed in mathematical models and tested by computers that random migration can account for homing in fishes. While I accept the fact that random search is important, all our data point to strong abilities of orientation. A salmon may be like the small boy en route home from school. He may dillydally at the swimming hole and meander through the woods but he nevertheless arrives home, having been completely oriented the whole while.

Adult salmon are known to move during the night in the sea. In order to take advantage of this activity the gill net fishermen set their nets at night. Clifford Barnes of the University of Washington observed salmon migrating at right angles to his oceanographic research vessel, which was on course at night in the northeastern Pacific. Because of a luminescent sea, this school of large salmon could be seen clearly. The fish swam on a fairly straight course until they were out of sight. We need to know more about the directed movements of salmon at night. Perhaps our sonic tag will aid us in tracking them in order to gain knowledge of their night activities at sea. We have here opportunities of unlimited potentiality, exciting to contemplate.

Acknowledgment

Acknowledgment is made to the University of Wisconsin Press, with whose permission we have reproduced the figures presented herein.

References

Clemens, W. A.; Foerster, R. E.; and Pritchard, A. L. 1939. The migration of Pacific salmon in British Columbia waters. In Migration and conservation of salmon. *Publ. Amer. Ass. Advance. Sci.* 8:51–59.

Donaldson, R., and Allen, G. H. 1957. Return of silver salmon, *Oncorhynchus kisutch* (Walbaum), to point of release. *Trans. Amer. Fish. Soc.* 87:13–22.

Hasler, A. D. 1966. *Underwater guideposts.* Madison: The University of Wisconsin Press.

Hasler, A. D., and Schwassmann, H. O. 1960. Sun orientation of fish at different latitudes. *Symp. Quant. Biol.* 25:429–41.

Hasler, A. D., and Wisby, W. J. 1951. Discrimination of stream odors by fishes and relation to parent stream behavior. *Amer. Nat.* 85:223–38.

Henderson, H. F.; Hasler, A. D.; and Chipman, G. C. 1966. An ultrasonic transmitter for use in studies of movements of fishes. *Trans. Amer. Fish Soc.* 95:350–56.

Matthews, G. V. T. 1955. *Bird navigation.* Cambridge: Cambridge University Press.

Neave, R. 1964. Ocean migrations of Pacific salmon. *J. Fisheries Res. Board Can.* 21:1227–44.

Powers, E. B. 1939. Chemical factors affecting the migratory movement of the Pacific salmon. *Publ. Amer. Ass. Advance. Sci.* 8:72–86.

Sato, R.; Hiyama, Y.; and Kajihara, T. 1966. The role of olfaction in return of chum salmon, *Oncorhynchus keta* (Walbaum), to its parent stream. *Proc. Pacific Sci. Congress, Pacific Sci. Ass., 11th.* Vol. 7.

Thorpe, W. H., and Jones, F. G. W. 1938. Olfactory conditioning in a parasite insect and its relation to the problem of host selection. *Proc. Roy. Soc., Ser. B* 124:56–81.

4

Comparative Studies of Learning in the Fish

M. E. Bitterman

Bryn Mawr College

I must warn you to begin with that I cannot talk about learning in the fish without talking also about learning in the rat. My experiments with the fish were patterned for the most part after experiments with the rat, and their main purpose was to look for similarities and differences in the learning of the two animals (Bitterman 1960, 1965). The rat is the animal about whose learning we know most. Early in this century, when the problem of animal intelligence first was being brought into the laboratory, many different animals were studied briefly; but the scope of research soon narrowed (as the conviction grew that the mechanisms of intelligence were the same everywhere in the animal series), and the rat became for the student of learning what the fruit fly has been for the student of genetics—a standard animal, chosen for reasons of custom and convenience, and treated as representative of animals in general. Other animals have been studied with considerable frequency, of course—for example, the dog has been the principal subject of the Russian experiments on conditioning—but none has been studied as thoroughly as the rat.

Both Thorndike and Pavlov believed the mechanisms of intelligence to be the same everywhere in the animal series. An animal comes into the world, said Thorndike (1911), with certain built-in connections between sensory and motor systems, and its intelligence lies simply in its ability to modify these connections in accordance with the demands of a particular environment. On the basis of his early comparative experiments with fish, bird, cat, dog, and monkey, Thorndike decided that however much animals may differ in "what" they learn, or in the "degree" of their learning ability, the principles which govern their learning are the same. This opinion was greeted with a good deal of skepticism, but it quickly gained wide acceptance, which it has even today. Pavlov also came rather early to the same conclusion. According to Voronin (1962), the dominant Russian opinion since Pavlov's day has been, and continues to be, that conditioning is a "universal mechanism" of intelligence which has undergone "only a quantitative growth or complication" in the course of evolution.

When I began to work on learning in the fish about ten years ago, there was little to contradict this popular view, but neither had there been very much in the way of systematic comparative study, and my aim was to remedy that deficiency. Taking the familiar rat as a standard, I turned first to the fish—specifically (and largely for practical reasons) to the goldfish and the African mouthbreeder—which seemed similar enough to the rat in general properties that it might meaningfully be studied by analogous methods (Bitterman 1966), yet different enough from the rat in brain structure that it might reasonably be expected to show some significant functional differences. My plan was not to compare the animals in terms of rate of learning (because differences in rate would not necessarily imply the operation of different learning mechanisms), but in terms of functional relations—to find out if their behavior was affected in the same way by the same variables. Since a variety of simple experiments had shown no striking differences in the learning of fish and rat, I decided to begin with some more elaborate procedures. My idea was that the simplest processes of learning might be the same in the two animals, but that in more complicated tasks the rat might display advanced capabilities or modes of adjustment which were not to be found in the fish. Let me now briefly describe some early results which seemed at first to support this idea, and then turn to some more recent results which have led me to question it.

Consider the problem of habit-reversal. Suppose that an animal is permitted on each trial to choose between two stimuli, *A* and *B*. If the choice of *A* is rewarded and the choice of *B* is not rewarded, the animal soon develops a preference for *A*. Fish and rat behave in much the same way. Now the positive and the negative stimuli are reversed—the choice of *B* is rewarded and the choice of *A* is not. Both animals persist for a time in the choice of *A*, but after a certain number of errors they reverse their preferences—that is, they begin consistently to choose *B*—and again it is impossible to tell from the learning curves which represents the performance of a fish and which the performance of a rat. As reversal training continues, however—that is, as the positive and negative stimuli are reversed again and again—a difference in the adjustment of the two animals appears. The rat shows what is called *progressive improvement in habit-reversal*—it shifts its preference more and more rapidly as the conditions change, until each reversal is accomplished with very few errors. The fish does not show progressive improvement. For the fish, the tenth (or the fiftieth) reversal is no less difficult than the first (Behrend, Domesick, and Bitterman 1965). Some representative data for rat and mouthbreeder are plotted in Figure 1.

Another striking difference in the adjustment of fish and rat appears in experiments on probability-learning. Again in these experiments, an animal is given a choice between two stimuli, *A* and *B*, both of which now are rewarded, but with different probabilities. For example, *A* may be rewarded on a random 70 per cent of trials and *B* on the remaining trials (a 70:30 problem), or *A* may be rewarded on a random half of the trials and *B* on the remaining trials (a 50:50 problem). The traditional procedure of rewarding one stimulus consistently and the other never may be regarded simply as a limiting case of probability-learning (a 100:0 problem). In these experiments, the fish shows *random probability-matching*, a phenomenon which has never been found in the rat. It is called "matching," because the choice-probabilities correspond closely to the reward-probabilities, and the matching is described as "random" because no sequential dependencies are to be found in the data—the fish chooses on each trial as though it were consulting a table of random numbers. For example, in a 70:30 problem, the fish chooses the higher-probability alternative on a random 70 per cent of trials and the lower-probability alternative on the remaining trials (Behrend and Bitterman 1966). In such experiments, the rat commonly *maximizes*—that is, it comes gradually to choose the higher-probability alternative on about 100 per cent of trials. Some representative data for rat and mouthbreeder are shown in Figure 2.

Two points should be made with respect to these differences. The first is that they are not merely quantitative differences (in the sense that one animal does something more rapidly or more efficiently than another) but qualitative—one animal does something which the

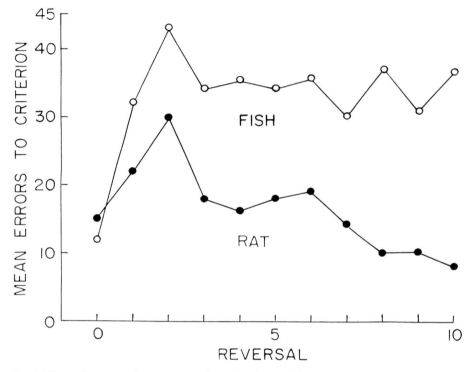

FIG. 1. The performance of rats and mouthbreeders in an original problem and ten subsequent reversals. The rats were trained in a horizontal-vertical discrimination (Gonzalez, Roberts, and Bitterman 1964) and the fish in a red-green discrimination (Behrend, Domesick, and Bitterman 1965).

other animal does not do at all. The rat shows progressive improvement in habit-reversal, while the fish does not, and the fish shows random probability-matching, while the rat does not. The second point is that the differences in performance do not seem to be attributable simply to sensory, or motor, or motivational differences. The test is *systematic variation*. A difference in performance which we find in any single experiment may perhaps be due to the fact that different sensory or motor demands are being made on the two animals (there is no way to equate these demands across species) or that the motivational conditions are different—the fish may be hungrier (or less hungry) than the rat, or it may for some other reason like the worms with which it is rewarded more (or less) than the rat likes food pellets (there is no way to equate these motivational conditions across species). If, however, the fish shows one mode of adjustment over a wide range of sensory, and motor, and motivational conditions, while the rat shows another, we must begin to look elsewhere than to those variables for an explanation of the difference. Let us look now to learning.

Learning theorists long have agreed that the primary products of learning are connections of some sort, although they have disagreed sharply about the nature of the connections which are established and about the variables which affect the connecting process (Bitterman 1967). Consider, for example, the central fact of instrumental learning, which is that behavior can be controlled by manipulating its consequences. If a hungry rat is rewarded with food for pressing a bar introduced into its chamber, it comes to press the bar more and more readily. Furthermore, large rewards produce better performance than do small rewards. How does reward work?

The earliest answer to this question was that the rat *learns about* reward—that its increasing readiness to respond reflects a growing anticipation of the reward. Performance is better with large rewards than with small rewards because large rewards are more attractive. This informational or *S-S-contiguity* interpretation (so called because the anticipation of reward was thought to be based on the development of new connections between con-

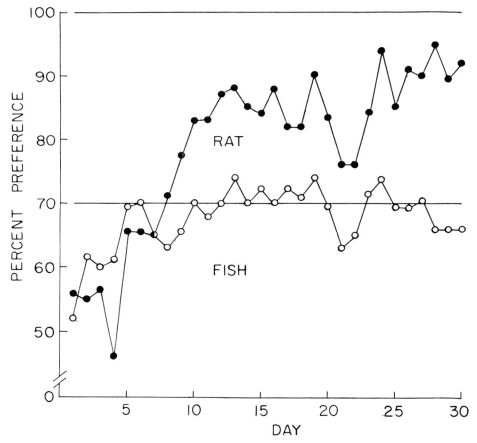

Fig. 2. The performance of rats and mouthbreeders in a 70:30 horizontal-vertical discrimination (Bitterman, Wodinsky, and Candland 1958). The percentage of each day's trials on which the 70 per cent stimulus was chosen is plotted.

tiguously activated sensory centers in the brain) soon gave way to the so-called *S-R-rein-forcement* interpretation, according to which the reward acts directly to establish and strengthen connections between sensory and motor centers (the sensory centers activated by the introduction of the bar and the motor centers for pressing). From this point of view, reward is not "learned about" but is a *condition* of learning. Performance is better with large rewards than with small because large rewards produce stronger connections. Although the S-R-reinforcement interpretation was widely accepted for a time, there has been a return in recent years to the contiguity view, which is supported by the results of a variety of experiments. One of the most important of those experiments—the Crespi experiment—we shall have to consider later.

Whatever the nature of the connecting process, the modification of behavior in learning situations cannot be accounted for in terms of connections alone. It is necessary also to postulate certain integrating-activating processes which put together the primary products of learning with each other and with information about the present state of the animal to generate appropriate patterns of behavior. For example, a rat which has learned to press a bar for food does not do very much bar-pressing unless it is hungry; the hungrier it is, the more enthusiastically it presses the bar. Whether or not a connection established in training will be reflected in behavior, and how it will be reflected, seems to depend on processes of a different kind than those that have produced the connection in the first place. Now we may ask this question: To which of these two kinds of process should we look for an explanation of different modes of adjustment such as those shown by fish and rat in experiments on habit-reversal and probability-learning? One possibility is that the laws of connection are the same in the two animals, but the integrating mechanisms are different. Consider the 70:30 probability experiment. It is conceivable that two competing response-tendencies are established according to the same laws in fish and rat, but that the conflict is resolved differently—in the fish by some probabilistic mechanism, and in the rat by a mechanism which selectively activates the stronger tendency. Another possibility is that the animals behave differently because different connections have been established.

Of the two possibilities, I have been inclined to favor the first for several reasons. One is that the complexity of the conditions under which the differences in behavior appear—at ratios other than 100:0 in probability-learning, and over an extended series of habit-reversals—suggest that they are second-order effects. Another reason is that modes of adjustment characteristic of the fish are shown in such experiments by adult rats which have been extensively decorticated in infancy (Gonzalez, Roberts, and Bitterman 1964). Cortical damage would seem much more likely to disrupt some second-order integrating process responsible for the behavior of normal rats than to alter the connecting process. From the very outset of this resarch, I considered it rather unlikely, in fact, that *any* experiment would show the elementary processes of connection to be different in the two animals. The only alternative to the contiguity principle (which seemed to be required by the rat data) was the reinforcement principle, and that seemed to me to be physiologically rather implausible. I shall review now some recent data which point to a different conclusion.

Soon after the first experiments on habit-reversal and probability-learning in the fish (Bitterman, Wodinsky, and Candland 1958), I thought it might be interesting to look also at the effect of partial (inconsistent) reinforcement on resistance to extinction in a simple instrumental situation (one which involves no choice between alternative responses—only one response is defined, and the readiness with which it is made is measured). The results of the first experiments on partial reinforcement in the fish (Wodinsky and Bitterman 1959,

1960; Longo and Bitterman 1960) were strikingly different from those of analogous experiments with the rat. In the rat, resistance to extinction is increased by partial reinforcement. Rats which have been rewarded on only 50 per cent of training trials for making some instrumental response persist longer in making that response after they are no longer rewarded at all (extinction) than do rats which have been rewarded on 100 per cent of training trials. This is a rather paradoxical outcome. Although reward is necessary to establish the response to begin with, and to maintain the response after it has been established, inconsistent reward (that is, occasional *nonreward*) produces more resistance to extinction than does consistent reward. By contrast, the first results for the fish were quite unparadoxical—resistance to extinction was greater after *consistent* reward—and they suggested that fish and rat might be differently affected by inconsistency of reinforcement. As it happened, however, this interpretation proved to be incorrect.

In the traditional experiments on partial reinforcement in the rat (after which the first experiments on the fish were modeled), number of training trials was equated. That is, partial (50 per cent) groups had the same number of training trials as consistent (100 per cent) groups, but half the number of reinforcements. It is impossible in a comparison of partial and consistent reinforcement to equate both number of training trials and number of reinforcements; number of reinforcements can be equated only if the partial group is given twice as many training trials as the consistent group. Whichever way the experiment is done with the rat, the paradoxical effect appears, but the results for the fish turned out to depend on method. When, in the course of the systematic variation in experimental conditions designed to explore the generality of the first results for the fish, reinforcements rather than trials were equated, the paradoxical effect appeared (Gonzalez, Eskin, and Bitterman 1962). How was this result to be interpreted? It now seemed reasonable to explain the earlier equated-trials results for the fish, not on the assumption that the fish is affected differently than the rat by inconsistency of reinforcement, but on the assumption that it is differently affected by frequency of reinforcement. According to this interpretation, inconsistency of reinforcement tends to increase resistance to extinction in both animals, but in the fish (unlike the rat) the resistance of the consistent group is increased by the greater frequency of reinforcement which it receives in an equated-trials experiment, and the effect of frequency is strong enough to override the effect of inconsistency. When, however, number of reinforcements is equated, the effect of inconsistency becomes evident.

The correctness of this interpretation was suggested by the results of some subsequent experiments on amount of reward. Hulse (1958) and Wagner (1961) had shown that the magnitude of the partial reinforcement effect increases with amount of reward in the rat, and an equated-reinforcements experiment with the goldfish now gave similar results, which are plotted in Figure 3 (Gonzalez and Bitterman 1967). The large difference between the two high-reward groups suggested that in might be possible to show the partial reinforcement effect in the fish even in an equated-trials experiment by pitting amount of reward against frequency. Accordingly, an equated-trials high-reward experiment was carried out with the goldfish, which yielded the extinction curves of Figure 4. The partial reinforcement effect is clear. These results provide further support for the conclusion that inconsistency of reinforcement tends to increase resistance to extinction in the fish as well as in the rat (and more so with high reward than with low), but that the fish is more sensitive than the rat to sheer frequency of reinforcement, and that this frequency effect is strong enough to override the effect of inconsistency when trials are equated and reward is low.

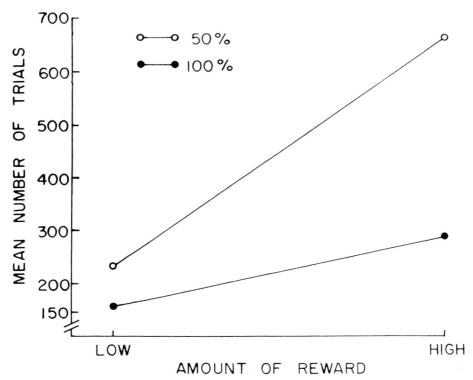

Fig. 3. Resistance to extinction in the goldfish as a function of consistency of reinforcement and amount of reward (Gonzalez and Bitterman 1967). Resistance is measured in terms of the mean number of trials to the criterion of extinction.

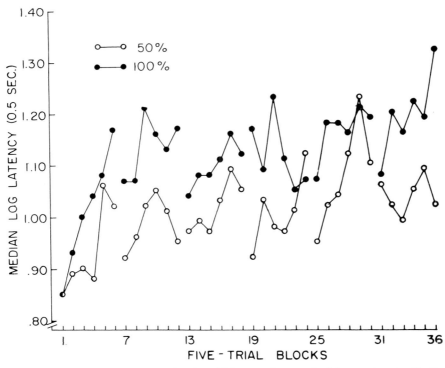

Fig. 4. The partial reinforcement effect in a high-reward equated-trials experiment with the goldfish (Gonzalez and Bitterman 1967). The course of extinction in the two groups is plotted in terms of the latency of response on successive 5-trial blocks.

One other difference between fish and rat became evident in these experiments—a difference in the way in which the two animals are affected by amount of reward. As may be seen in Figure 3, resistance to extinction in the fish increased with amount of reward in both consistently and partially reinforced fish. The partial reinforcement effect was greater with high reward because resistance increased more in the partial animals than in the consistent ones. The results for the rat were different in one important respect. Although resistance to extinction increased with amount of reward in partially reinforced rats, the relation was inverse in consistently reinforced rats—with consistent reinforcement, resistance to extinction in the rat *decreased* as amount of reward increased. Now, clearly, it had become necessary to look carefully at the way in which consistently reinforced fish and rats were affected by frequency and amount of reinforcement. Differences in the effects of these variables would point to

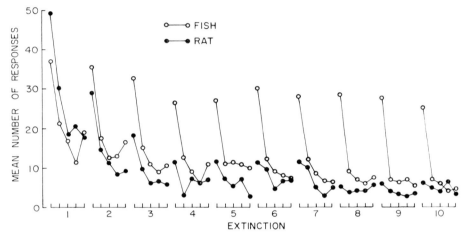

FIG. 5. The course of extinction in rat and goldfish plotted in terms of mean number of responses for successive 3-min periods in each of ten 15-min extinction sessions separated by retraining sessions (Gonzalez, Holmes, and Bitterman 1967a).

more fundamental differences in the learning of the two animals than had previously been suspected.

Rats and goldfish were consistently reinforced in a free-operant situation (that is, for response to a continuously available lever), then extinguished, retrained, extinguished again, and so forth, the retraining and extinction sessions being given on separate days (Gonzalez, Holmes, and Bitterman 1967a). Their performance in each of ten 15-min extinction sessions is plotted in Figure 5 in terms of the mean number of responses in successive 3-min periods. Initially, the curves for rat and fish are very much the same in shape. Both animals respond at a high rate in the first 3 min of extinction, and the rate declines as the session continues. In later extinctions, the rat curves flatten markedly, while the fish curves do not. The meaning of this difference became apparent when, after the tenth extinction, we began systematically to vary the amount of retraining interpolated between successive extinctions. The extinction curves for the rat on any given day were the same whether the rat had been retrained or extinguished on the preceding day. What seems to be important for the sophisticated rat is only whether or not it is reinforced at the time of testing. If the first response in a given session is reinforced, the rat responds at a high rate; if the first response is not reinforced, it responds at a very low rate. For the goldfish, by contrast, it continues to matter very much whether the preceding day was an extinction day or a retraining day. On days following retraining days, its extinction curves look as they do in Figure 5 (sharply peaked in the first three minutes). On days following extinction days, its extinction curves are flat, indistinguishable from those for the rat.

While the goldfish in this experiment were not found to be differently affected by the number of retraining sessions which preceded extinction (six days of retraining produced no more marked an initial burst of responding in extinction than did one day of retraining), resistance to extinction in mouthbreeders of an earlier experiment (Gonzalez, Eskin, and

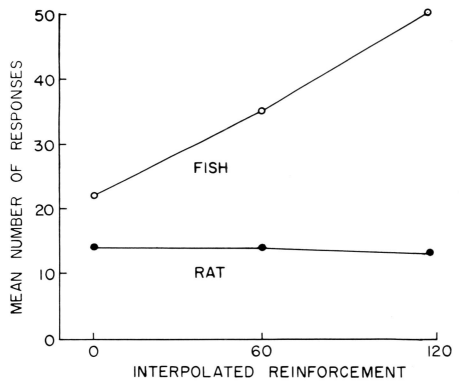

FIG. 6. Resistance to extinction in rat and mouthbreeder as a function of amount of interpolated reinforcement (Gonzalez, Eskin, and Bitterman 1961).

Bitterman 1961) increased with number of interpolated retraining sessions in essentially linear fashion over a six-day period. In that experiment, a group of mouthbreeders and a group of rats were subjected to a series of extinction sessions separated by three interpolated retraining sessions of 20 reinforcements each until resistance to extinction had declined to a stable level in both groups. Then the number of interpolated retraining sessions was varied systematically—0, 3, or 6, in balanced order, with each animal as his own control. The results are shown in Figure 6. For the rat, again, the frequency of interpolated reinforcement matters not at all; for the fish, again, it matters a great deal.

In another recent experiment, the effect of amount of reward on resistance to extinction was studied (Gonzalez, Holmes, and Bitterman 1967b). Two groups of rats and two groups of goldfish were given 15 sessions of consistently reinforced free-operant training with 30 reinforcements per session. For one group of rats, each response was rewarded with one 45-mg Noyes pellet; for the other, the reward was 7 pellets. For one group of fish, the reward was one *Tubifex* worm; for the other, 10 worms. Then each group was extinguished for 30 min. In Figure 7, the extinction curves are plotted in terms of mean number of responses in 5-min periods. As you see, high reward produced a higher initial level of responding in both animals, but there the resemblance ends. Rate of responding declined more rapidly in the high-reward rats than in the low-reward rats, but the high-reward fish continued throughout the session to respond at a higher level than the low-reward fish. Here is further evidence that the relation between resistance to extinction and amount of reinforcement is direct in the fish but inverse in the rat.

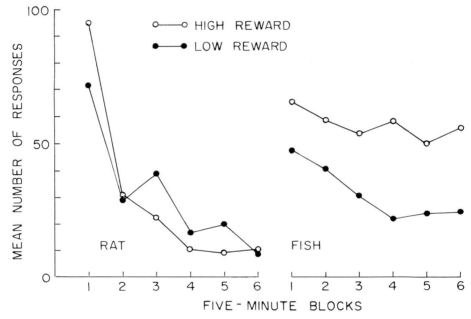

Fɪɢ. 7. Resistance to extinction in rat and goldfish as a function of amount of reward (Gonzalez, Holmes, and Bitterman 1967*b*).

There followed a series of 16 additional 12-min extinction sessions separated by retraining sessions. The extinction curves for the rat were found to flatten rapidly, as do the rat curves of Figure 5, and the difference due to amount of reward disappeared after the second extinction. By contrast, the extinction curves for the goldfish (shaped like the goldfish curves in Figure 5) continued to show a marked difference in level correlated with magnitude of reinforcement. The performance of the two groups of goldfish is plotted in Figure 8 in terms of the mean number of responses in each 12-min extinction session, along with the performance of two other groups of goldfish which were trained exactly as the first, except with only 10 instead of 20 reinforcements per training session. At each frequency, as you see, high reward produced a higher level of response in extinction; at each amount of reward, high frequency produced a higher level of response in extinction. Both effects persisted without sign of diminution (the interactions were statistically insignificant) over the 16 extinctions.

Frequency and amount of reward clearly have rather different effects on the performance of fish and rat in these situations, and the simplicity of the conditions under which the differences appear suggests that we may have come here upon a difference in connecting processes. Specifically, the results suggest that reward may operate directly in the fish to establish and strengthen connections between sensory and motor systems. Is the fish an S-R-reinforcement animal? To answer this question we have only to do experiments with the fish like those which were designed to answer the question at the level of the rat. One such experiment has already been completed. Let us look first at the rat model.

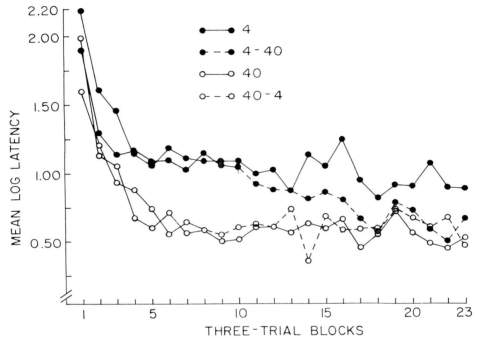

FIG. 8. Resistance to extinction in the goldfish as a function of amount and frequency of reward (Gonzalez, Holmes, and Bitterman 1967*b*). Data are plotted for 16 extinction sessions separated by retraining sessions.

Suppose that two groups of rats are trained to make some instrumental response, one group with large reward and one group with small reward. As training proceeds, speed of responding increases progressively in both groups, but the learning curve of the large-reward group approaches a higher asymptote than does that of the small-reward group. The S-R-reinforcement interpretation is that the different asymptotic speeds reflect different asymptotic habit-strengths produced by the different amounts of reward. What should happen when half the small-reward animals are shifted to large reward? Their speed should increase gradually to the large-reward level. What should happen if half the large-reward animals are shifted to low reward? Nothing at all! These animals should continue to perform at the large-reward level, because strong S-R connections have already been established in them by the large reward.

The results obtained by Crespi (1942) in just such an experiment were quite different from those which S-R-reinforcement theory predicts. Both shifted groups showed dramatic changes in performance. The speed of the animals shifted from small to large reward increased rapidly to a level well *above* that of the unshifted large-reward animals (which Crespi called an "elation" effect), while the speed of the animals shifted from large to small reward fell well *below* that of the unshifted low-reward animals (a "depression" effect). These so-called contrast effects suggested that the animals were reacting in terms of the difference between preshift and postshift amounts of reward, which meant that they must have learned and remembered something about the preshift amounts of reward as such. The suddenness and the bidirectionality of the changes in performance with change in reward, as well as the magnitude of these changes, were difficult to understand in S-R-reinforcement terms, and

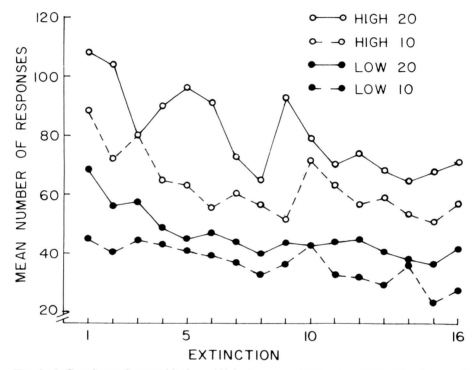

FIG. 9. A Crespi experiment with the goldfish (Lowes and Bitterman 1967). The data are for four groups rewarded with either 4 or 40 worms in different stages of training.

it was largely on the basis of these results that C. L. Hull (1952), long the leading exponent of the S-R-reinforcement principle, found it necessary to make a major change in his conception of the role of reward in learning which led inevitably to the abandonment of the principle.

An analogue of the Crespi experiment, with the fish instead of the rat as its subject, has just been completed (Lowes and Bitterman 1967). Four groups of goldfish were trained to strike a target for food, and the latency of response was measured. For two of the groups, each response was rewarded with 4 *Tubifex* worms; for the other two groups, each reward was 40 worms. One of the two small-reward groups was continued throughout on 4 worms, while the second was shifted to 40 worms on trial 30. One of the two large-reward groups was continued throughout on 40 worms, while the other was shifted to 4 worms on trial 24. The performance of all four groups is plotted in Figure 9 in terms of mean log latency of response per block of three trials. (Low latency, of course, means high speed, and the values are logged, in accordance with the usual practice, to normalize the distributions for statistical treatment.) As in the rat, the different amounts of reward produce different asymptotic speeds of reaction in the fish, but the effects of shift in reward are quite different from those which Crespi found in the rat. The speed of the small-reward goldfish shifted to large reward approaches that of the unshifted large-reward animals, but the approach is gradual and there is no evidence of a contrast effect. The speed of the large-reward animals shifted to small reward remains unchanged! These results, then, are precisely those which the S-R-reinforcement principle would lead us to expect.

Whether or not the fish is an S-R-reinforcement animal, many more experiments will be necessary to decide. I need not caution you that results of a single experiment on so large a question cannot be given too much weight, however substantial the empirical context which led us to ask it in the first place. A good deal of systematic variation will be required to test the generality of the first results. It will be necessary, too, to do experiments of other kinds, especially on latent learning (Bitterman 1957). Nevertheless, it is difficult now to escape the impression that the connecting processes of fish and rat are different in some fundamental respect. A difference in connecting processes would not, of course, rule out the possibility of a difference in integrating processes. It is, in fact, difficult to conceive of a difference in connecting processes without some correlated difference in integrating processes. The infantile decortication procedure and related procedures will have an important bearing on these issues.

I cannot conclude without mentioning a new and, I think, rather exciting line of research on learning in the fish which is under way in my laboratory. There has been a good deal of work on learning in animals which have less than the normal amount of brain tissue, but nobody has studied learning in animals which have more than the normal amount of brain tissue. With David Bresler, a graduate student, I am getting ready now to do just that. Minnows and fish of other species with duplicated brain parts have, of course, been produced before (Oppenheimer 1950), but they have not been allowed to grow up, and nothing is known about their learning. With our first superbrained mouthbreeders almost full-grown, we hope soon to remedy that deficiency.

Acknowledgment

The experiments reported in this paper were supported for the most part by Grant MH-02857 from the United States Public Health Service.

References

Behrend, E. R., and Bitterman, M. E. 1966. Probability matching in the goldfish. *Psychon. Sci.* 6:327–28.

Behrend, E. R.; Domesick, V. B.; and Bitterman, M. E. 1965. Habit reversal in the fish. *J. Comp. Physiol. Psychol.* 60:407–11.

Bitterman, M. E. 1960. Toward a comparative psychology of learning. *Amer. Psychol.* 15: 704–12.

———. 1965. Phyletic differences in learning. *Amer. Psychol.* 20:396–410.

Bitterman, M. E. 1966. Animal learning. In *Experimental methods and instrumentation in psychology*, ed. J. Sidowski, pp. 451–84. New York: McGraw-Hill.

―――. 1967. Learning in animals. In *Contemporary approaches to psychology*, ed. H. Helson and W. Bevan, pp. 140–79. Princeton, N.J.: Van Nostrand.

Bitterman, M. E.; Wodinsky, J.; and Candland, D. K. 1958. Some comparative psychology. *Amer. J. Psychol.* 71:94–110.

Crespi, L. 1942. Quantitative variation of incentive and performance in the white rat. *Amer. J. Psychol.* 55:467–517.

Gonzalez, R. C., and Bitterman, M. E. 1967. Partial reinforcement effect in the goldfish as a function of amount of reward. *J. Comp. Physiol. Psychol.* 64:163–67.

Gonzalez, R. C.; Eskin, R. M.; and Bitterman, M. E. 1961. Alternating and random partial reinforcement in the fish with some observations on asymptotic resistance to extinction. *Amer. J. Psychol.* 74:561–68.

―――. 1962. Extinction in the fish after partial and consistent reinforcement with number of reinforcements equated. *J. Comp. Physiol. Psychol.* 55:381–86.

Gonzalez, R. C.; Holmes, N. K.; and Bitterman, M. E. 1967a. Asymptotic resistance to extinction in fish and rat as a function of interpolated retraining. *J. Comp. Physiol. Psychol.* 63:342–44.

―――. 1967b. Resistance to extinction in the goldfish as a function of frequency and amount of reward. *Amer. J. Psychol.* 80:269–75.

Gonzalez, R. C.; Roberts, W. A.; and Bitterman, M. E. 1964. Learning in adult rats extensively decorticated in infancy. *Amer. J. Psychol.* 77:547–62.

Hull, C. L. 1952. *A behavior system.* New Haven, Conn.: Yale Univ. Press.

Hulse, S. H. 1958. Amount and percentage of reinforcement and duration of goal confinement in conditioning and extinction. *J. Exp. Psychol* 56:48–57.

Longo, N., and Bitterman, M. E. 1960. The effect of partial reinforcement with spaced practice on resistance to extinction in the fish. *J. Comp. Physiol. Psychol.* 53:169–72.

Lowes, G., and Bitterman, M. E. 1967. Reward and learning in the goldfish. *Science* 157:455–57.

Oppenheimer, J. 1950. Functional regulation in *Fundulus heteroclitus* embryos with abnormal central nervous systems. *J. Exp. Zool.* 115:461–92.

Thorndike, E. L. 1911. *Animal intelligence.* New York: Macmillan Co.

Voronin, L. G. 1962. Some results of comparative-physiological investigations of higher nervous activity. *Psychol. Bull.* 59:161–95.

Wagner, A. R. 1961. Effects of amount and percentage of reinforcement and number of acquisition trials on conditioning and extinction. *J. Exp. Psychol.* 62:234–42.

Wodinsky, J., and Bitterman, M. E. 1959. Partial reinforcement in the fish. *Amer. J. Psychol.* 72:184–99.

―――. 1960. Resistance to extinction in the fish after extensive training with partial reinforcement. *Amer. J. Psychol.* 73:429–34.

Index

271